student book volume 1

Science

VISIONS

MATHEMATICS

Secondary
Cycle Two, Year Two

Jean-François Cardin
Jean-Claude Hamel
Antoine Ledoux
Steeve Lemay

9001, boul. Louis-H.-La Fontaine, Anjou, Québec, Canada H1J 2C5
Telephone: 514 351-6010 • Fax: 514 351-3534

ORIGINAL VERSION

Publishing Manager
Katie Moquin

Production Manager
Danielle Latendresse

Coordination Manager
Rodolphe Courcy

Project Manager
Diane Karneyeff

Linguistic Review (LES)
Denis Desjardins

Proofreader
Viviane Deraspe

Graphic Design
Dessine-moi un mouton

Technical Illustrations
Bernard Lachance (page 4, page 50, page 51)
Stéphan Vallières

General Illustrations
Yves Boudreau

Iconographic Research
Jean-François Beaudette
Perrine Poiron

These programs are funded by Quebec's Ministère de l'Éducation, du Loisir et du Sport, through contributions from the Canada-Québec Agreement on Minoroty-Language Education and Second-Language Instruction.

Visions, Science, Student Book, Volume 1, Secondary Cycle Two, Year Two

9001, boul. Louis-H.-La Fontaine
Anjou, Québec H1J 2C5

Translation of *Visions, Sciences naturelles, manuel de l'élève, volume 1,* (ISBN 978-2-7617-2603-0) © 2009, Les Éditions CEC inc.

Legal Deposit : 2009
Bibliothèque et Archives nationales du Québec
Library and Archives Canada

ISBN 978-2-7617-2805-8

Printed in Canada
1 2 3 4 5 13 12 11 10 09

The authors and publisher wish to thank the following people for their collaboration in the evolution of this project.

Collaboration
Jocelyn Dagenais, Teacher, École Secondaire André-Laurendeau, CS Marie-Victorin
Isabelle Gendron, Teacher, Collège Mont-Royal

Scientific Consultants
Éysée-Robert Cadet, Professor, Université du Québec en Abitibi-Témiscamingue
Matthieu Dufour, Professor, Université du Québec à Montréal

Pedagogical Consultants
Stéphane Brosseau, Teacher, École Secondaire l'Horizon, CS des Affluents
Richard Cadieux, Teacher, École Jean-Baptiste Meilleur, CS des Affluents
Sivia Comsa, Teacher, École Saint-Luc, CS de Montréal
Nadia Hammache, Teacher, École Marguerite-De Lajemmerais, CS de Montréal
Jonathan Lafond, Teacher, Collège Notre-Dame-de-Lourdes
Teodora Nadu, Teacher, École Jeanne-Mance, CS de Montréal
Dominic Paul, Teacher, École Pierre-Bédard, CS des Grandes-Seigneuries

ENGLISH VERSION

Translators and Linguistic Review
Donna Aziz
Daniella Berglas
Donna Boychuk
Don Craig
Gordon Cruise
Cecilia Delgado
Jean-Guy Dufort
Shona French
Alain Groven
Jennifer McCann

Pedagogical Consultant
Joanne Malowany

Pedagogical Review
Don Craig
Peggy Drolet
Kirk Robinson
Vilma Scattolin

Project Management
Patrick Bérubé
Rite De Marco
Stephanie Vucko
Valerie Vucko

A special thank you to the following people for their collaboration in the evolution of this project.

Collaboration
Michael J. Canuel
Robert Costain
Sylvie Desrochers
Margaret Dupuis
Christiane Dufour
Rosie Himo
Doris Kerec
Nancy Kerec
Louis-Gilles Lalonde
Denis Montpetit
Mital Patel
Mary Stewart
Bev White

TABLE OF CONTENTS

volume 1

VISION 3

VISION 4

PRESENTATION OF STUDENT BOOK

This *Student Book* contains four chapters each called "Vision." Each "Vision" presents various "Learning and evaluation situations (LES)" sections and special features "Chronicle of the past," "In the workplace" and "Overview." At the end of the *Student Book*, there is a "Reference" section.

Revision

The "Revision" section helps to reactivate prior knowledge and strategies that will be useful in each "Vision" chapter. This feature contains one or two activities designed to review prior learning, a "Knowledge summary" which provides a summary of the theoretical elements being reviewed and a "Knowledge in action" section consisting of reinforcement exercises on the concepts involved.

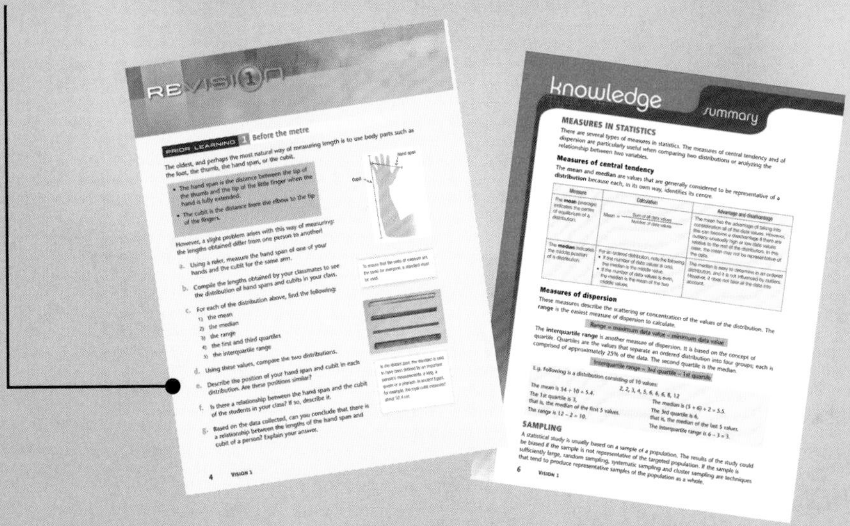

The Sections

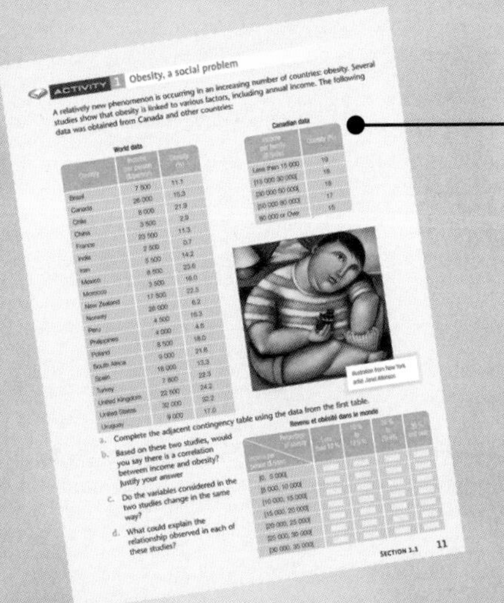

A "Vision" chapter is divided into sections, each starting with a problem and a few activities, followed by the "Technomath," "Knowledge" and "Practice" features. Each section is related to a LES that contributes to the development of subject-specific and cross-curricular competencies, as well as to the integration of mathematical concepts that underscore the development of these competencies.

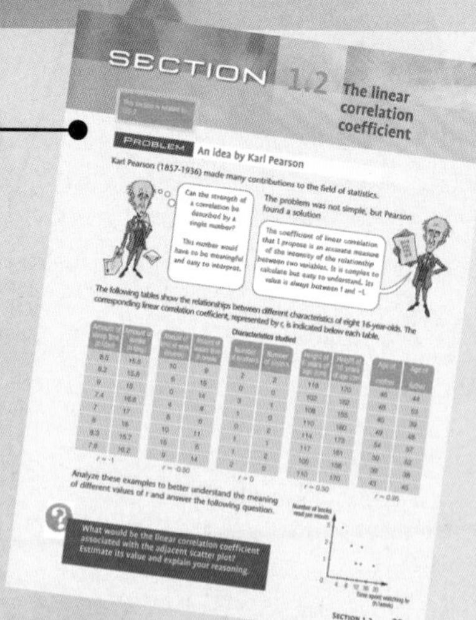
SECTION 1.2 The linear correlation coefficient

PROBLEM An idea by Karl Pearson

Problem

The first page of a section presents a problem that serves as a launching point and is made up of a single question. Solving the problem engages several competencies and various strategies while calling upon the mobilization of prior knowledge.

Activity

The activities contribute to the development of subject-specific and cross-curricular competencies, require the use of various strategies, mobilize knowledge and further the understanding of mathematical notions. These activities can take on several forms: questionnaires, material manipulation, construction, games, stories, simulations, historical texts, etc.

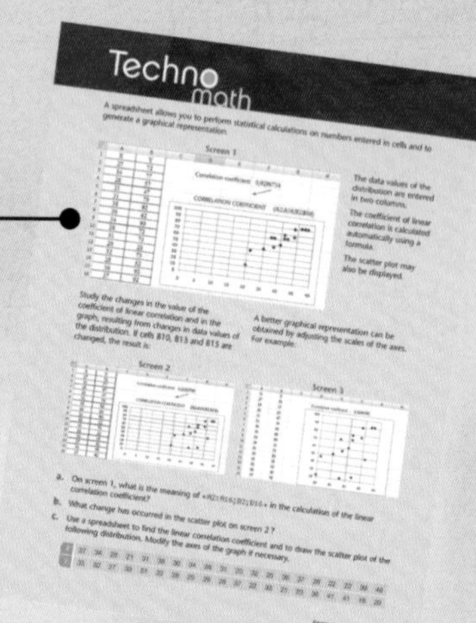
Technomath

Technomath

The "Technomath" section allows students to use technological tools such as a graphing calculator, dynamic geometry software or a spreadsheet program. In addition, the section shows how to use these tools and offers several questions in direct relation to the mathematical concepts associated with the content of the chapter.

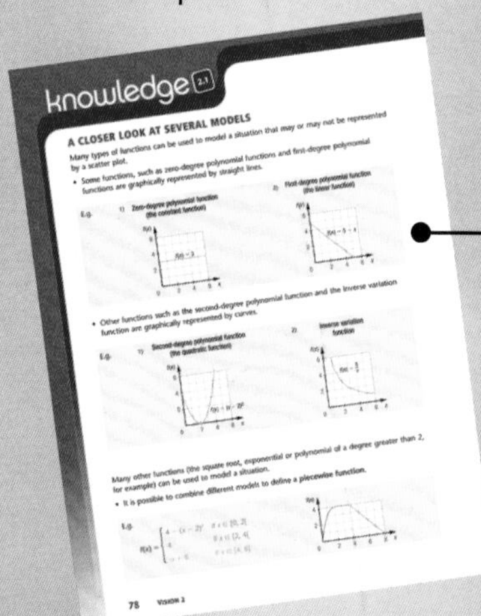
knowledge 2.1

A CLOSER LOOK AT SEVERAL MODELS

Knowledge

The "Knowledge" section presents a summary of the theoretical elements encountered in the section. Theoretical statements are supported with examples in order to foster students' understanding of the various concepts.

Practice

The "Practice" section presents a series of contextualized exercises and problems that foster the development of the competencies and the consolidation of what has been learned throughout the section.

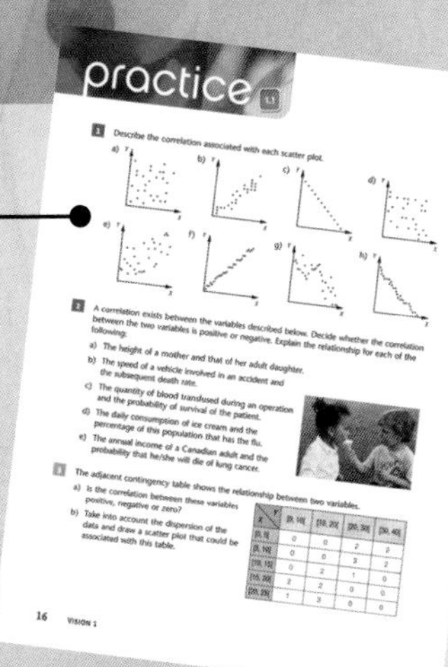

practice

SPECIAL FEATURES

Chronicle of the past

The "Chronicle of the past" feature recalls the history of mathematics and the lives of certain mathematicians who have contributed to the development of mathematical concepts that are directly related to the content of the "Vision" chapter being studied. This feature includes a series of questions that deepen students' understanding of the subject.

Chronicle of the past

Isaac Newton

In the workplace

The "In the workplace" feature presents a profession or a trade that makes use of the mathematical notions studied in the related "Vision" chapter. This feature includes a series of questions designed to deepen students' understanding of the subject.

Overview

The "Overview" feature concludes each "Vision" chapter and presents a series of contextualized exercises and problems that integrate and consolidate the competencies that have been developed and the mathematical notions studied. This feature ends with a bank of problems, each of which focuses on solving, reasoning or communicating.

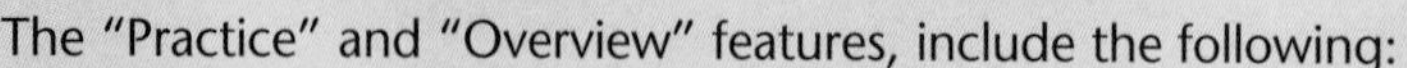

The "Practice" and "Overview" features, include the following:

- A number in a blue square refers to a Priority **1** and a number in an orange square a Priority **2**.
- When a problem refers to actual facts, a keyword written in red uppercase indicates the subject with which it is associated.

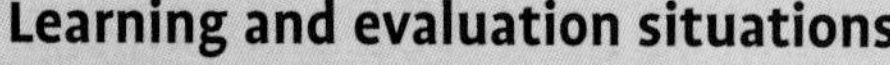

Learning and evaluation situations

The "Learning and evaluation situations" (LES) are grouped according to a common thematic thread; each focuses on a general field of instruction, a subject-specific competency and two cross-curricular competencies. The knowledge acquired through the sections helps to complete the tasks required in the LES.

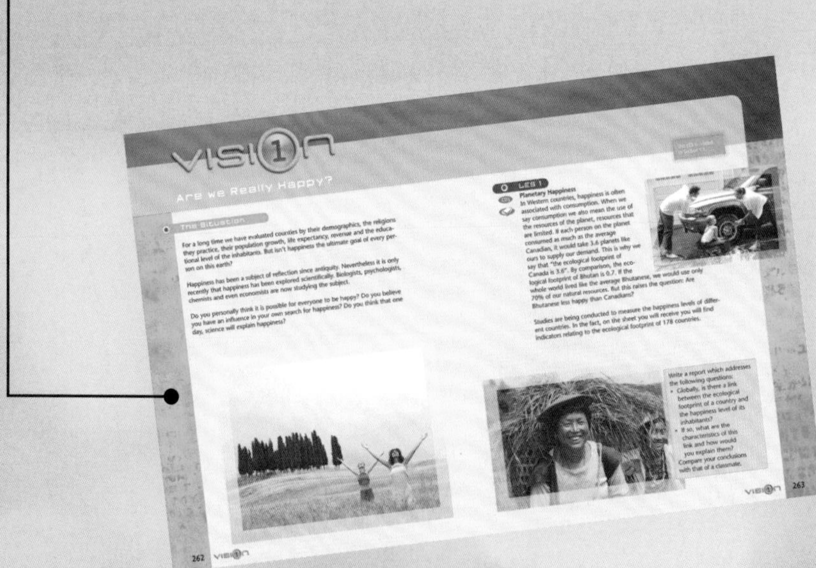

Reference

Located at the end of the *Student Book*, the "Reference" section contains several tools that support the student-learning process. It consists of two distinct parts.

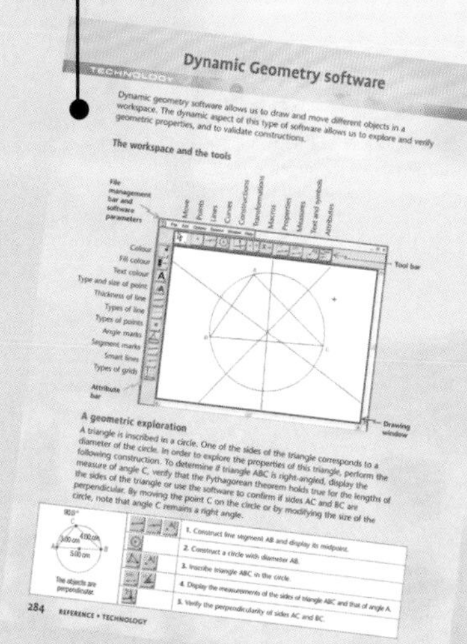

The "Technology" part provides explanations pertaining to the functions of a graphing calculator, the use of a spreadsheet program as well as the use of dynamic geometry software.

The "Knowledge" part presents notations and symbols used in the *Student Book*. Geometric principles are also listed. This part concludes with a glossary and an index.

Icons

Indicates that a worksheet is available in the *Teaching Guide*.

Indicates that the activity can be performed in teams. Details on this topic are provided in the *Teaching Guide*.

Indicates that some key features of subject-specific competency 1 are mobilized.

Indicates that some key features of subject-specific competency 2 are mobilized.

Indicates that some key features of subject-specific competency 3 are mobilized.

Indicates that subject-specific competency 1 is being targeted in the LES.

Indicates that subject-specific competency 2 is being targeted in the LES.

Indicates that subject-specific competency 2 is being targeted in the LES.

Vision 1

From correlation to modelling

Are the rich happier than the poor? Is there a relationship between the height of a student and his or her academic success? Look at the world around you; there are many variables. Are they related? If a relationship can be established between two variables, what is its nature? Is the relationship strong or weak? Is it simply due to chance, or is there another explanation? In "Vision 1," you will analyze statistical data related to various variables, for example, characteristics of populations of people, of countries or of objects. You will determine whether or not there is a correlation between these variables and you will quantify it. When you find a strong relationship between two quantitative variables, you will attempt to model it using a function, just as men and women of science do in their area of expertise.

Arithmetic and algebra

- Modelling
- Interpolation and extrapolation

Geometry

Statistics

- Two-variable distribution
- Contingency table
- Scatter plot
- Correlation
- Linear correlation coefficient
- Regression line
- Equation of the regression line

15
10
150
100

REVISION 1

PRIOR LEARNING 1 Before the metre

The oldest, and perhaps the most natural way of measuring length is to use body parts such as the foot, the thumb, the hand span, or the cubit.

- The hand span is the distance between the tip of the thumb and the tip of the little finger when the hand is fully extended.
- The cubit is the distance from the elbow to the tip of the fingers.

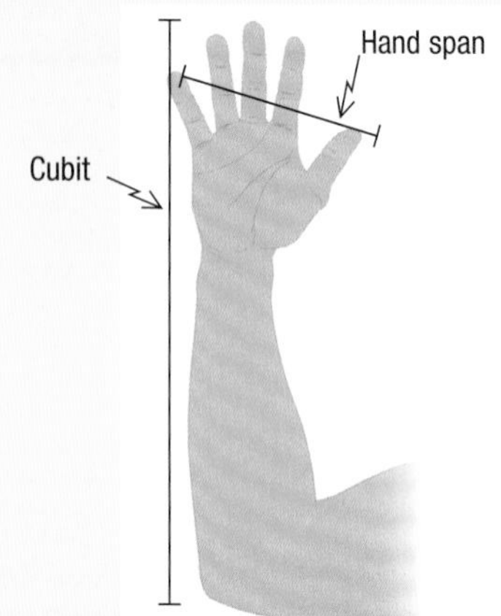

However, a slight problem arises with this way of measuring: the lengths obtained differ from one person to another!

a. Using a ruler, measure the hand span of one of your hands and the cubit for the same arm.

b. Compile the lengths obtained by your classmates to see the distribution of hand spans and cubits in your class.

To ensure that the units of measure are the same for everyone, a standard must be used.

c. For each of the distribution above, find the following:

1) the mean
2) the median
3) the range
4) the first and third quartiles
5) the interquartile range

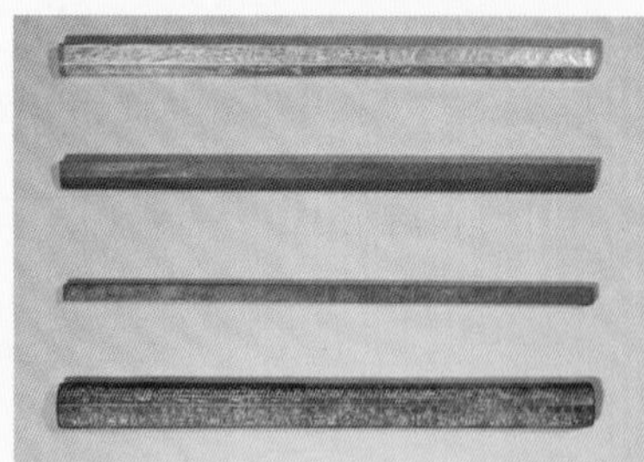

d. Using these values, compare the two distributions.

e. Describe the position of your hand span and cubit in each distribution. Are these positions similar?

In the distant past, the standard is said to have been defined by an important person's measurements, a king, a queen or a pharaoh. In ancient Egypt, for example, the royal cubit measured about 52.4 cm.

f. Is there a relationship between the hand span and the cubit of the students in your class? If so, describe it.

g. Based on the data collected, can you conclude that there is a relationship between the lengths of the hand span and cubit of a person? Explain your answer.

PRIOR LEARNING 2 Are two measurements better than one?

Since 1971, Canadians have seen the old Imperial System replaced by the International System of Units. However, units from both systems are still commonly used. Following are a few examples:

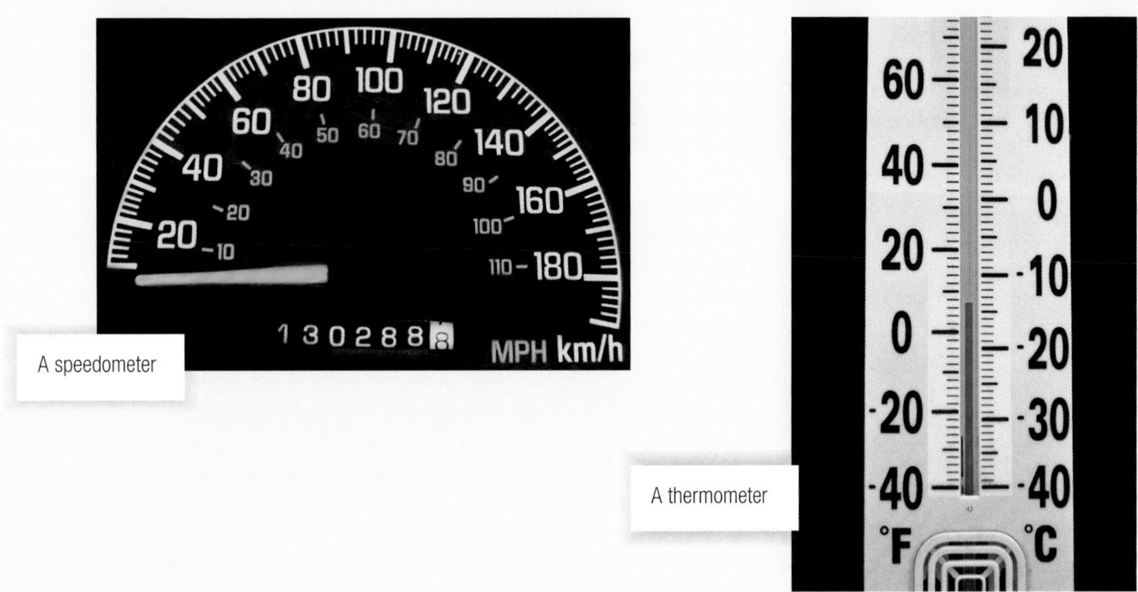

A speedometer

A thermometer

The double scale on the speedometer shows that a functional relationship exists between speed expressed in kilometres per hour and in miles per hour.

a. Using speed expressed in kilometres per hour as the independent variable, represent this function graphically.

b. What is the rule of this function?

c. In the United States of America, speed limits on roads are indicated in miles per hour. Express the speed limit of the adjacent road sign in kilometres per hour.

As you can see, there are also two scales on a thermometer. Temperature expressed in degrees Fahrenheit can be expressed as a function of degrees Celsius.

d. Draw the graph of this function and determine its rate of change.

e. What is the rule of this function?

f. Given that the boiling point of water is 100°C, what is it on the Fahrenheit scale?

g. To cook a pizza, the oven must be set to 450°F. Express this temperature in degrees Celsius.

MEASURES IN STATISTICS

There are several types of measures in statistics. The measures of central tendency and of dispersion are particularly useful when comparing two distributions or analyzing the relationship between two variables.

Measures of central tendency

The **mean** and **median** are values that are generally considered to be representative of a **distribution** because each, in its own way, identifies its centre.

Measure	Calculation	Advantage and disadvantage
The **mean** (average) indicates the centre of equilibrium of a distribution.	$\text{Mean} = \dfrac{\text{Sum of all data values}}{\text{Number of data values}}$	The mean has the advantage of taking into consideration all of the data values. However, this can become a disadvantage if there are outliers: unusually high or low data values relative to the rest of the distribution. In this case, the mean may not be representative of the data.
The **median** indicates the middle position of a distribution.	For an ordered distribution, note the following: • If the number of data values is odd, the median is the middle value. • If the number of data values is even, the median is the mean of the two middle values.	The median is easy to determine in an ordered distribution, and it is not influenced by outliers. However, it does not take all the data into account.

Measures of dispersion

These measures describe the scattering or concentration of the values of the distribution. The **range** is the easiest measure of dispersion to calculate.

Range = maximum data value – minimum data value

The **interquartile range** is another measure of dispersion. It is based on the concept of quartile. Quartiles are the values that separate an ordered distribution into four groups; each is comprised of approximately 25% of the data. The second quartile is the median.

Interquartile range = 3rd quartile – 1st quartile

E.g. Following is a distribution consisting of 10 values:

2, 2, 3, 4, 5, 6, 6, 6, 8, 12

The mean is 54 ÷ 10 = 5.4.

The median is (5 + 6) ÷ 2 = 5.5.

The 1st quartile is 3,
that is, the median of the first 5 values.

The 3rd quartile is 6,
that is, the median of the last 5 values.

The range is 12 – 2 = 10.

The interquartile range is 6 – 3 = 3.

SAMPLING

A statistical study is usually based on a sample of a population. The results of the study could be biased if the sample is not representative of the targeted population. If the sample is sufficiently large, random sampling, systematic sampling and cluster sampling are techniques that tend to produce representative samples of the population as a whole.

RATE OF CHANGE

The rate of change of a relation involving two variables is a comparison between two variations that correspond to each other.

$$\text{Rate of change} = \frac{\text{variation of the dependent variable}}{\text{corresponding variation of the independent variable}}$$

Symbolically, the rate of change between the ordered pairs (x_1, y_1) and (x_2, y_2) is: $\frac{y_2 - y_1}{x_2 - x_1}$.

E.g. The rate of change between the ordered pairs (9, 7) and (17, 19) is: $\frac{19 - 7}{17 - 9}$.

FIRST-DEGREE POLYNOMIAL FUNCTION

- The rate of change of a first-degree polynomial function is always constant and not equal to zero.
- Its graphical representation is a straight line.
- Its rule is in the form $y = ax + b$, where **a** is the rate of change and **b** is the initial value.

E.g. Table of values	Graphical representation	Rule
x: -2, 0, 3, 4; y: -3, 1, 7, 9 (x: +2, +3, +1; y: +4, +6, +2) The following rates of change are equivalent: $\frac{4}{2} = \frac{6}{3} = \frac{2}{1} = 2$	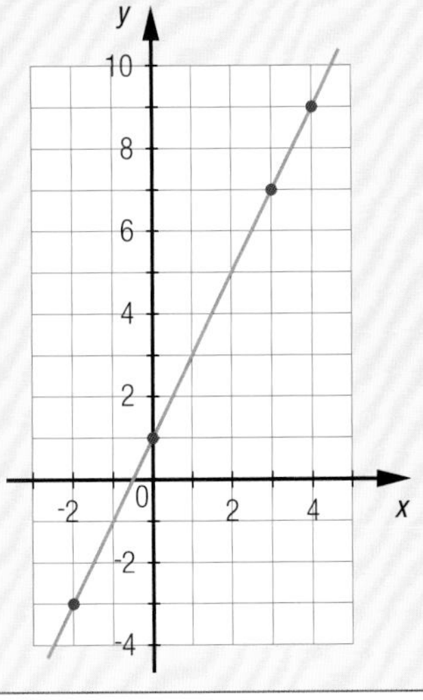	$y = 2x + 1$ 2 is the rate of change; 1 is the initial value.

x	y
-2	-3
0	1
3	7
4	9

Finding the rule

The rule of a function represented by a straight line can be determined if the coordinates of two points on the line are known. To find the rule of a straight line, proceed as follows:

- Calculate the rate of change associated with the two points to determine the value of **a.**
- Substitute the coordinates of one of the points for variables x and y, and solve the resulting equation to find the value of **b.**

E.g. The coordinates of two points on a line are (3, 28) and (7, 72).

$$a = \frac{72 - 28}{7 - 3} = \frac{44}{4} = 11$$

$$y = ax + b$$
$$y = 11x + b$$
$$28 = 11 \times 3 + b$$
$$28 = 33 + b$$
$$28 - 33 = 33 + b - 33$$
$$b = -5$$

Therefore, the rule is $y = 11x - 5$.

knowledge in action

1 Find the mean, the median, the range, and the interquartile range of the following distributions:

a) 1, 2, 2, 4, 7, 8, 9

b) 0, 2, 5, 6, 7, 7, 11, 12

c) 2, 6, 3, 4, -7, 9, 1, 10, 6, -5

d) 1, 1, 1, 1, 1, 1, 2, 2, 2, 3, 3, 3, 3, 3, 3, 3, 3, 3, 4, 4

2 Magic, particularly mentalism, has always fascinated people. Imagine that you are about to participate in one of these mental experiments. Follow these instructions carefully.

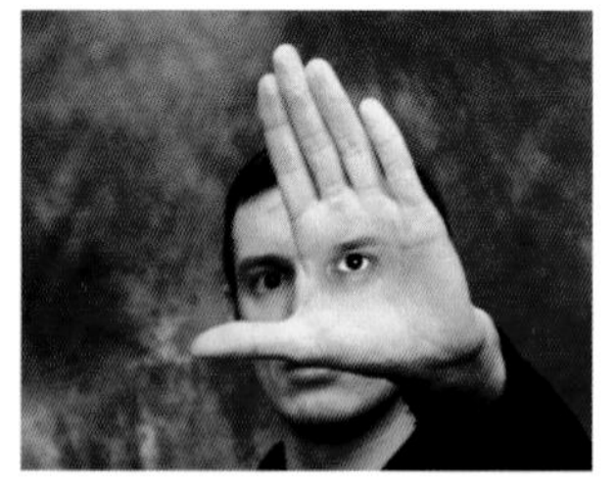

- Write down five natural numbers and calculate the mean.
- Subtract the mean from each of the five original numbers.
- Calculate the mean of the results obtained in the previous step.

A mentalist could easily have predicted your answer. Explain why.

3 A science teacher asked her students to weigh a 100 g object using two different types of scales. Below are the results collected by eight teams:

Team	Roman scale Unit is the *libra* (1 *libra* = 327.5 g)	Roberval scale Unit is the gram
1	0.35	96.8
2	0.37	101.7
3	0.35	99.2
4	0.36	103.4
5	0.37	98.9
6	0.36	99.6
7	0.36	99.3
8	0.35	99.0

Roman scale

Roberval scale

At the beginning of the 17th century, the mathematician Gilles Personne de Roberval (1602-1675) introduced a revolutionary new scale that made the Roman scale obsolete after being used for over 2000 years.

A measuring instrument is considered more *precise* when the measured value is closer to the real value. When repeated measurements tend to cluster around the same value, the instrument is considered more *reliable.*

a) Which scale is more precise?

b) Which scale is more reliable?

4 For each of the following situations, find the rule that corresponds to the information provided.

a)

x	3	5	7	10
y	6π	10π	14π	20π

b)

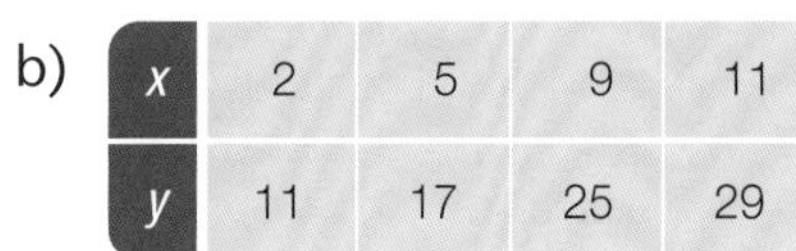

x	2	5	9	11
y	11	17	25	29

c)

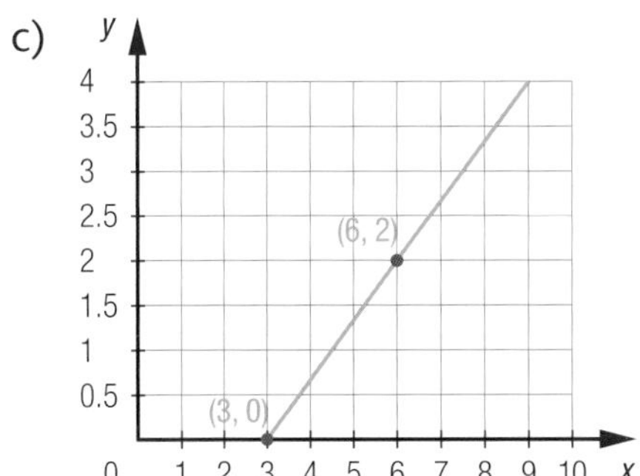

d)

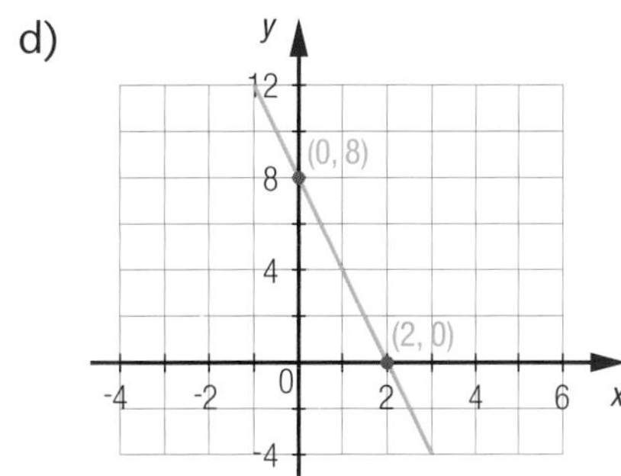

5 A fisherman built a spring scale to determine the mass of his catch. To do so, he had to calibrate his instrument using known masses.

a) Plot the graph representing the relation between the mass and the observed spring extension.

Calibration of the spring scale

Mass (kg)	0.5	2.5	5.0	8.0
Extension (cm)	0.4	2.0	4.0	6.4

b) What would be the extension of the spring if the the fisherman weighed a 500 kg tuna? What would happen?

6 Following is some information on two hybrid cars: the Hydrobrid and the Ecobrid. The adjacent graph shows the amount of gas left in the tank of the Hydrobrid in relation to distance travelled. A relation can also be found for the Ecobrid given that it can travel 1140 km on a full tank of gas and that it consumes 5.7 L per 100 km.

a) Determine the rule for each function.

b) What is the capacity of the Hydrobrid's tank if it has the same operating range as the Ecobrid?

c) If the capacity of the Hydrobrid's tank is as calculated in **b)**, how would the adjacent graph need to be modified?

Hydrobrid

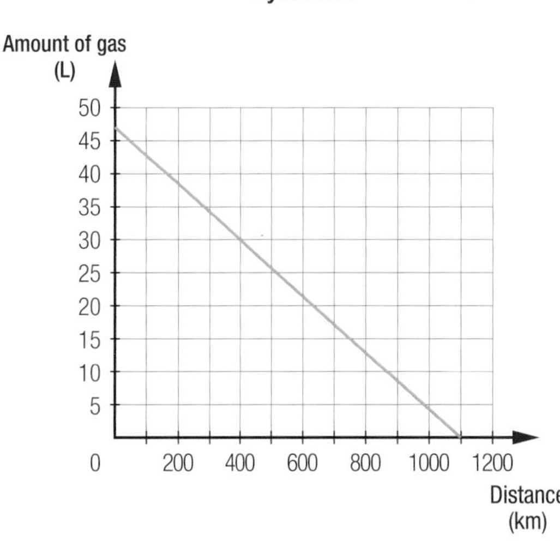

SECTION 1.1 The qualitative estimation of a correlation

This section is related to LES 1.

PROBLEM Society as portrayed by newspapers

Read the following newspaper excerpts carefully.

Associated Press, Tuesday, July 17, 2007

Does height really matter? Many economists would answer yes, because there is a **correlation** between height and many indicators of the well-being of a population. Taller people are in better health, are richer and have a greater life expectancy than shorter people.

GIORDANO JODI, *VIOLENCE IN VIDEO GAMES* [online] (CONSULTED MARCH 14, 2008)

Many researchers have found a relationship between violence in video games and violent behaviour. However, this relationship is a **correlation** and consequently not a cause and effect relationship.

American Geophysical Union Sunday, August 5, 2007

Sun Spots Linked to Abundant Rainfall in East Africa

A new study reveals a correlation between abundant sunspots and periods of heavy rain in east Africa. This study contradicts several other studies which state that no such connection exists.

La Presse, Wednesday, September 26, 2007

Somalia, Iraq and Myanmar Head the List of Corrupt Countries

...The perception of corruption index (PCI) ranges from 10 for a country considered "clean" to zero for a country where corruption is perceived to be "rampant."... Myanmar "is a very good example of the correlation between poverty and corruption," insists Hughette Labelle.

Country	Income per person ($/year)	PCI
Canada	26,000	8.7
China	3,500	3.5
India	2,500	3.5
Iran	5,500	2.5
New Zealand	17,500	10.0
Peru	4,500	3.5
Spain	18,000	6.7
United Kingdom	22,500	8.4
United States	32,000	7.2
Uruguay	9,000	6.7

Agence Science-Presse, Thursday, August 2, 2007

More Wars in Cold Weather

"War seems to occur more often... in cold weather.... And the correlation is surprising," writes David Zhang from Hong Kong University, in *Human Ecology*.

On the Internet, use a search engine to find newspaper articles that contain the word "correlation."

Based on the examples on this page or using the articles you have found, what type of relationship is there between the variables involved? Does one variable depend on the other? If yes, explain. If not, find an explanation for the reported correlation.

ACTIVITY 1 Obesity: a growing social problem

Obesity is a growing social concern in an increasing number of countries. Several studies show that obesity is linked to a variety of factors including annual income. The following data was obtained from Canada and other countries:

World data

Country	Income per person ($/year)	Obesity (%)
Brazil	7,500	11.1
Canada	26,000	15.3
Chile	8,000	21.9
China	3,500	2.9
France	23,500	11.3
India	2,500	0.7
Iran	5,500	14.2
Mexico	8,500	23.6
Morocco	3,500	16.0
New Zealand	17,500	22.5
Norway	28,000	6.2
Peru	4,500	16.3
Philippines	4,000	4.6
Poland	8,500	18.0
South Africa	9,000	21.6
Spain	18,000	13.3
Turkey	7,800	22.3
United Kingdom	22,500	24.2
United States	32,000	32.2
Uruguay	9,000	17.0

Canadian data

Income per family ($/year)	Obesity (%)
Less then 15,000	19
[15,000, 30,000[	18
[30,000, 50,000[	18
[50,000, 80,000[	17
80,000 and over	15

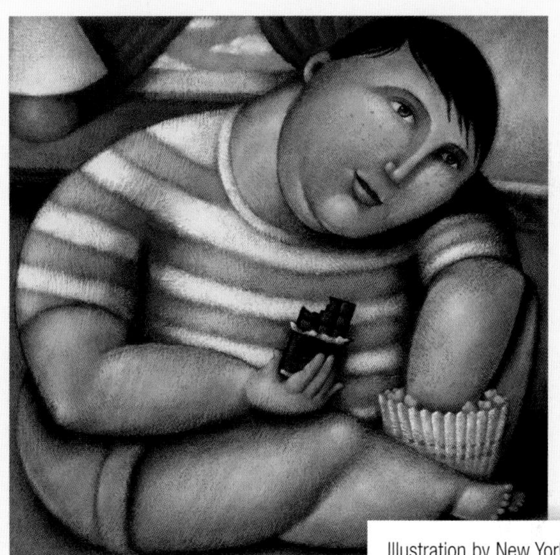

Illustration by New York artist Janet Atkinson

a. Complete the adjacent contingency table using the data from the first table.

b. Based on these two studies, would you say there is a correlation between income and obesity? Justify your answer.

c. Do the variables considered in the two studies change in the same way?

d. What could explain the relationship observed in each of these studies?

Income and global obesity

Income per person ($/year) \ Percentage of obesity	Less than 10%	Percentage [10, 20[	Percentage [20, 30[	30% and over
[0, 5,000[				
[5,000, 10,000[				
[10,000, 15,000[				
[15,000, 20,000[				
[20,000, 25,000[				
[25,000, 30,000[				
[30,000, 35,000[				

ACTIVITY 2 A visit to the doctor

When visiting the doctor, patients are faced with a ritual. Their height and mass are measured, their pulse is taken, etc. Much to his patients' surprise, Dr. Robert also measures the height of their navels. Below is the data compiled for 15 of his patients:

Dr. Roberts' patients

Name	Height (cm)	Mass (kg)	Body mass index (kg/m^2)	Heart rate at rest (pulsations/min)	Number of physical activities per month	Height of navel (cm)
1. Adams	175	67	22	55	12	108
2. Barrett	178	72	23	70	10	111
3. Campbell	185	85	25	72	6	123
4. Donahue	172	85	29	88	4	104
5. Ellis	162	76	29	85	3	101
6. Franklin	162	70	27	87	5	95
7. Gonzalez	154	54	23	71	8	96
8. Hawah	162	50	19	60	9	105
9. Iacono	165	51	19	58	8	100
10. Jones	179	63	20	64	8	110
11. Khang	157	81	33	102	2	92
12. Libman	167	52	19	74	10	98
13. Marceau	167	47	17	62	8	97
14. Nguyen	182	93	28	94	4	112
15. Otis	184	85	25	78	7	123

Complete the following exercises and display your results with a scatter plot.

The body mass index (BMI), used for 20 to 65-year-olds, is calculated as follows:

$$BMI = \frac{\text{mass}}{(\text{height})^2}$$

a. Using the information in the table, find an example of a positive correlation as well as a negative correlation between variables.

b. Identify two variables from the table with a weak linear correlation between them and explain this correlation.

c. Identify two variables from the table with a strong linear correlation between them and explain this correlation.

In Spain, since 2005, a model with a BMI below 18 is no longer permitted to participate in fashion shows.

Techno math

A graphing calculator allows you to display different types of graphs. The following explains how you would display a scatter plot of a two-variable distribution and how to describe the correlation:

X	23	25	25	30	30	32	33	34	35	35	36	39	40	44	44
Y	40	55	64	35	53	66	55	41	66	77	47	61	78	62	84

This screen allows you to enter each ordered pair from the table of values.

Screen 1

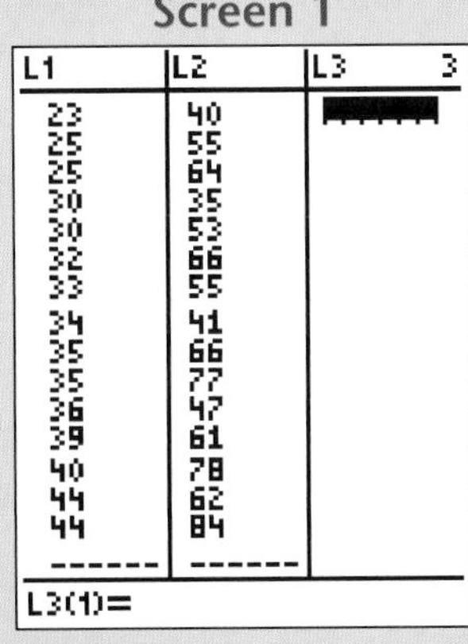

This screen allows you to choose the scatter plot as the display mode.

Screen 2

The graphical display must be configured to adequately represent the scatter plot displaying the correlation.

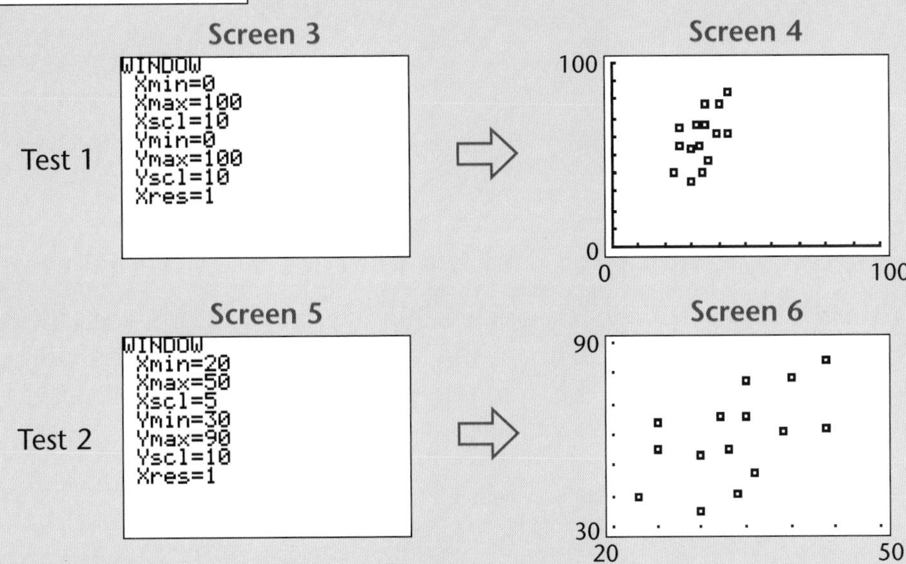

a. How has the graph changed from Screen **4** to Screen **6**?

b. What happens to the graph when the following ranges are chosen for the display screen?

1)

WINDOW
Xmin=0
Xmax=100
Xscl=5
Ymin=30
Ymax=90
Yscl=10
Xres=1

2)

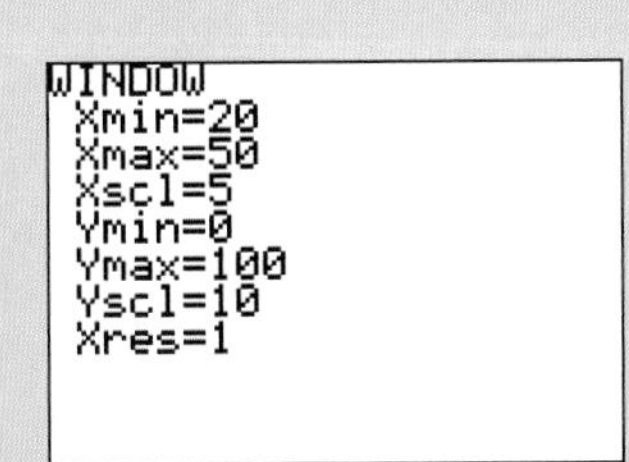

3)

WINDOW
Xmin=0
Xmax=50
Xscl=10
Ymin=30
Ymax=70
Yscl=10
Xres=1

c. Using a graphing calculator, display the scatter plot of the following points and describe the observed correlation.

X	1	2	3	4	5	6	7	8	9	10
Y	4	3	5	6	4	5	5	6	5	6

knowledge 1.1

ASSESSING A CORRELATION QUALITATIVELY

Some statistical studies investigate more than one characteristic of a population. In these cases, the data collected forms a **distribution** of two or more variables.

E.g. The following is data pertaining to income and happiness in various countries:

Country	Income per person ($/year)	Happiness index (scale of 100)
Canada	26,000	93
China	3,500	74
France	23,500	85
India	2,500	63
Japan	25,500	80
Morocco	3,500	66
New Zealand	17,500	90
Pakistan	2,000	53
Peru	4,500	64

Country	Income per person ($/year)	Happiness index (scale of 100)
Romania	6,000	47
Russia	7,500	40
South Korea	16,000	75
Spain	18,000	79
Turkey	7,800	60
Ukraine	4,000	38
United Kingdom	22,500	88
Uruguay	9,000	78
United States	32,000	90

Data representation and the concept of correlation

A **correlation** describes the relationship that may exist between the **quantitive variables** of a population. These variables are also called **statistical variables**. Using a method of representation such as a **contingency table** or a **scatter plot** makes it easier to study the correlation between two variables of this type.

E.g.

The contingency table

Income per person ($/year) \ Happiness index	[20, 40[	[40, 60[	[60, 80[	[80, 100[
[0, 5,000[	1	1	4	
[5,000, 10,000[		2	2	
[10,000, 15,000[				
[15,000, 20,000[			2	1
[20,000, 25,000[				2
[25,000, 30,000[				2
[30,000, 35,000[				1

The scatter plot

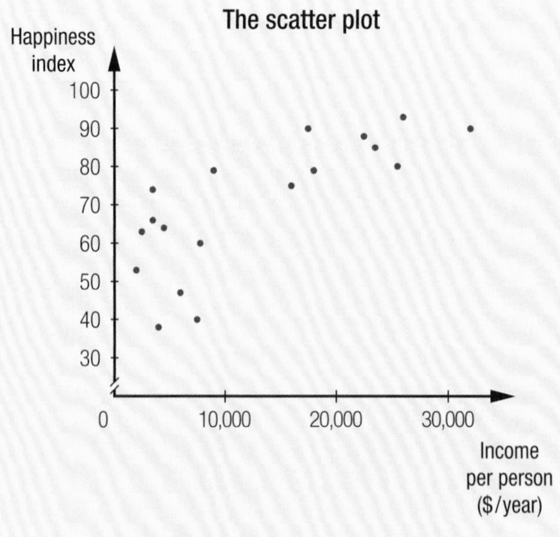

A correlation seems to exist between these two variables. The happiness index is generally greater in countries where people have a higher income.

Linear correlation

- The correlation between two variables is linear if the scatter plot is close to forming a straight line. The linear correlation is positive or negative depending on the slope of this line.
- The shape of the scatter plot allows you to classify the linear correlation between variables. Linear correlation is said to be perfect, strong or weak. Closely aligned points imply a stronger correlation.
- To classify a linear correlation properly, it is essential that the scale of the *x*- and *y*-axes take into account the dispersion of each of the variables studied. It is usually sufficient to choose the scales so that the range of each variable corresponds approximately to the same length on both axes of the graph.

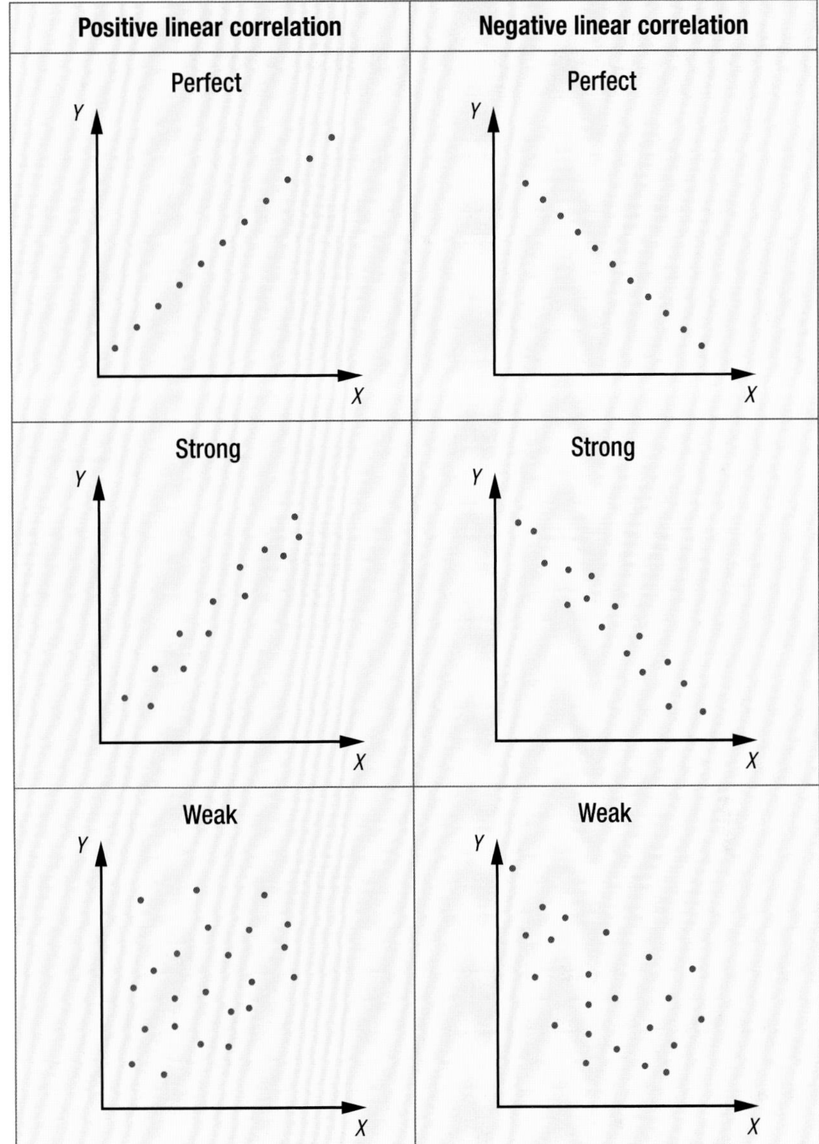

- If the points of the scatter plot are distributed randomly or do not align, then there is no correlation. The correlation is then said to be zero.

Interpreting the correlation

A strong correlation does not necessarily imply there is a cause and effect relationship between the two variables studied. Although this could in fact be the case, studying their correlation does not provide that information. Some cases of correlation are simply due to chance while others can be explained by the influence of a third variable.

E.g. A salesman working at a beach resort observed that the number of sunburned tourists is strongly correlated to the number of sunglasses sold. However, you cannot deduce from this correlation that sunglasses cause sunburn.

practice 1.1

1 Describe the correlation associated with each scatter plot.

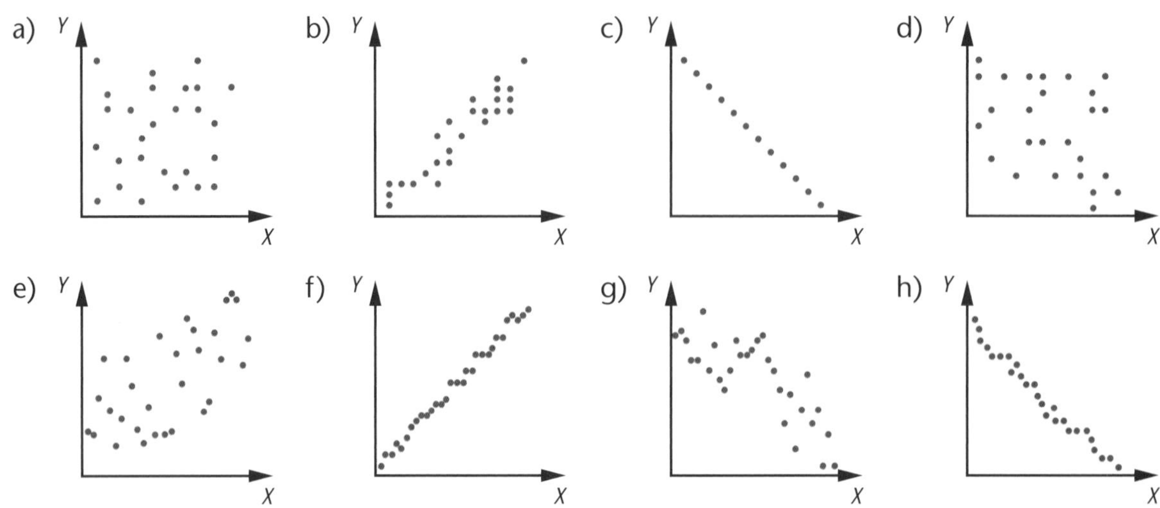

2 A correlation exists between the variables described below. Decide whether the correlation between the two variables is positive or negative. Propose an explanation for the correlation.

a) The height of a mother and the height of her adult daughter.

b) The speed of a vehicle involved in an accident and the subsequent death rate from the accident.

c) The quantity of blood transfused during an operation and the probability the patient survives.

d) The daily consumption of ice cream and the percentage of this population with the flu.

e) The annual income of a Canadian adult and the probability that he/she will die of lung cancer.

3 The adjacent contingency table shows the relationship between two variables.

a) Is the correlation between these variables positive, negative or zero?

b) Take into account the dispersion of the data and draw a scatter plot that represents the relationship shown on the table.

X \ Y	[0, 10[	[10, 20[	[20, 30[	[30, 40[
[0, 5[	0	0	2	2
[5, 10[	0	0	3	2
[10, 15[	0	2	1	0
[15, 20[	2	2	0	0
[20, 25[	1	3	0	0

4 Using the following data, construct a contingency table and describe the observed relationship between the two variables.

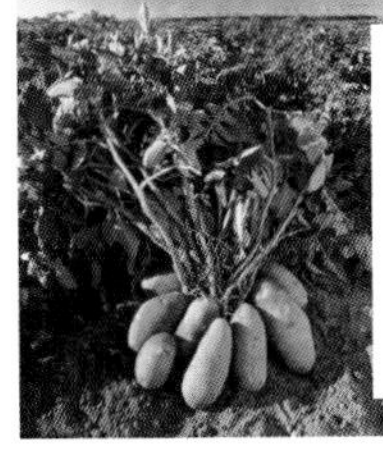

The potato is a tuber native to America whereas the sweet potato is from India. These plants are from two completely different families. The sweet potato is not cultivated in Canada because the Canadian climate is unsuitable.

a) A farmer is interested in the effect of soil acidity on the number of potatoes produced per plant.

pH of the soil	5.5	5.1	8.0	8.4	7.0	6.2	5.8	5.7	6.6	6.3	7.9	6.2	7.2	8.2	5.8
Number of potatoes per plant	29	24	10	6	13	18	17	21	19	22	8	13	13	9	22

pH of the soil	5.1	5.5	6.2	7.8	8.4	6.4	7.2	8.1	8.1	7.2	5.5	6.1	7.0	6.2	6.9
Number of potatoes per plant	27	28	24	18	13	27	19	8	10	14	23	21	15	19	14

b) In hockey, the fans are said to be *the seventh player* on the ice. A coach wants to know whether the size of the crowd at home games has an effect on the number of goals scored by his team.

Attendance (thousands)	11.2	14.5	10.5	19.7	20.8	18.2	17.1	13.4	16.2	21.0	20.1	14.3
Number of goals scored	3	2	0	1	4	0	1	2	4	2	2	1

Attendance (thousands)	21.0	17.7	11.4	12.9	15.8	15.1	21.0	21.0	18.9	20.5	16.0	16.5
Number of goals scored	0	0	1	5	3	4	4	3	2	0	0	2

5 Arrange each of the two series of scatter plots below according to the intensity of the correlation represented, from the weakest to the strongest.

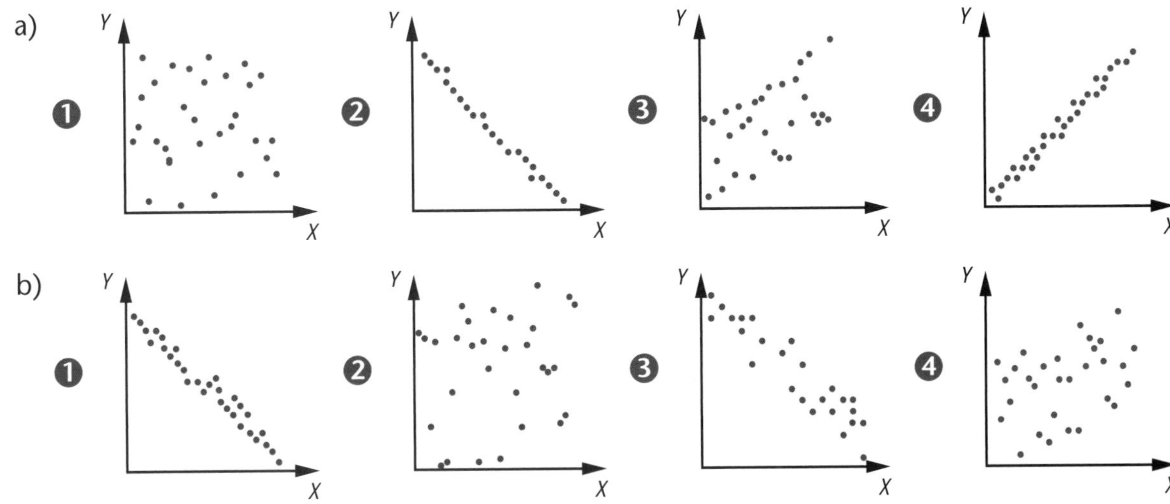

6 Ismaël is interested in identifying the material composition of ten cubes. To help identify their composition, he measures the volume and the mass of each one. The table below shows the data obtained:

Cubes

Volume (cm³)	3	4	5	10	12	15	16	20	24	25
Mass (g)	8.0	11.0	13.5	27.0	32.5	40.5	43.0	54.0	64.5	67.5

a) Describe the correlation that exists between these two variables.

b) Is Ismaël right in thinking that all the cubes are composed of the same substance? Justify your answer.

7 **WEATHER** A teacher gives his students meteorological statistics for the Montréal area. The data consists of 12 monthly means calculated using meteorological data for the years 1961 to 1991. Below are the graphs produced by three students:

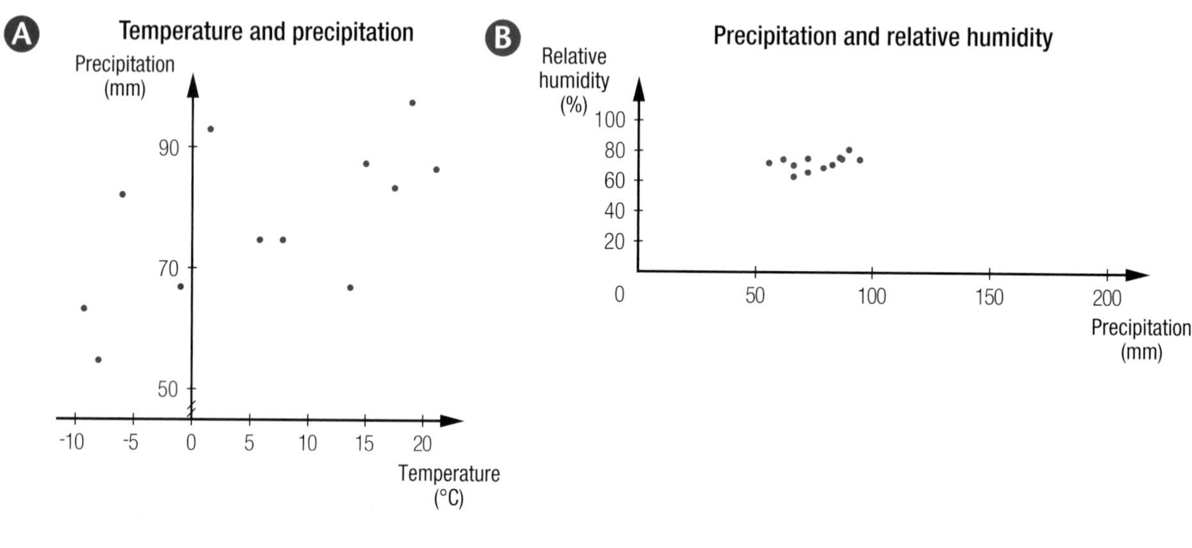

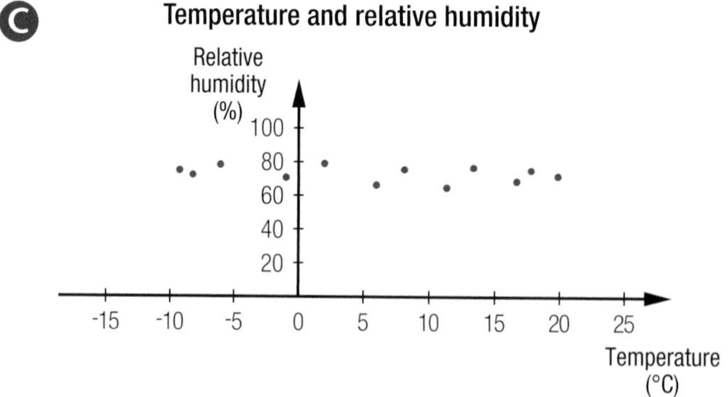

Which of these graphs best evaluates the relationship between the variables presented? Explain your answer, and specify how the other two graphs should be modified.

8 Lucy plays backgammon using a computer program that generates the possible numbers obtained when tossing two dice. However, she thinks that the white die has a tendency to yield a large number when the red die yields a small number and vice versa. Analyze the results she obtains to verify whether her intuition is correct.

Backgammon is played with a pair of dice and a third doubling die. The numbers 2, 4, 8, 16, 32 and 64 are shown on the sides of the third die.

Results

Red die	1	3	2	2	4	2	4	5	2	5	1	3	3	5	1	4	5	3	3	4
White die	6	4	5	4	4	6	1	3	5	5	5	4	5	1	6	2	5	3	1	3

Red die	5	1	2	5	6	2	2	3	6	2	3	5	6	1	3	6	3	4	1	1
White die	1	6	6	2	3	2	6	2	2	6	3	6	1	5	2	5	4	3	4	4

Red die	4	4	5	4	2	1	4	5	2	2	6	5	1	4	5	2	4	2	5	5
White die	1	3	3	1	5	5	1	5	6	6	2	3	6	4	1	4	6	3	2	2

9 a) Based only on the contexts given below, describe the correlation that could be observed between the following variables and explain your prediction.

1) The number of beds in a hospital and the mean duration of hospitalization.
2) The performance of the French players at the Roland-Garros tennis tournament in June and the success rate of students on university exams.
3) The number of people detained in prison and the life expectancy of men.

b) Represent the following data using scatter plots to validate or contradict your predictions. Interpret each context based on the scatter plot.

Hospital

Number of beds	Mean duration of hospitalization (days)
68	1
1230	14
1000	10
750	6
650	9
200	2
138	1
180	1
600	4
500	8

Tennis

Performance of French players (points)	Examination success rate (%)
115	80
87	63
88	63
90	66
100	74
102	76
109	79
104	80

Prison

Number of detainees (per 100 000 inhabitants)	Life expectancy of men (years)
96.6	75.5
55.3	74.6
37.6	77.7
36.1	68.6
114.7	60.5
41.8	78.1
92.2	75.5
389.0	66.0
227.3	64.5
678.2	59.0

10 Can the size of a person's head be an indicator of their mathematical aptitude? Twenty-eight elementary students were selected randomly, and the circumference of their heads was measured. They were then submitted to a mathematical aptitude test. The following ordered pairs represent the circumference of each student's head (in cm) and the result obtained by the student on an aptitude test (as a percentage).

(46, 10)	(77, 14)	(48, 82)	(48, 17)	(49, 14)	(49, 55)
(50, 30)	(50, 31)	(50, 65)	(52, 90)	(52, 45)	(53, 76)
(53, 95)	(54, 66)	(54, 87)	(54, 89)	(54, 40)	(55, 15)
(55, 70)	(55, 82)	(56, 92)	(56, 48)	(56, 52)	(56, 79)
(57, 86)	(57, 61)	(57, 73)	(58, 81)		

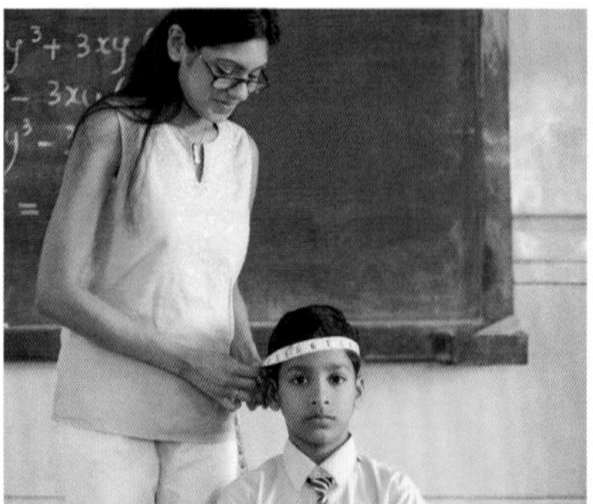

a) Draw the scatter plot for this distribution.

b) Using a qualitative analysis, describe the correlation between the circumference of a student's head and their mathematical aptitudes.

c) Give one explanation for the observed results.

11 Are we happier if we think we will live to a ripe old age? The following are the statistics on life expectancy in various countries and the happiness index of the inhabitants:

Country	Life expectancy (years)	Happiness index (scale of 10)	Country	Life expectancy (years)	Happiness index (scale of 10)
Australia	79.0	7.8	New-Guinea	55.3	6.3
Burundi	43.6	3.0	Nicaragua	69.7	6.3
Chad	43.6	4.5	Nigeria	43.4	5.5
Greece	78.3	6.3	Republic of Vanuatu	68.6	7.4
Guyana	63.1	7.2	São Tomé and Principe	63.0	6.7
Kyrgyzstan	66.8	6.6	Singapore	78.7	6.9
Lebanon	72.0	5.6	Sri Lanka	74.0	6.1
Mauritius	72.2	6.5	Tajikstan	63.6	6.6
Moldavia	67.7	3.5	Thailand	70.0	6.5
Netherlands	78.4	7.5	Tunisia	73.3	6.4

Determine whether a relationship exists between these two variables and, if so, describe it. Use any method of representation to draw your conclusions.

12 Eight teams of students performed an experiment to determine the relationship between the mass of a free-falling object and its final speed as it reached ground level. The experiment consisted of dropping, from the same height, balls of equal volume but different mass and then recording the final speed. The results are as follows:

Free fall of a ball 15 cm in diameter from a height of 1.5 m

Team	1	2	3	4	5	6	7	8
Mass (kg)	Final speed (m/s)	Final speed (m/s)	Final speed (m/s)	Final speed (m/s)	Final speed (m/s)	Final speed (m/s)	Final speed (m/s)	Final speed (m/s)
0.1	55	55	49	47	49	51	55	49
0.2	54	50	48	49	53	50	49	49
0.3	48	46	47	51	55	55	51	52
0.4	53	50	48	51	55	49	50	48
0.5	48	52	53	49	52	47	48	51
0.6	47	49	50	48	52	50	47	48
0.7	53	54	49	48	46	55	55	53
0.8	48	53	53	54	47	48	48	49
0.9	51	46	55	47	53	50	47	53
1.0	54	49	53	51	49	46	55	50

a) Analyze the results obtained by Team **3** and comment on them.

b) Include the results of the other teams and analyze the situation again.

c) What is the relationship between the mass of the ball and its final speed as it reaches ground level? Justify your answer.

Galileo Galilei (1554-1642)

Galileo is recognized as having introduced the experimental method in science. For example, to determine the influence of mass on the speed of falling bodies, he is said to have dropped heavy spheres from the top of the Tower of Pisa. Afterwards, he used pendulums to more precisely measure this relationship.

13 For over 20 years, *L'Association des Sceptiques du Québec* has been promoting critical thinking and scientific rigour in studies that examine allegations of paranormal phenomena. This association even offers a $10,000 prize to anyone who can scientifically prove the existence of such a power. A person claiming to be clairvoyant participated in an experiment in an attempt to prove the existence of this power. This experiment consisted of predicting a series of computer-generated random numbers from 1 to 20. The results were as follows:

Some people claim they can bend keys or spoons using only the power of thought. None of them has been able to prove this claim.

Experimental results

Generated numbers	18	18	14	19	13	4	19	10	3	9	3	9	14	13
Predicted numbers	8	7	8	5	12	11	6	14	9	10	12	6	8	10

Generated numbers	18	18	6	10	14	6	14	14	6	8	8	18	3	13
Predicted numbers	19	5	4	9	16	2	5	2	8	17	10	17	16	8

a) At times the gap between the clairvoyant's prediction and the generated number was very large as in the first prediction. Sometimes the difference was small. Was the clairvoyant right to claim that small differences are less important errors than the large ones? Explain your point of view.

b) How should members of l'*Association des Sceptiques du Québec* have interpreted the results had the clairvoyant always predicted a number that was one unit smaller than the number generated by the software?

c) Should the association award the $10,000 prize for this person's power of clairvoyance? Justify your answer.

14 The following data is from 20 countries where part of the population lacks the resources to feed itself properly. Analyze this data and interpret the relationship between the two variables.

The situation in 20 countries

Country	Literacy rate (%)	Malnutrition (%)	Country	Literacy rate (%)	Malnutrition (%)
Argentina	96	3	Ivory Coast	39	16
Brazil	82	23	Jordan	82	19
China	78	46	Lesotho	78	37
Cyprus	94	3	Madagascar	58	17
Congo	67	47	Nigeria	49	27
Egypt	47	26	Panama	89	17
El Salvador	72	45	Syria	65	16
Ghana	59	24	Togo	44	29
Guyana	97	19	Uruguay	97	3
Indonesia	80	47	Yemen	33	54

SECTION 1.2 The linear correlation coefficient

This section is related to LES 2.

PROBLEM An idea by Karl Pearson

Karl Pearson (1857-1936) made many contributions to the field of statistics.

Can the strength of a correlation be described by a single number?

This number would have to be meaningful and easy to interpret.

The problem was not simple, but Pearson found a solution.

The linear correlation coefficient that I propose is an accurate measure of the intensity of the relationship between two variables. It is complex to calculate but easy to understand. Its value is always between 1 and −1.

BIO ME TRI KA

The following tables show the relationships between different characteristics of eight 16-year-olds. The corresponding linear correlation coefficient, represented by *r*, is indicated below each table.

Characteristics studied

Amount of sleep (h/day)	Amount of time awake (h/day)
8.5	15.5
8.2	15.8
9	15
7.4	16.6
7	17
8	16
8.3	15.7
7.8	16.2

$r = -1$

Amount of time at work (h/week)	Amount of leisure time (h/week)
10	9
6	15
0	14
4	8
8	6
10	11
15	6
9	14

$r \approx -0.50$

Number of brothers	Number of sisters
2	2
0	0
3	1
1	0
0	2
1	1
1	2
2	0

$r = 0$

Height at 6 years of age (cm)	Height at 16 years of age (cm)
118	170
102	162
108	155
110	160
114	173
117	161
105	158
110	170

$r \approx 0.50$

Age of mother	Age of father
46	44
48	53
40	39
49	48
54	57
50	52
39	38
43	45

$r = 0.95$

Analyze these examples to better understand the meaning of different values of *r* and answer the following question.

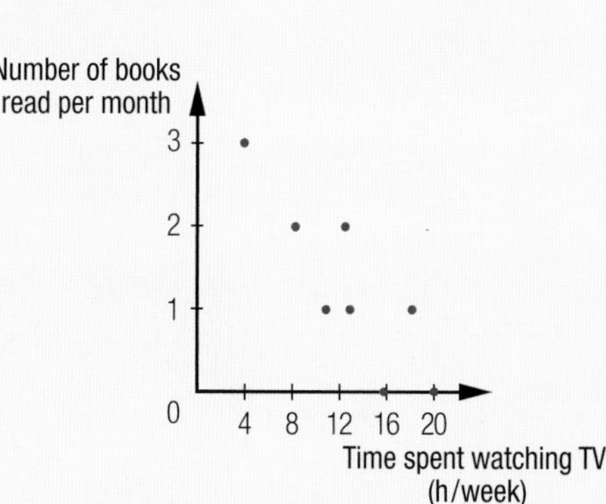

What would be the linear correlation coefficient associated with the adjacent scatter plot? Estimate its value, and explain your reasoning.

ACTIVITY 1 Estimation using the rectangle method

Below are six scatter plots representing correlations of different strengths between two variables. A rectangle containing all the points has been drawn in Graph **1**.

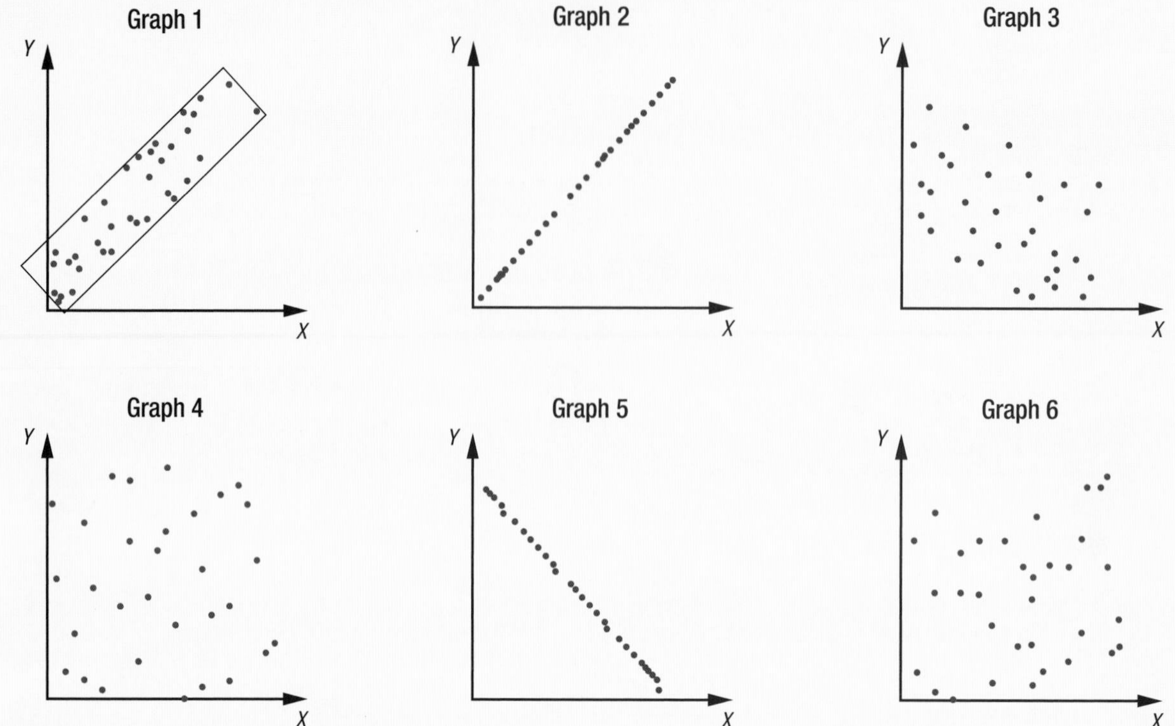

a. For each of these graphs, do the following:

1) Draw the smallest rectangle that can contain all of the points.
2) Measure the dimensions of the rectangle.

Match each graph to one of the linear correlation coefficients *r* in the adjacent table and add the dimensions of the corresponding rectangle to the table.

Graph number	*r*	Width of rectangle (mm)	Length of rectangle (mm)
	1		
	0.8		
	0.2		
	0		
	-0.5		
	-1		

b. Is there a relationship between the dimensions of the rectangle and the strength of the correlation between the two variables? Justify your answer.

c. Using the information you collect, find a rule that allows you to estimate the value of the correlation coefficient based on the dimensions of the rectangle.

d. Compare your rule to the rule found by other students, and together decide on the best method to estimate a linear correlation coefficient.

Make a critical judgement

Scatter plots make it possible to quickly detect the interaction between two variables. However, it is important to think carefully about how they are interpreted. In each of the following cases, the conclusion expressed by the person seems doubtful.

You should walk to school. Follow your friends' example: the more time they take to get to school, the better they succeed.

Success, a question of time

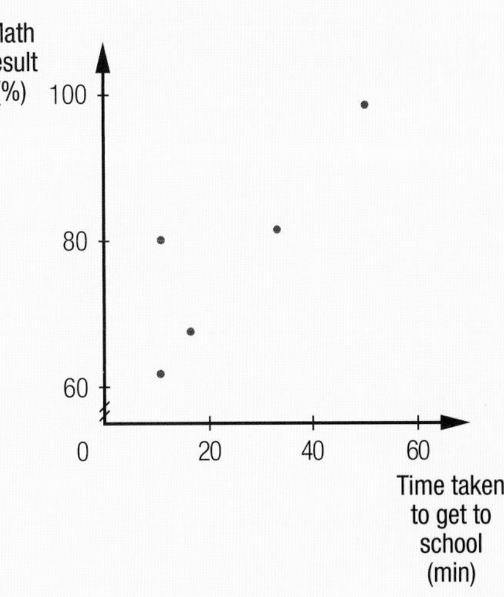

You understand, boss, the correlation coefficient associated with this graph is negative. It explains it all. The more time people spend in the store, the less they buy. That's why we think you should hire an extra salesperson; service will be faster.

Amount spent in a store

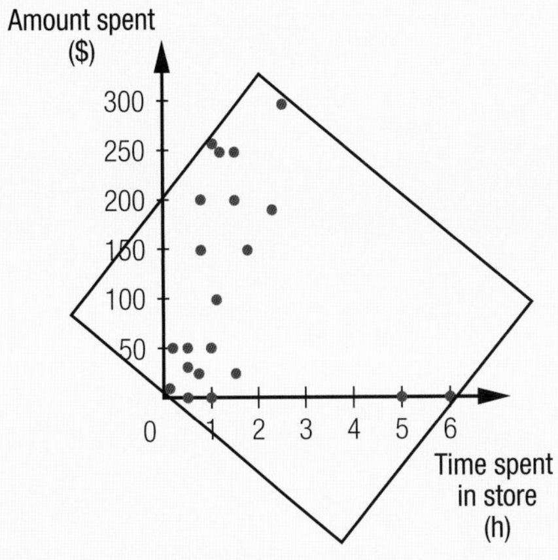

Stop chatting. It distracts from your schoolwork.

But Mom, I never chat more than an hour a day.

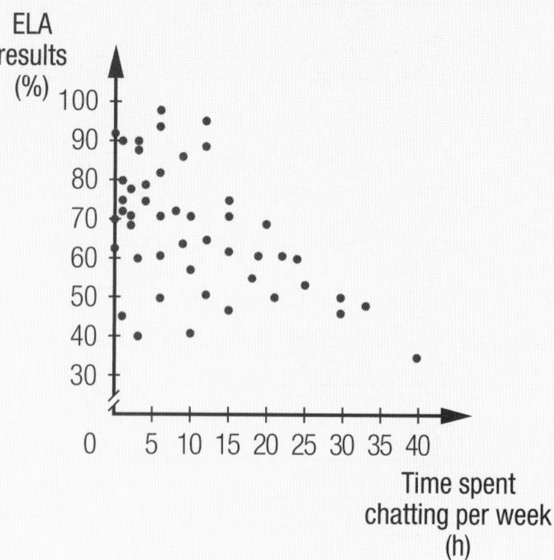

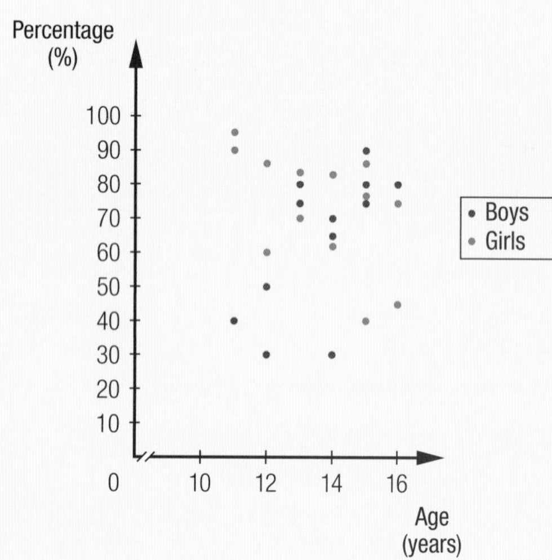

This graph illustrates that young smokers are in the habit of smoking with their friends. If you look closely at the graph, you will see that the correlation is nearly zero. I conclude that age does not influence the percentage of time students spend smoking with their friends.

a. For each of the four situations above, explain why the conclusion is doubtful.

b. How would you proceed to get a valid estimate of each correlation coefficient?

c. Interpret each situation.

Techno math

A spreadsheet allows you to perform statistical calculations on numbers entered into cells and to generate a graphical representation based on the data entered. For example:

Screen 1

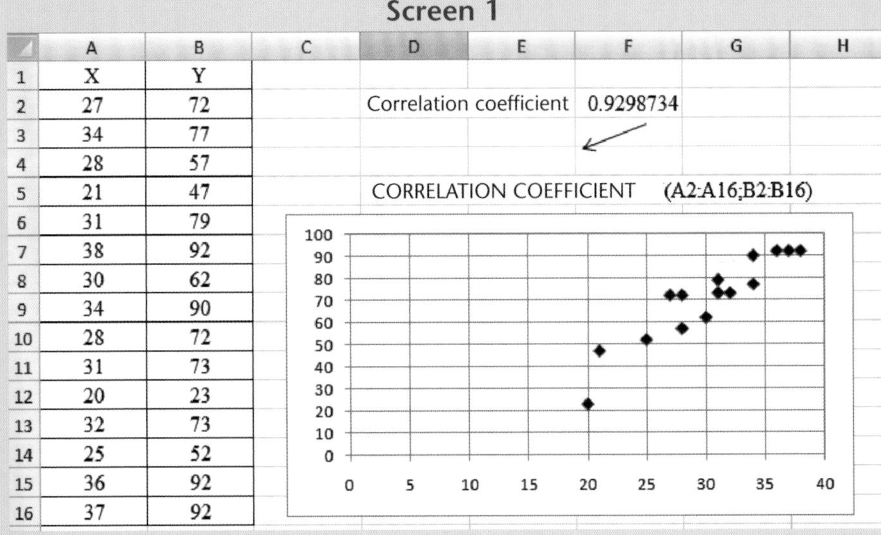

	A	B
1	X	Y
2	27	72
3	34	77
4	28	57
5	21	47
6	31	79
7	38	92
8	30	62
9	34	90
10	28	72
11	31	73
12	20	23
13	32	73
14	25	52
15	36	92
16	37	92

The data values of the distribution are entered into two columns.

The linear correlation coefficient is calculated automatically using a formula.

The scatter plot may also be displayed.

Study the changes in the value of the linear correlation coefficient in the graph resulting from changes in data values of the distribution. If the values in cells B10, B13 and B15 are changed, the result is:

A better graphical representation can be obtained by adjusting the scales of the axes. For example:

Screen 2

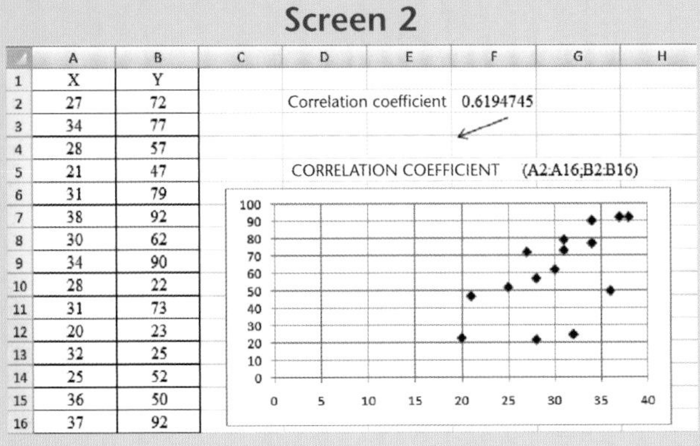

	A	B
1	X	Y
2	27	72
3	34	77
4	28	57
5	21	47
6	31	79
7	38	92
8	30	62
9	34	90
10	28	22
11	31	73
12	20	23
13	32	25
14	25	52
15	36	50
16	37	92

Screen 3

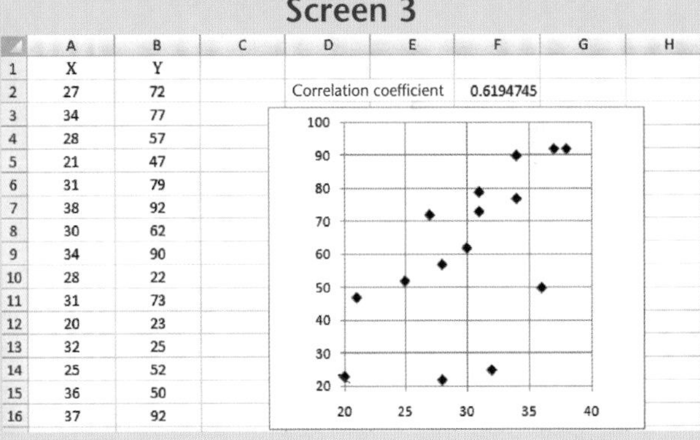

	A	B
1	X	Y
2	27	72
3	34	77
4	28	57
5	21	47
6	31	79
7	38	92
8	30	62
9	34	90
10	28	22
11	31	73
12	20	23
13	32	25
14	25	52
15	36	50
16	37	92

a. In Screen **1**, what is the meaning of «`A2:A16;B2:B16`» in the calculation of the linear correlation coefficient?

b. What change has occurred in the scatter plot on Screen **2**?

c. Use a spreadsheet to find the linear correlation coefficient and to draw the scatter plot of the following distribution. Modify the axes of the graph if necessary.

X	27	34	28	21	31	38	30	34	28	31	20	32	25	36	37	28	22	22	39	49
Y	33	32	27	33	51	22	28	25	29	28	37	22	33	21	23	36	41	41	18	29

LINEAR CORRELATION COEFFICIENT

The linear correlation coefficient, represented by *r*, is used to quantify the intensity of the linear relationship between two variables. The value of this coefficient is in the interval [-1,1].

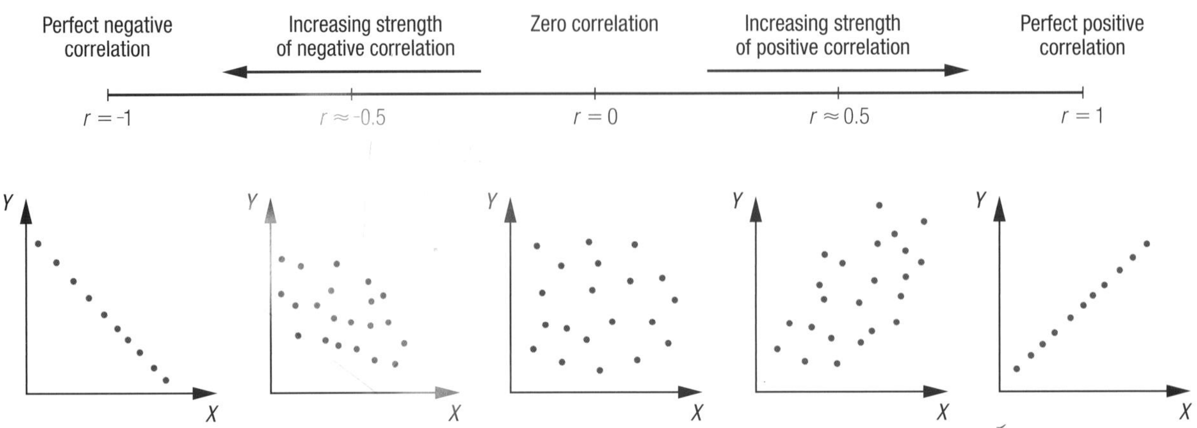

Calculating the linear correlation coefficient is a complex process; technology is usually used to facilitate this task.

Estimating the linear correlation coefficient

You can estimate the value of *r* using a graphical method called the rectangle method. This method consists of the following steps:

1. Measure the longer side *L* and shorter side *l* of the rectangle that best contains all the points of the scatter plot.
2. Use the following expression to calculate the approximate value of the correlation coefficient *r*:

$$\pm\left(1 - \frac{l}{L}\right)$$

The sign in front of the brackets is decided by looking at the direction of the points that form the scatter plot.

This estimate is valid only if the scatter plot is constructed properly. The scales on the axes must take into account the dispersion of each variable.

E.g.

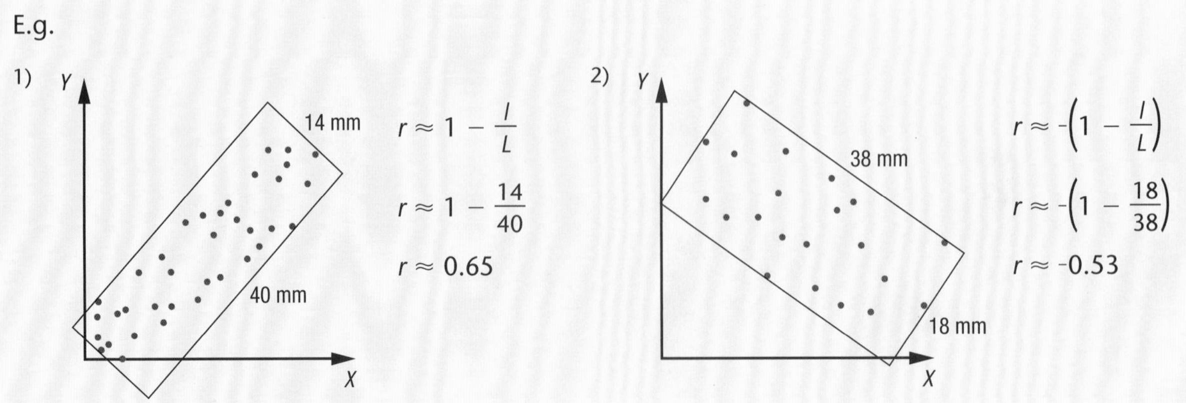

1) $r \approx 1 - \frac{l}{L}$

$r \approx 1 - \frac{14}{40}$

$r \approx 0.65$

2) $r \approx -\left(1 - \frac{l}{L}\right)$

$r \approx -\left(1 - \frac{18}{38}\right)$

$r \approx -0.53$

INTERPRETING THE CORRELATION COEFFICIENT

The interpretation of the value of a correlation coefficient varies from one area of study to another. In the physical sciences (chemistry, physics, etc.), a correlation coefficient of 0.5 would be considered a weak correlation. On the other hand, in the social sciences (psychology, sociology, etc.), it would be considered an indication of a strong correlation.

E.g. If you are analyzing the number of deaths that occur and the number of people taking a certain drug, a correlation coefficient of 0.3 would be considered to be a strong correlation.

Some sources of bias can lead to incorrect conclusions.

Source of bias	Example
Non-representative sample A sample which is not representative can give a false impression of the correlation between two variables of the population.	A very small sample can suggest that the correlation is stronger or weaker than it really is.
Outliers The rectangle method of estimating the correlation coefficient is less reliable when outliers are present. It is better to exclude these isolated points from the estimation process.	Y X
Two distinct groups The presence of two groups in the sample can lead us to believe that the correlation is stronger or weaker than it really is.	Y X The correlation is positive if all the points are considered but it is zero within each of the two groups.
Interval-based correlation Sometimes, differences in correlation are observed over different intervals. In that case, it is preferable to make a distinction.	Y X The correlation is strong for the smaller values of X but weak for the greater values.

practice 1.2

1 Select the scatter plot that best represents each of the following linear correlation coefficients:

a) −0.98; −0.86; 0.61; 0.94

A 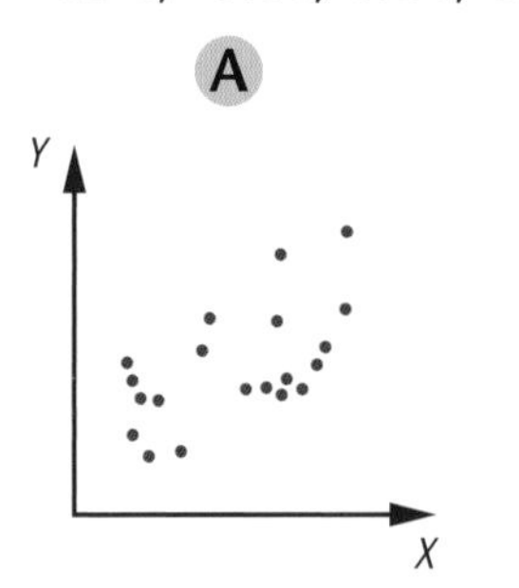

B 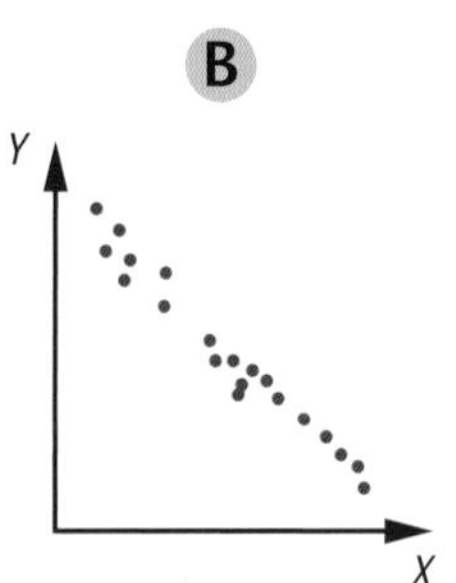

C 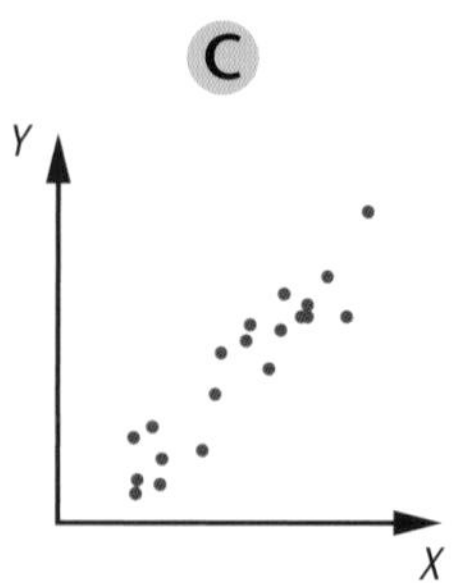

D 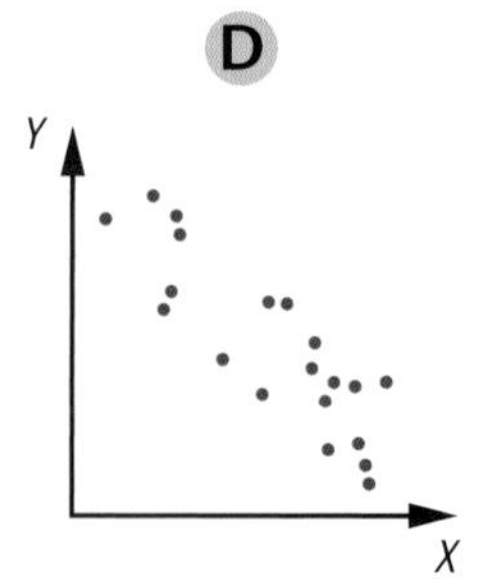

b) 0.05; 0.38; 0.51; 0.78

A 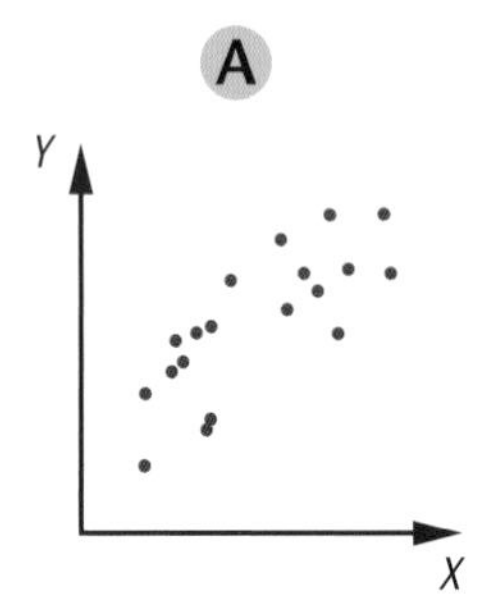

B 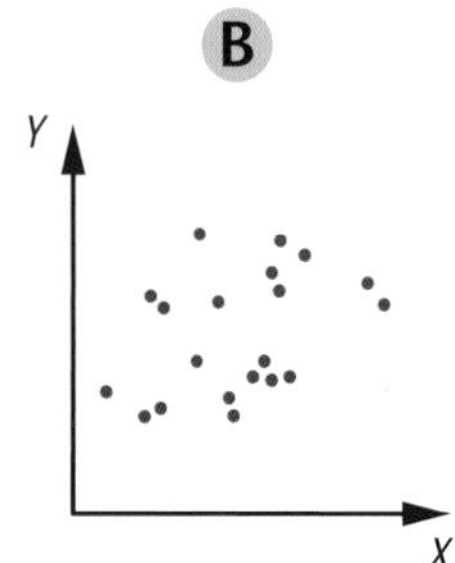

C 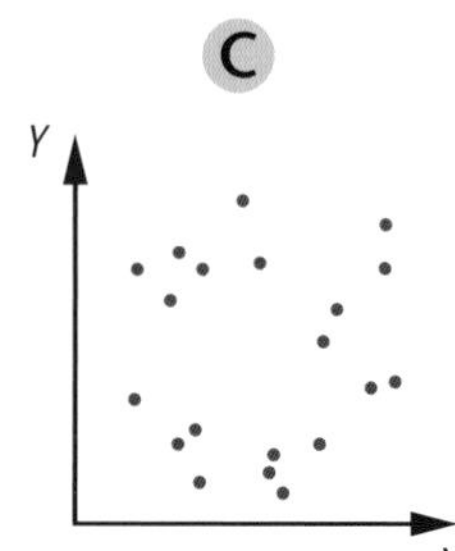

D 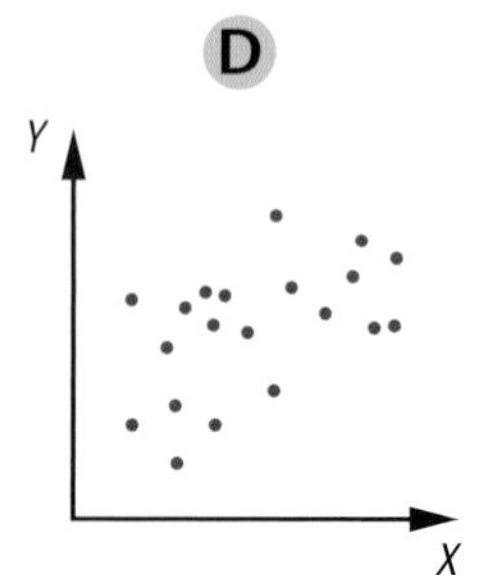

c) −0.58; −0.30; 0.24; 0.57

A 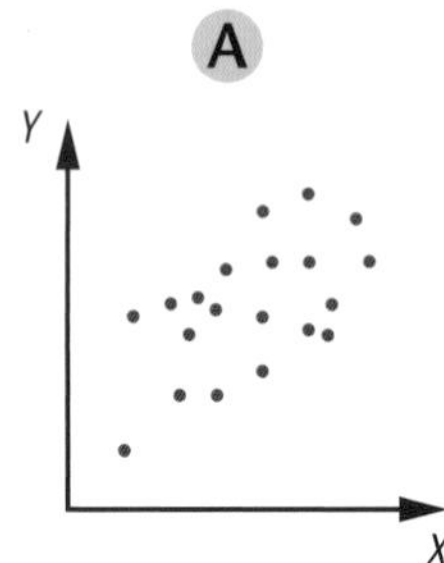

B 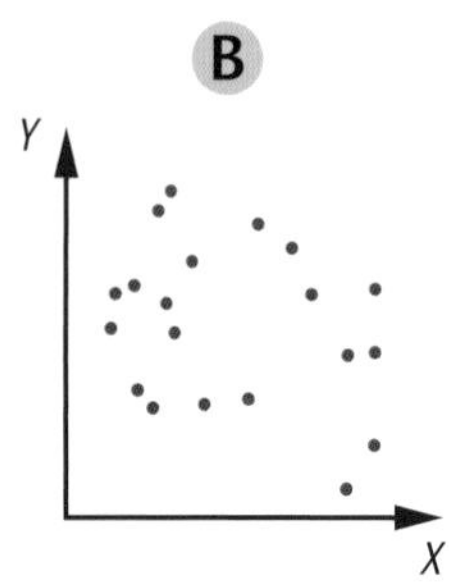

C 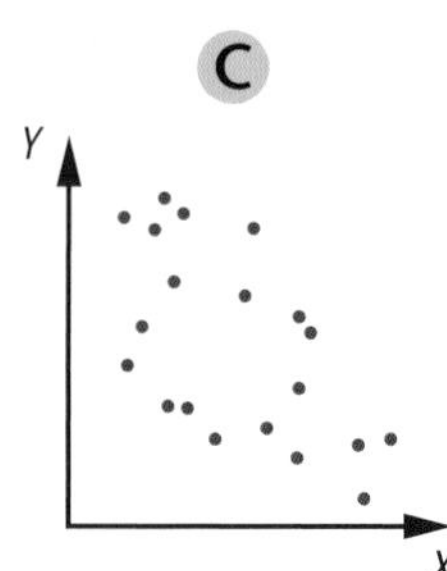

D 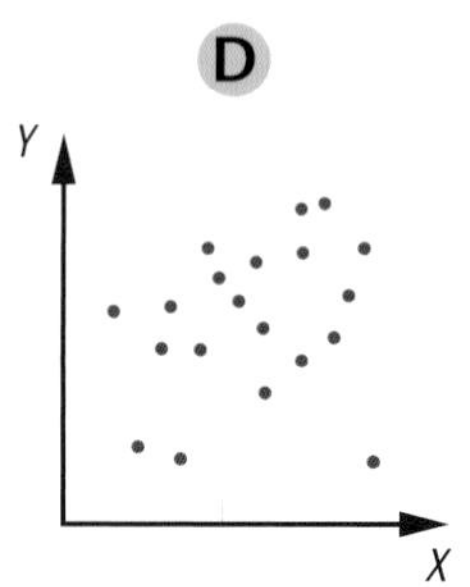

2 In each table of values, assign a number from 1 to 5 to the variable *Y*, so that the correlation coefficient of the two variables will be as close as possible to the indicated value of *r*.

a) $r = -1$

X	Y
1	
2	
3	
4	
5	

b) $r = 0$

X	Y
1	
2	
3	
4	
5	

c) $r = 0.5$

X	Y
1	
2	
3	
4	
5	

3 Use the rectangle method to approximate the linear correlation coefficient associated with each of the following scatter plots.

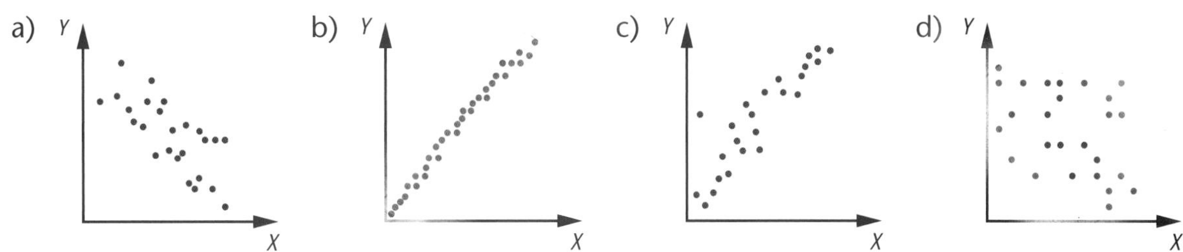

4 Draw a sketch of a scatter plot corresponding to each of the following correlation coefficients.

a) -0.2 b) 0.4 c) 0.8 d) -0.9

5 The administration at Four Corners School asked students to participate in a survey to evaluate their satisfaction with school services. The results are shown in the table below, where 0 represents complete dissatisfaction, and 10 represents complete satisfaction:

Four Corners School

	Satisfaction of boys (from 0 to 10)	Satisfaction of girls (from 0 to 10)
Sports	9	8
Sports facilities	8	9
Sports-study program	7	8
Cultural activities	7	3
Technology	8	9
Teachers	7	7
Student body	6	7
Administrative staff	6	6
Support staff	5	5
School location	3	4
Air quality	4	5
Cleanliness	4	4
Cafeteria	3	2
School auditorium	3	8
Library	2	3

a) Estimate the linear correlation coefficient between the degree of satisfaction of boys and that of girls.

b) Can you conclude that there is not much difference between the degree of satisfaction of boys and that of girls? Why?

c) Can you conclude that all is well in this school? What is your understanding of the situation?

6 HEALTH INDICATORS

The following table shows the provincial breakdown from a study on Canadian health:

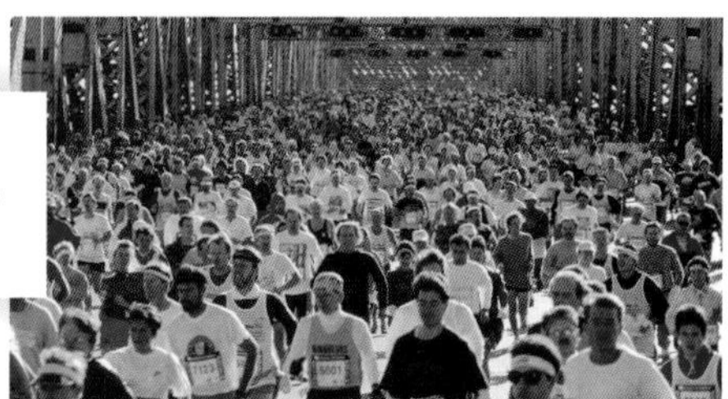
In 2007, close to 9000 people participated in the races at the Montréal Marathon.

Health indicators

	Individuals aged 12 years and over who practice one recreational physical activity (%)	Individuals who consume 5 or more portions of fruit and vegetables per day (%)	Adults who smoke regularly or occasionally (%)	Adults who drink more than 5 glasses of alcohol a day, more than 12 times a year (%)	Obese adults (%)
British Columbia	59	40	19	24	13
Alberta	55	36	24	24	16
Saskatchewan	52	33	26	28	21
Manitoba	50	32	23	25	18
Ontario	53	40	23	24	15
Québec	49	50	26	22	14
New Brunswick	48	34	25	29	24
Nova Scotia	52	34	25	29	22
Price Edward Island	47	30	24	29	24
Newfoundland	47	22	25	35	25

a) Which of the first four variables listed (physical activity, portions of fruit and vegetables, smoking, alcohol consumption) has the strongest correlation with obesity? Justify your answer.

b) Explain the strong correlation identified above.

c) In view of this data, what would you suggest to an individual who is concerned about their mass?

7

A sports medicine specialist studied the relationship between the muscle mass of her patients and their physical strength. Her results are displayed in the scatter plot below:

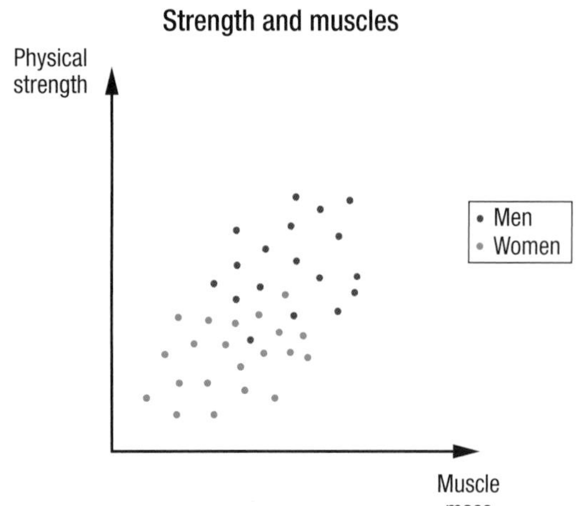

a) Estimate the linear correlation coefficient between the variables for:
   1) men
   2) women
   3) all patients

b) Based on this graph, draw a conclusion about the relationship between muscle mass and physical strength. Justify your conclusion.

8 Québec sociologists have studied the relationship between annual family income and the birth rate in five different cultural communities. The linear correlation coefficients are as follows:

Community	A	B	C	D	E
r	0.6	-0.3	0	-0.8	0.1

a) Arrange the communities according to the intensity of the correlation, from weakest to strongest.

b) Identify which community is described in each of the following statements.
   1) In this community, the richest families have noticeably fewer children than the poorest families.
   2) Generally speaking, the richer the families in this community, the more children they have, but there are exceptions.
   3) In this community, all families have many children. Family income does not influence the number of children.

9 In a clinical trial carried out before a new analgesic was approved for use on arthritic patients, researchers studied the possible relationship between the daily dosage and the frequency of psychological problems such as depression during the trial period. The data collected is presented in the adjacent scatter plot.

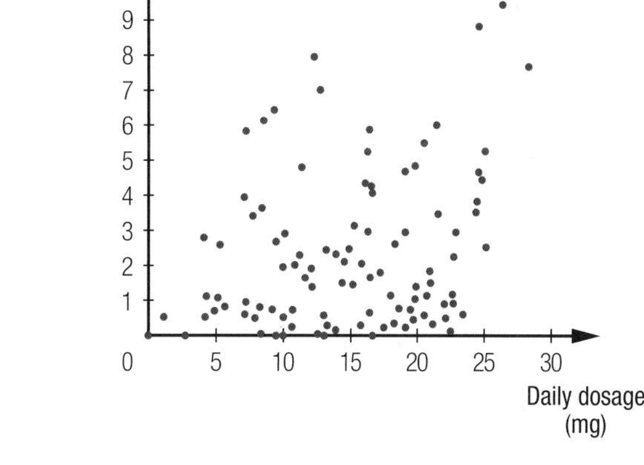

a) Estimate the linear correlation coefficient between these two variables.

b) Considering that it is an effective painkiller, should this drug be commercialized? Defend your point of view.

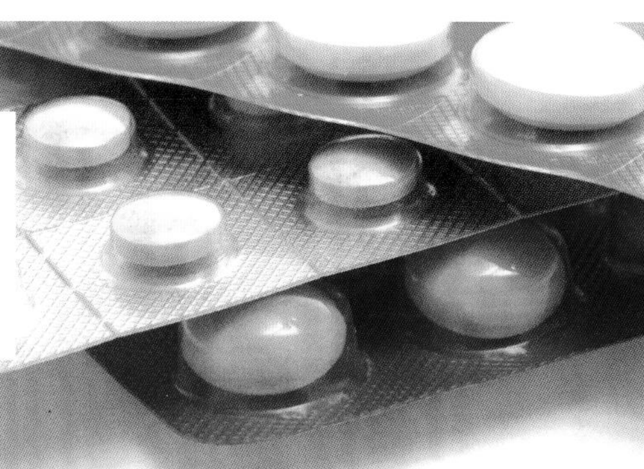

Clinical trials do not end when a drug is commercialized. Phase IV trials continue in order to detect any undesirable effect that may have been missed during the preceding trials.

10 Thirty-five goaltenders in the National Hockey League were the subjects of Peter's study on the relationship between the mean number of goals scored against them per game and their ice time. Peter drew the scatter plot below and estimated the correlation coefficient to be -0.86.

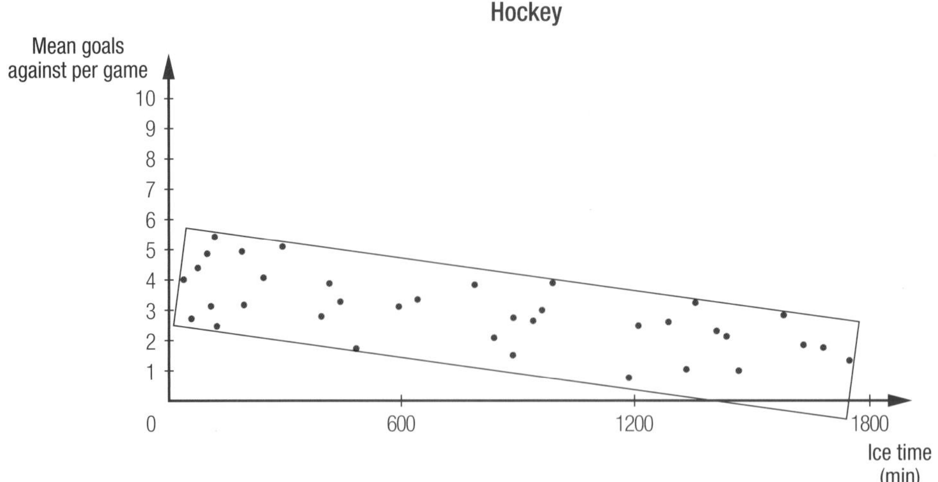

Caroline carried out the same analysis and arrived at slightly different conclusions using the same data. According to her, Peter is overestimating the strength of the correlation. She calculated the coefficient to be -0.6.

a) Who is right? Present your arguments.

b) How could the relationship between these two variables be explained?

c) If you had to draw the graph of the relationship between these two variables, how would it differ from Peter's graph?

11 Thirty students aged 15 to 16 years were asked how much time they spend each week working at a paid after-school job. Their academic achievement was evaluated on a scale of 1 to 10. The following data was obtained:

Students at work

Time worked (h)	0	0	0	0	0	0	3	3	3	3	4	5	6	6	8
Academic achievement	9	8	6	5	4	3	10	8	7	4	6	8	10	9	10

Time worked (h)	8	9	10	10	12	12	12	12	15	15	15	16	16	20	20
Academic achievement	8	6	9	6	8	7	6	5	8	6	4	6	4	4	3

a) Analyze the correlation between these two variables.

b) Considering this data, would you say that working interferes with academic achievement? Explain your answer.

It is estimated that close to half the students in the last two years of secondary school have a paid job.

12 In the table below, $\overline{X}$ and $\overline{Y}$ represent the respective means of the X and Y values, and the expressions $X - \overline{X}$ and $Y - \overline{Y}$ are the mean deviations.

a) Complete this table.

b) On a Cartesian plane, draw a scatter plot of the mean deviations.

c) In which quadrants are most of the points located?

d) Estimate the linear correlation coefficient of this distribution.

e) Is there a relationship between the answers in **c)** and in **d)**? Explain.

	X	Y	$X - \overline{X}$	$Y - \overline{Y}$
	1	3		
	1	4		
	1	2		
	2	5		
	3	1		
	3	2		
	4	2		
	4	0		
	5	1		
	6	0		
Sum				
Mean				

13 The linear correlation coefficient can be calculated using different methods; using the mean deviations is one method. The table from above is repeated below, but three new columns have been added:

X	Y	$X - \overline{X}$	$Y - \overline{Y}$	$(X - \overline{X})(Y - \overline{Y})$	$(X - \overline{X})^2$	$(Y - \overline{Y})^2$
1	3					
1	4					
1	2					
2	5					
3	1					
3	2					
4	2					
4	0					
5	1					
6	0					
			Sum			
				↓ A	↓ B	↓ C

a) Complete this table.

b) If A represents the sum of the products of the deviations from the mean, and B and C represent the sum of the squares of the deviations from the mean for the variables X and Y, respectively, then r is expressed as $\frac{A}{\sqrt{B \times C}}$. Calculate the correlation coefficient r and check your answer using a technological tool.

SECTION 1.3 The line as a model

This section is related to LES 3.

PROBLEM Should we sell today?

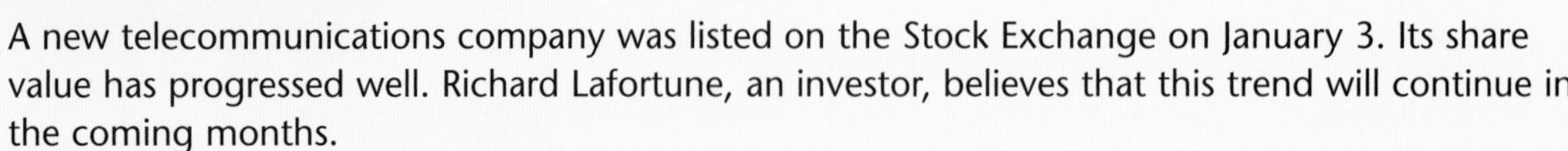

A new telecommunications company was listed on the Stock Exchange on January 3. Its share value has progressed well. Richard Lafortune, an investor, believes that this trend will continue in the coming months.

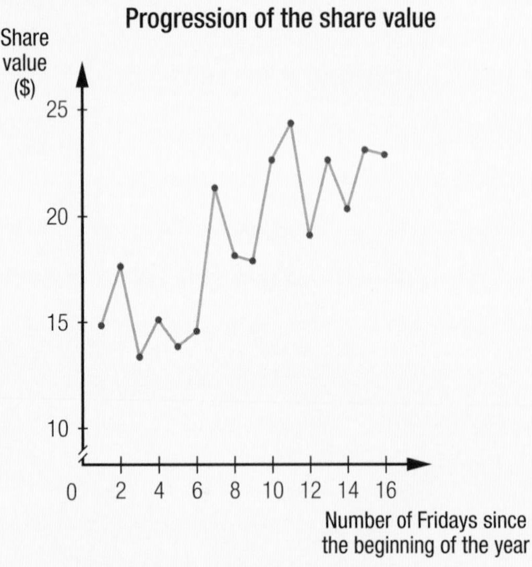

First quarter yield

Month	Mean share value Friday at closing ($)	Value of share on last Friday of month ($)
January	15.13	15.00
February	16.88	18.00
March	20.88	19.00

Share value Friday at closing

Date	Share value ($)
January 7	14.75
January 14	17.50
January 21	13.25
January 28	15.00
February 4	13.75
February 11	14.50
February 18	21.25
February 25	18.00
March 4	17.75
March 11	22.50
March 18	24.25
March 25	19.00
April 1	22.50
April 8	20.25
April 15	23.00
April 22	22.75

If Richard Lafortune is right, at what date will the share have doubled its initial value? Be sure that others can use your method to arrive at the same date as you.

ACTIVITY 1 A quick, simple method

Yassim would like to find a method to quickly define a line that best represents the set of points of a scatter plot. To better understand the problem he starts by considering a simple case consisting of three points.

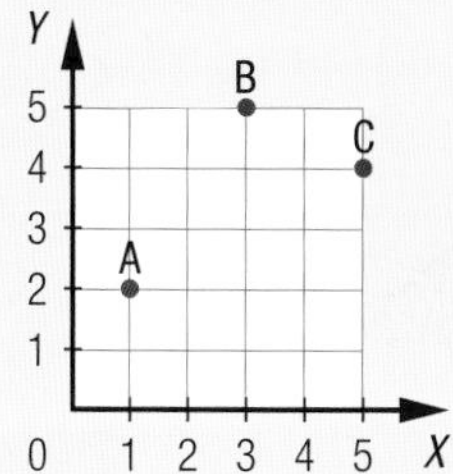

a. Of points A, B and C on the adjacent graph, which two best define the direction of the line?

Yassim feels that the line should not pass through these two points because the third would then not have been considered at all. He thinks the line should pass through another point that represents all three.

b. What are the coordinates of this representative point? Justify your answer.

c. Draw the line defined by your answers to questions **a.** and **b.**, and find its equation.

After having found a method using three points, Yassim examines a more elaborate scatter plot.

X	Y
1	54
1	45
2	40
3	46
5	42
5	14
6	45
7	22
7	38
8	33
9	26
10	46
10	14

X	Y
11	30
11	15
13	19
14	22
14	13
15	38
15	4
17	13
18	3
18	25
19	4
20	8

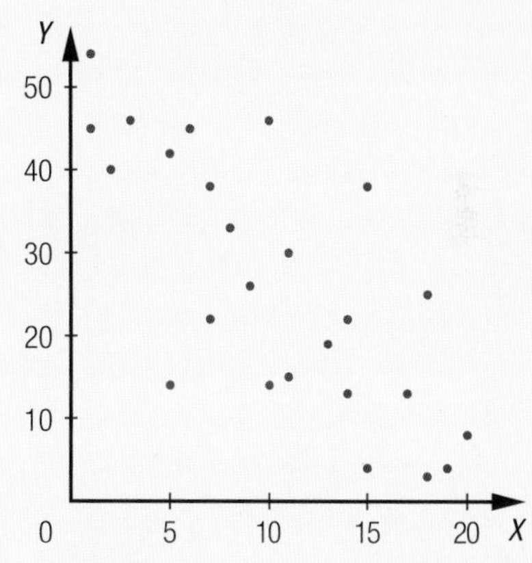

If I could represent all of the data using only three points, I could apply the same method I used previously.

d. Suggest an appropriate statistical method to quickly determine three representative points of this distribution. Share your proposal with other students.

e. Using these three points, draw the line that best represents the scatter plot and find its equation.

ACTIVITY 2 May the best line win!

During an experiment, Camilla obtained the results recorded in the adjacent table. She wants to model the situation using a line, but she wonders: "Could one line be a better fit than any other possible line? A criterion is required." Such a criterion does exist. It was put forward by the mathematician Karl Friedrich Gauss at the beginning of the 19th century.

Value of X	Observed value of Y
0	2
2	6
4	4
6	8
8	7
10	9

Carl Friedrich Gauss (1777-1855)

« The observed values always deviate from the values predicted by a model. These deviations should be as small as possible. This is a good criterion to use when judging a model. But if we simply add the differences between the observed and predicted values, then the positive and negative values will cancel out. That is why I suggest finding the model that *minimizes the sum of the squares of the differences.* »

Examine the adjacent graph. Camilla used this scatter plot to display her experimental data. The relationship between the variables can be modelled using the linear equation $y = 0.8x + 2$. The red segments represent the deviations of the theoretical values from the observed values of Y.

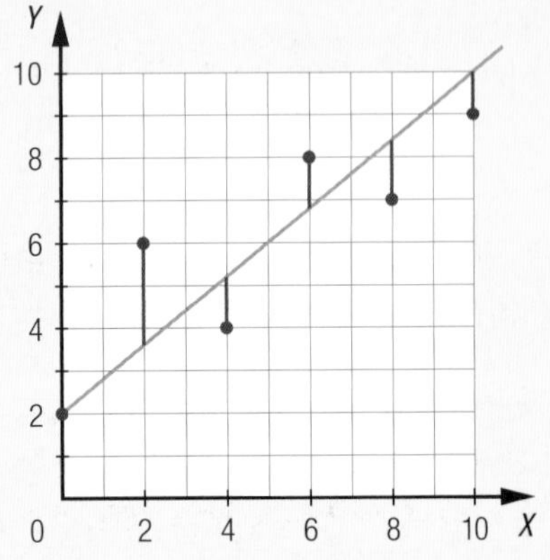

a. Use the equation $y = 0.8x + 2$ to find the theoretical values of Y; complete the adjacent table; then calculate the sum of the squares of deviation.

b. Suggest a line that fits the scatter plot better than Camilla's. Justify your answer using the Gauss criterion.

Value of X	Observed value of Y	Theoretical value of Y	Deviation $Y_{obs} - Y_{th}$	Square deviations $(Y_{obs} - Y_{th})^2$
0	2			
2	6			
4	4			
6	8			
8	7			
10	9			
			Sum:	

ACTIVITY 3 A new auditorium

The owner of a new theatre in the Laurentians must decide on the admission fee she should charge. She does not want the fee to be so high as to discourage potential customers. She decides to hire a market analyst to survey the target market. The scatter plot below illustrates the results collected. The regression line is drawn in orange; its equation is $y = -4.74x + 247.89$.

a. Estimate the correlation coefficient of this distribution.

b. Using the line drawn on the graph, estimate the number of spectators if the admission fee is:

1) \$5

2) \$25

3) \$50

c. Does this regression line adequately represent the scatter plot? Justify your answer.

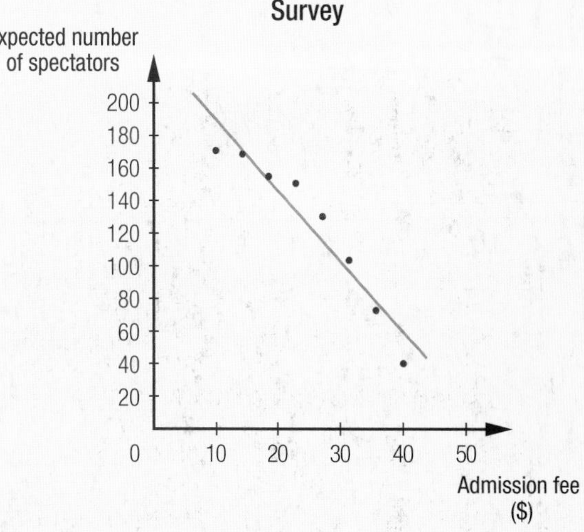

In order to suggest an admission fee to the owner, the analyst calculates the expected ticket revenue for each show.

Expected revenue per show for different admission fees

Admission fee (\$)	12	16	20	24	28	32	36	40
Revenue (\$)	2,064	2,720	3,120	3,648	3,668	3,328	2,628	1,560

The software used by the analyst also produces the equation of the regression line and the linear correlation coefficient between these two variables.

d. Considering the weak value of r, can you conclude that the admission price has little effect on the predicted revenue? Justify your answer.

e. What should the analyst's recommendation be?

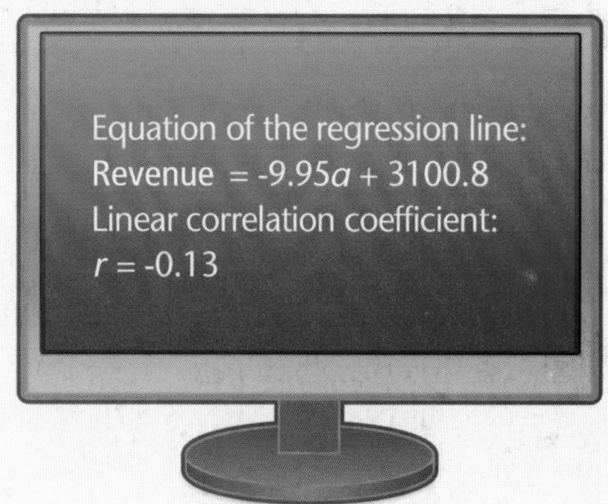

Techno math

A graphing calculator allows you to display a scatter plot and determine the equation of the regression line using the least squares method.

This table of values shows the results of an experiment involving two variables.

X	0	1	2	3	4	5	6	7
Y	6.90	7.00	7.20	7.30	7.45	7.60	7.75	8.00

This screen allows you to enter each ordered pair from the table of values.

Screen 1

L1	L2	L3 3
0	6.9	
1	7	
2	7.2	
3	7.3	
4	7.45	
5	7.6	
6	7.75	
7	8	

L3(1)=1

This screen allows you to choose the scatter plot as the display mode.

Screen 2

Screen 3

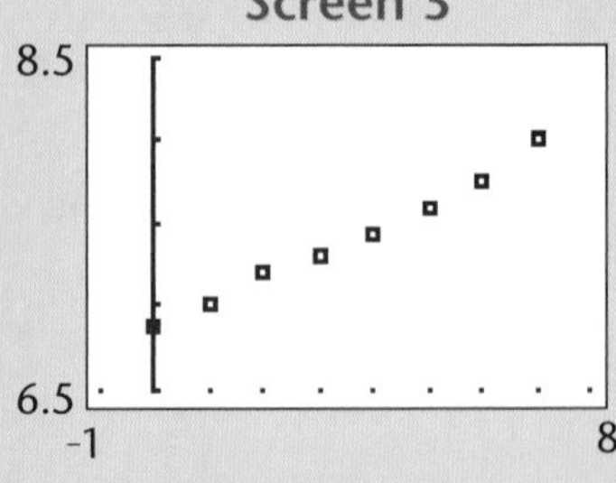

This screen allows you to find the equation of the regression line using the least squares method.

Screen 4

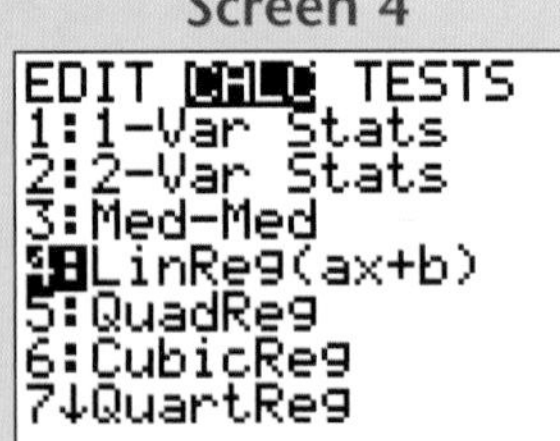

This screen allows you to place the equation of the regression line in the equation editor, and to display the equation and the correlation coefficient *r*.

Screen 5

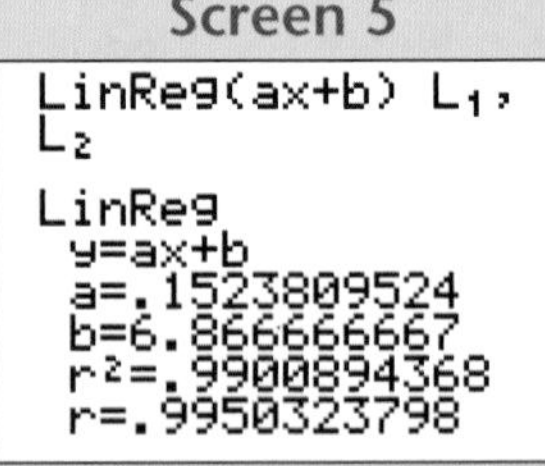

Move the cursor on the screen to display the coordinates of the points on the regression line.

Screen 6

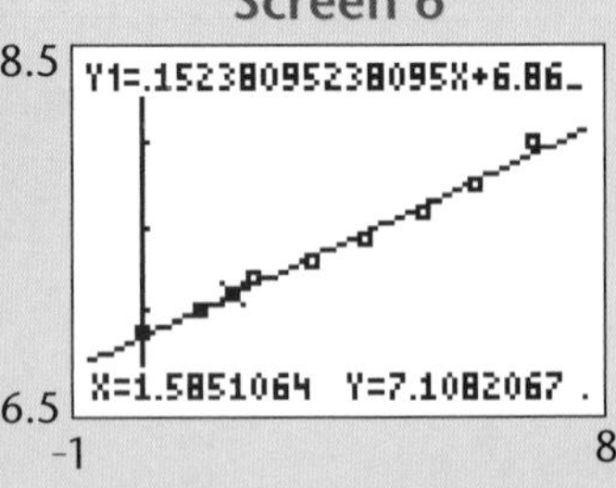

a. Use a graphing calculator to generate the scatter plot of the data below and to draw the regression line using the least squares method.

X	10	15	20	25	30	35	40
Y	65.2	71.1	73.1	76.7	77.4	78.8	80.5

b. What is the equation of this regression line?

c. Estimate the value of *Y* for *X* = 0 and for *X* = 50.

d. Is this line the best model to represent this data? Justify your answer.

knowledge 1.3

MODELLING WITH A FIRST-DEGREE POLYNOMIAL FUNCTION

If the linear correlation between the two variables of a distribution is strong enough to reveal a dependency relationship, it becomes worthwhile to model the situation using a first-degree polynomial function. With this model, using interpolation or extrapolation, it is possible to predict the values of the variables involved. In general, the stronger the correlation the more reliable the prediction will be. The rule of this function can be determined by any one of several methods with each method yielding a different regression line.

The least squares method

The use of this method generates the line of best fit for a scatter plot. However, the calculations required to determine its position are complex. The graph of this line and its equation are usually determined with the help of a technological tool.

E.g.

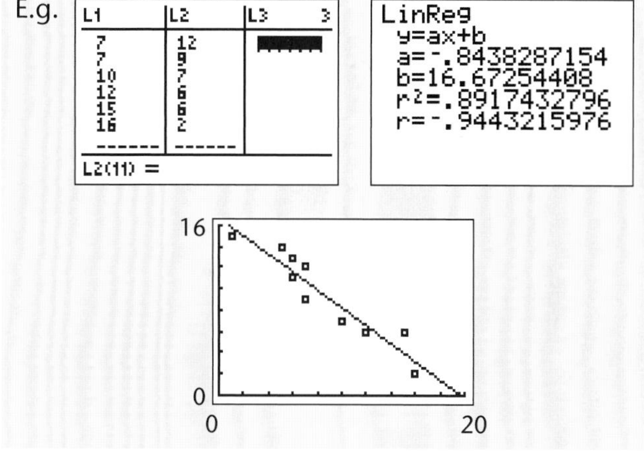

The Mayer line method

The use of this method results in a line that passes through two representative points of the distribution. Follow these steps to define this line:

Step 1 Arrange the distribution in increasing order with respect to the *x*-variable, then split it into two groups that are equal, if possible.

Step 2 Calculate the mean of the data in each group and obtain points P_1 and P_2.

E.g.

	Mean of the *x*-coordinates: 5					Mean of the *x*-coordinates: 12				
X	1	5	6	6	7	7	10	12	15	16
Y	15	14	13	11	12	9	7	6	6	2
	Mean of the *y*-coordinates: 13					Mean of the *y*-coordinates: 6				
	$P_1(5, 13)$					$P_2(12, 6)$				

Step 3 Find the equation of the Mayer line that passes through these two points.

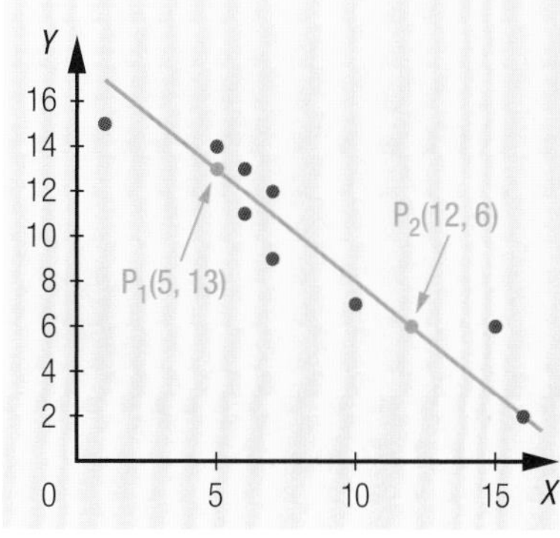

Rate of change from P_1 to P_2: $\frac{6 - 13}{12 - 5} = -1$

Value of **b**: $y = -x + b$

$13 = -5 + b$

$b = 18$

The equation of the Mayer line is:

$y = -x + 18$

The median-median line method

When dealing with a large amount of data for a distribution, this method has the advantage of requiring fewer calculations to determine the position of the line of best fit. Follow these steps to define this line:

Step 1 Arrange the distribution in increasing order with respect to the *x*-variable, then divide the distribution into three equal groups. If this is not possible, the first and third groups must contain the same number of data values.

E.g.

	Median of the *x*-coordinates: 5			Median of the *x*-coordinates: 7				Median of the *x*-coordinates: 15		
X	1	**5**	6	6	**7**	**7**	10	12	**15**	16
Y	15	**14**	13	**11**	12	**9**	7	6	**6**	2
	Median of the *y*-coordinates: 14			Median of the *y*-coordinates: 10				Median of the *y*-coordinates: 6		
	$M_1(5, 14)$			$M_2(7, 10)$				$M_3(15, 6)$		

Step 2 Find the median of the data values in each group to get the coordinates of points M_1, M_2, and M_3.

Step 3 Calculate the mean of the coordinates of these three points to find those of point P.

The mean of the medians is as follows:

x-coordinate: $(5 + 7 + 15) \div 3 = 9$

y-coordinate: $(14 + 10 + 6) \div 3 = 10$

point P is: P(9, 10)

Step 4 Find the equation of the median-median line passing through P and parallel to line M_1M_3.

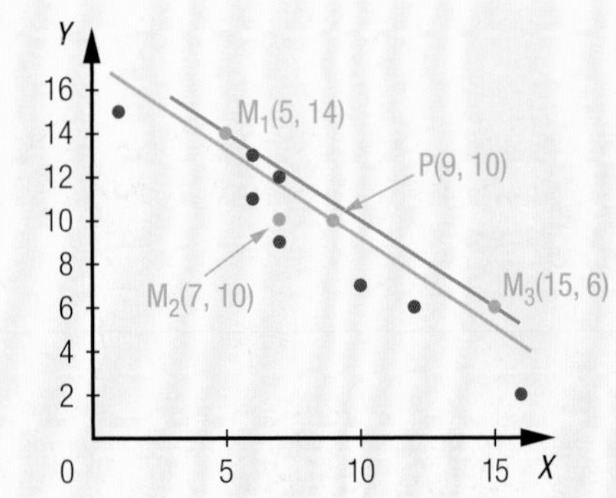

The line must pass through P(9, 10).

Rate of change from M_1 to M_3: $\frac{6 - 14}{15 - 5} = -0.8$

The parallel line passing through P has the same rate of change.

Value of **b**: $y = -0.8x + b$

$10 = -0.8(9) + b$

$b = 17.2$

The equation of the median-median line is:

$$y = -0.8x + 17.2$$

MODELLING USING OTHER FUNCTIONAL MODELS

A weak or zero linear correlation does not mean that no relationship exists between the variables. A **correlation** can be **non-linear**. In such a case, the situation is modelled graphically with a curve of best fit.

E.g.

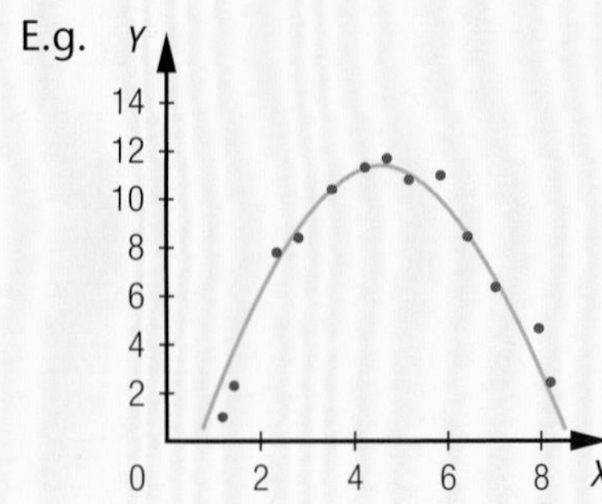

Linear correlation is close to zero. However, the orange curve reveals a strong non-linear correlation.

practice 1.3

1 Each of these scatter plots was modelled using the Mayer line method.

1) 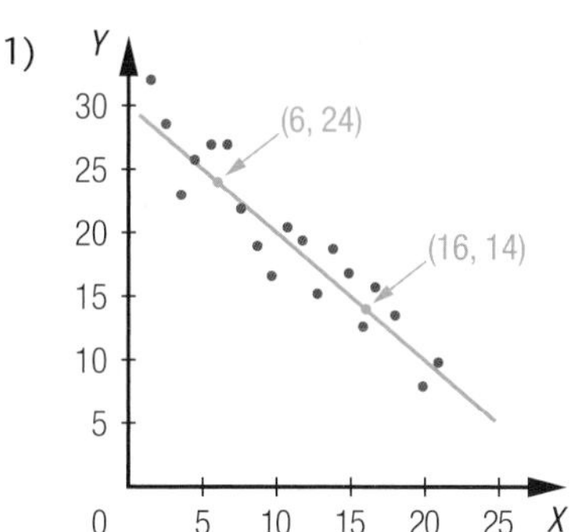

2) 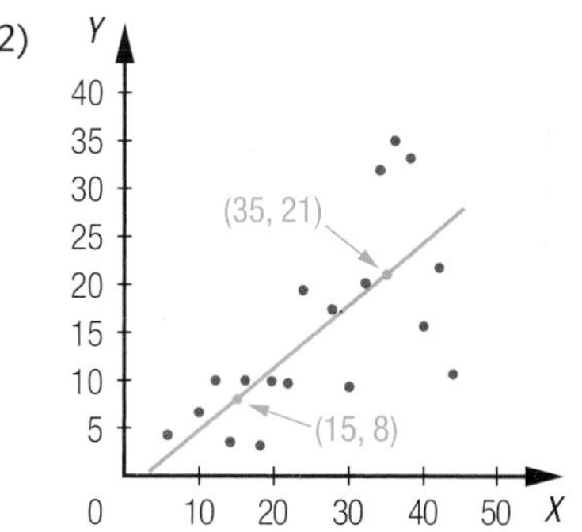

3) 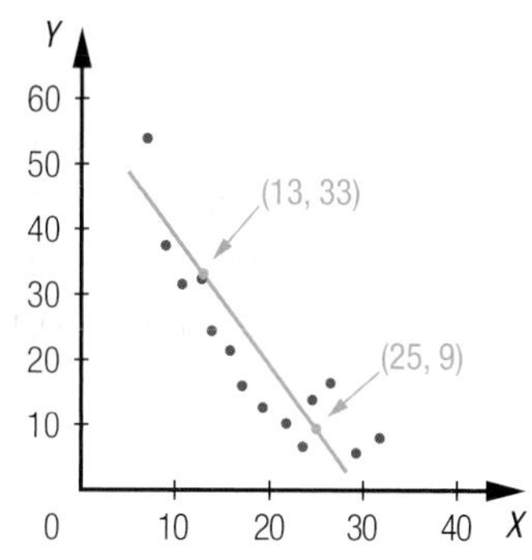

a) Find the equation of these lines.

b) In each case, consider the distribution of points on the scatter plot, and decide if the line is an adequate model. Justify your answer.

2 The three median points of a distribution are $M_1(4, 2)$, $M_2(8, 8)$ and $M_3(12, 20)$.

a) Provide an example of a two-variable distribution, composed of nine data values, that could represent the distribution described above. Draw the scatter plot for this distribution.

b) Draw the median-median line for this scatter plot and find its equation.

c) Is this line representative of the distribution? Why?

3 Over the past six years, Francophone adults were polled on whether they intended to start a business. A journalist compared the results of the poll to the actual number of businesses that were started annually.

a) Find the equation of the line of best fit for this data.

b) If 50% of Francophone adults had intended to start a business, how many businesses would actually have been started?

c) Do you think that this model is representative of reality? Explain your point of view.

Poll

Number of adults intending to start a business (%)	Number of businesses started (thousands)
29	262
31	269
27	269
23	292
25	319
20	342

4 For each of the distributions below, do the following:

a) Draw the scatter plot.

b) Draw the Mayer line, and find its equation.

c) Draw the median-median line, and find its equation.

d) For each line, determine the value of Y when $X = 25$.

Distribution 1

X	11	14	19	20	21	23	24	26	27	30
Y	8	5	9	10	18	17	15	20	22	21

Distribution 2

X	1	2	3	4	5	6	7	8	9	10	11	12
Y	20	29	29	27	34	35	35	45	47	59	49	47

Distribution 3

X	2	2	4	4	4	6	6	7	8	9	9	11	12	12	13	13	13	13	15	17
Y	30	23	26	21	28	22	24	20	16	18	14	12	28	11	14	9	8	4	6	4

5 Victoria loves science, especially when it's fun. Last summer she practised skipping pebbles on the surface of the water. Later on, to study this phenomenon, she precisely measured the speed of 12 throws executed under optimal conditions and recorded the number of skips.

a) According to the data, is there a relationship between the initial speed of the pebble and the number of skips?

b) Model this situation using a first-degree polynomial function.

c) Estimate the speed needed to produce 52 skips.

Results of the experiment

Initial speed of pebble (m/s)	Number of skips
7.6	8
7.4	5
7.2	8
9.8	16
5.5	4
9.0	11
6.0	5
8.2	8
8.7	9
7.9	11
9.5	15
6.5	4

In 2007, American Russell Bryars established a world record with 51 skips off the water resulting from one throw of a pebble.

6 **GAS CONSUMPTION** The price of gas has increased substantially in Canada over the past few years, and yet, gas consumption has continued to rise. Consider the data presented below:

Evolution of gas consumption and price in Canada

Year	Total consumption (millions of kL)	Price index at the pump (percentage of 1990 price)
1990	33.9	100
1991	32.8	98
1992	33.3	95
1993	34.0	94
1994	35.0	92
1995	35.1	97
1996	35.5	101
1997	36.3	103
1998	37.4	94
1999	38.3	103
2000	38.3	125
2001	38.8	122
2002	39.6	121
2003	40.2	129
2004	41.0	142

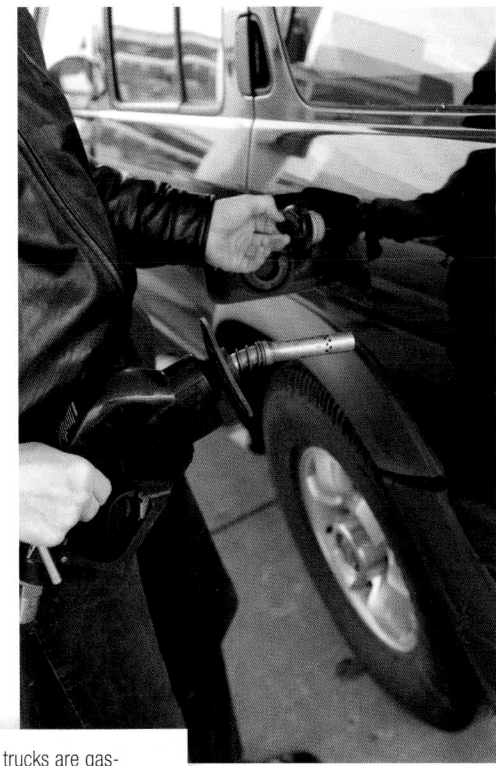

Minivans and trucks are gas-guzzlers. Despite this, 37% of Canadian families owned these types of vehicles in 2005.

a) Draw the scatter plot associated with each of these relationships:
   1) gas consumption and number of years since 1990
   2) gas price index and number of years since 1990
   3) gas consumption and gas price index

b) Draw the line of best fit for each scatter plot and find its equation.

c) In each case, is the line a good model for the data? Explain your point of view.

d) As an economist, you are asked to predict the level of gas consumption and the price index in the year 2025. What are your predictions? Justify them.

7 **WINGSPAN** An ornithologist measured the mass and wingspan of different species of birds. The data obtained and the corresponding scatter plot are shown below:

The wingspan is the distance between the tips of a bird's outstretched wings.

Birds

Mass (g)	Wingspan (cm)	Mass (g)	Wingspan (cm)
18	24	220	42
21	26	270	73
23	31	360	80
30	32	450	54
40	18	750	145
50	52	800	135
50	34	1030	79
61	33	1300	115
155	73	2250	160
210	76	3500	182

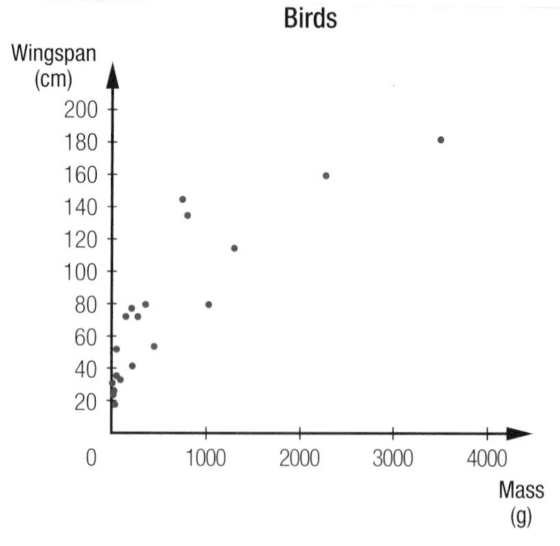

a) Find the equation of the regression line.

b) Draw the curve of best fit.

c) Estimate the wingspan of an 11 kg swan using the following:

1) the equation of the regression line

2) the curve of the best fit

d) Which estimate is more realistic?

Before they offer a scientific opinion, biologists take a variety of samples and measurements in the field.

8 **SEA LEVEL** For the past few decades, rising sea levels have been seen as one of the consequences of global warming. The data below refers to this subject. Estimate what the total rise of the sea level will be in 2050.

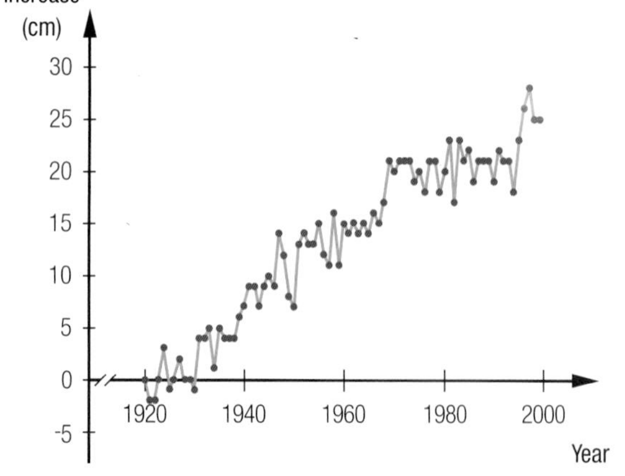

Mean rise per decade

Decade	Variation (cm)
1920 - 1929	0.0
1930 - 1939	3.6
1940 - 1949	9.4
1950 - 1959	12.5
1960 - 1969	15.6
1970 - 1979	20.0
1980 - 1989	20.8
1990 - 1999	22.8

9 At a private secondary school, students must write a math entrance exam. A Cycle One teacher compared the results of this exam to those obtained on a major evaluation that these students wrote in October. One student was absent for this evaluation.

Mark on the entrance exam (%)	Mark on the October evaluation (%)	Mark on the entrance exam (%)	Mark on the October evaluation (%)	Mark on the entrance exam (%)	Mark on the October evaluation (%)	Mark on the entrance exam (%)	Mark on the October evaluation (%)
75	68	79	74	82	65	88	88
75	65	79	66	83	74	88	78
76	72	79	62	84	77	90	90
76	55	80	68	84	82	90	82
77	50	80	75	85	75	92	80
77	68	80	85	85	85	94	84
77	75	81	Absent	85	82	96	95
78	72	82	84	87	80	100	92

Estimate the mark that the absent student could have obtained had he or she been present for the October evaluation.

10 The adjacent table associates employees' years of experience in a company and their weekly salary:

a) Draw a scatter plot of this data and describe the correlation between these two variables.

b) Would it be appropriate to model this using a line? Justify your answer.

c) Would your answer to **b)** be different if you used only data for employees with 10 years or less experience? Why?

d) Describe the model you consider best suited to represent the relationship between these variables.

e) Use this model to estimate the weekly salary of employees with 5, 10, and 15 years experience.

Years of experience	Weekly salary ($)
1	560
1	550
2	580
2	560
3	1,100
4	700
4	610
5	670
6	760
7	700
8	710
8	770
9	820
10	850
12	830
12	850
15	830
16	830
18	850
20	850

11 **HIV** The table below presents data on the number of HIV-positive test results for Canadian adults from 1996 to 2005.

a) For each year, calculate the percentage of women from the total number of HIV-positive cases. Round your answer to the nearest tenth.

b) Draw a scatter plot of the relationship between these percentages and the number of years since 1995. Describe the observed correlation.

c) Based on this data and assuming that the same trend continues, what will be the percentage of HIV-positive women in 2025?

Positive test result

Year	Number of women	Number of men
1996	535	2054
1997	483	1861
1998	470	1697
1999	515	1596
2000	486	1538
2001	526	1580
2002	620	1809
2003	627	1822
2004	655	1825
2005	628	1830

The red ribbon symbolizes the fight against AIDS: its colour represents blood and its shape brings to mind the broken infinity sign. It is worn as an inverted "V." But the day that a cure is discovered, it will be worn the other way around as a sign of victory.

12 A graphing calculator was used to determine the equation of the regression line from a scatter plot.

a) Show that this line passes through the mean point of this distribution, that is, the point whose coordinates correspond to the mean value of each variable.

b) Using a technological tool, create another two-variable distribution and determine the equation of its regression line. Check that this line passes through the mean point.

L1	L2	L3 3
8	5	
14	10	
16	14	
12	13	
4	3	
6	9	

L3(1)=

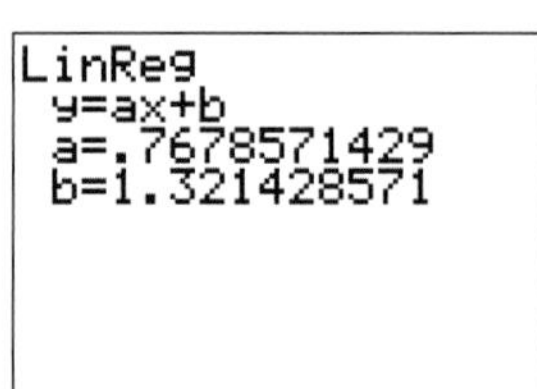

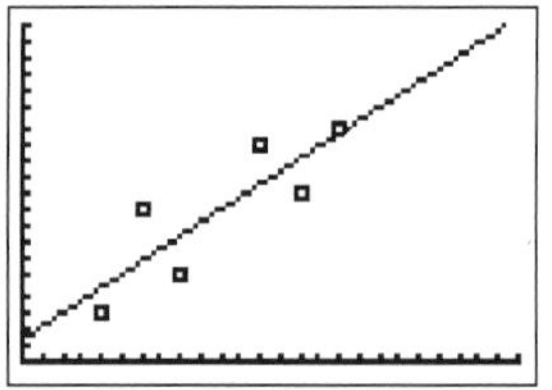

13 The following table shows the steps used to calculate the exact value of the linear correlation coefficient for the variables X and Y using the deviations from the mean $X - \overline{X}$ and $Y - \overline{Y}$.

	X	Y	$X - \overline{X}$	$Y - \overline{Y}$	$(X - \overline{X})(Y - \overline{Y})$	$(X - \overline{X})^2$	$(Y - \overline{Y})^2$
	1	3	-2	1	-2	4	1
	1	4	-2	2	-4	4	4
	1	2	-2	0	0	4	0
	2	5	-1	3	-3	1	9
	3	1	0	-1	0	0	1
	3	2	0	0	0	0	0
	4	2	1	0	0	1	0
	4	0	1	-2	-2	1	4
	5	1	2	-1	-2	4	1
	6	0	3	-2	-6	9	4
Sum	30	20		Sum	-19	28	24
Mean	3	2			↓ A	↓ B	↓ C

The linear correlation coefficient is expressed as: $r = \dfrac{A}{\sqrt{B \times C}}$

From this table you can also find the equation of the regression line $y = ax + b$; proceed as follows:

- Find the value of **a**, given that $a = \dfrac{A}{B}$.
- Find the value of **b** using the fact that the regression line always passes through the mean point $(\overline{X}, \overline{Y})$.

In other words, the rate of change of the regression line is the sum of the products of the deviations from the mean of the X and Y values, divided by the sum of the squares of the deviations from the mean of the X values.

a) What is the equation of the regression line of the above distribution? Check your answer using a technological tool.

b) The following is another distribution:

X	1	3	5	7	9	11	13	15	17	19
Y	3	5	9	12	12	16	15	18	21	29

Calculate the correlation coefficient and find the equation of the regression line. Check your answer using a technological tool.

Chronicle of the

past

Francis Galton

His life

Francis Galton was born on February 16, 1822, in Sparkbrook, England. He is considered to have been a multidisciplinary genius. Anthropologist, explorer, geographer, meteorologist and statistician, he invented the concepts of correlation and regression, among other things. Galton invented the weather chart and was the first to suggest the existence of anticyclones. He is also the founder of psychometrics and worked on the classification of fingerprints. It is even believed that he invented the sleeping bag! Galton died on January 17, 1911, in Haslemere, England.

Galton published over 340 works in his lifetime. His cousin is Charles Darwin, creator of The Theory of Evolution.

The heritability of characteristics

Galton was very interested in heritability which is the probability that a person's descendants will inherit some of his or her characteristics. In 1886, he published a study in which he compared the height of 928 adult children to the height of their parents, for a total of 205 couples. In this study, Galton observed the following:

- Parents who are taller than the mean of the population give birth to children who are also taller than the mean of the population but are not as tall as their parents.
- Parents who are shorter than the mean of the population give birth to children that are also shorter than the mean of the population but are taller than their parents.

In this study Galton also noticed that the mean height of men is 8% greater than that of women. This is why, when processing his data, he multiplied the height of each woman by 1.08.

Contingency table showing the results of this study.

TABLE 1.

Number of Adult Children of Various Statures Born of 205 Mid-parents of Various Statures.
(All Female heights have been multiplied by 1·08).

Heights of the Mid-parents in inches.	Heights of the Adult Children.														Total Number of		Medians.
	Below	62·2	63·2	64·2	65·2	66·2	67·2	68·2	69·2	70·2	71·2	72·2	73·2	Above	Adult Children.	Mid-parents.	
Above ..	..	..	..	..	..	..	..	..	..	..	..	1	3	..	4	5	..
72·5	..	..	..	..	..	..	..	1	2	1	2	7	2	4	19	6	72·2
71·5	..	..	..	..	1	3	4	3	5	10	4	9	2	2	43	11	69·9
70·5	1	..	1	..	1	1	3	12	18	14	7	4	3	3	68	22	69·5
69·5	..	..	1	16	4	17	27	20	33	25	20	11	4	5	183	41	68·9
68·5	1	..	7	11	16	25	31	34	48	21	18	4	3	..	219	49	68·2
67·5	..	3	5	14	15	36	38	28	38	19	11	4	..	..	211	33	67·6
66·5	..	3	3	5	2	17	17	14	13	4	..	..	..	..	78	20	67·2
65·5	1	..	9	5	7	11	11	7	7	5	2	1	..	..	66	12	66·7
64·5	1	1	4	4	1	5	5	..	2	..	..	..	..	..	23	5	65·8
Below ..	1	..	2	4	1	2	2	1	1	..	..	..	..	..	14	1	..
Totals ..	5	7	32	59	48	117	138	120	167	99	64	41	17	14	928	205	..
Medians ..	..	..	66·3	67·8	67·9	67·7	67·9	68·3	68·5	69·0	69·0	70·0	..	..	..	..	..

Source: Galton, Francis. *Regression towards Mediocrity in Hereditary Stature,* 1886.

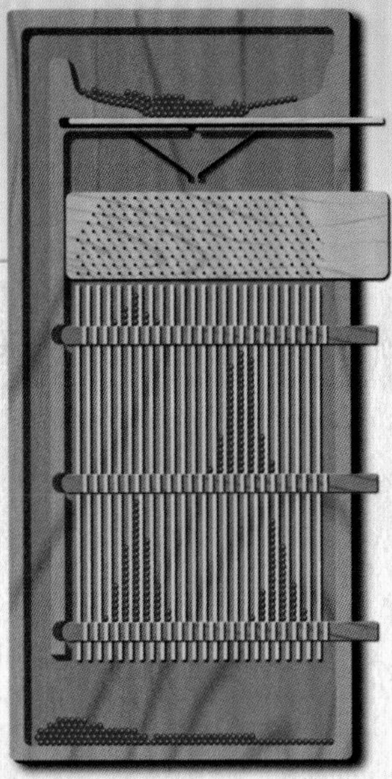

The Galton board

In order to simulate random events, Galton constructed the device shown in the adjacent illustration. A number of nails are arranged in staggered rows on an inclined board. Marbles fall one by one from a funnel-shaped reservoir and slide down the board. Each time a marble hits a nail, it has an equal probability of going either left or right. Containers, placed below the last row of nails, collect the marbles so that the results can be compiled.

Psychometric psychology

The objective of the science of psychometric psychology is to evaluate the capacity of the human mind. Galton created this subject because he wanted to measure and compare levels of intelligence. The Intelligence Quotient, or IQ test, is probably the best-known tool of psychometrics. Today, tests are used to evaluate different aspects of intelligence, such as, learning ability, knowledge, personality and emotional intelligence. However, before using these tests it is important to confirm their validity, that is, their ability to actually evaluate what they seek to measure.

IQ results from a recognized and validated test	Number of correct answers on new tests	
	Test A	Test B
90	10	37
95	10	39
98	12	44
98	9	34
100	12	55
100	11	35
104	14	46
105	11	41
108	14	53
114	15	42
120	16	48
125	14	52

1. Some of Galton's original data is reported in the table below. Use this data to find the rule of the first-degree polynomial function that best represents the relationship between the height of parents and that of their children. Given that 1 inch is approximately equal to 2.54 cm, use your own parents' height to see if this function represents your personal situation.

Height of parents (in inches)	Median height of adult children (in inches)
72.5	72.2
71.5	69.9
70.5	69.5
69.5	68.9
68.5	68.2
67.5	67.6
66.5	67.2
65.5	66.7
64.5	65.8

2. An experiment consists of releasing 100 marbles from point **A** of the Galton board depicted below and recording the amount collected in each container at the bottom. The experiment is repeated a number of times with the containers emptied each time. On average, how many marbles should you expect to find in each container?

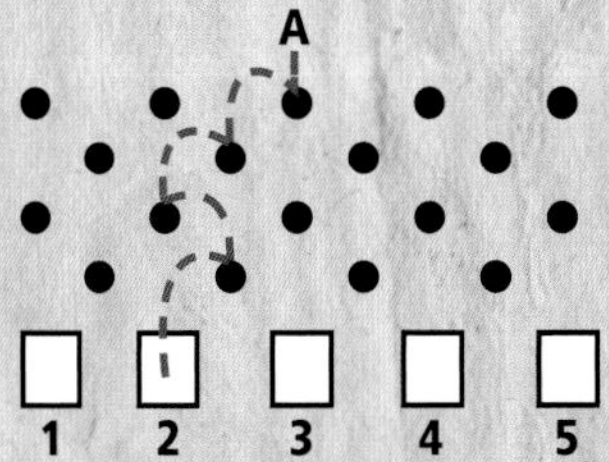

3. To validate a new test, it is sometimes compared to a test that has already been validated. Examine the adjacent data. Which of the two tests seems more valid? Justify your answer.

In the workplace

Epidemiologists

Population disease control

An epidemiologist is a medical doctor who conducts research to understand the outbreak and evolution of disease in humans. This specialist makes recommendations on sanitation and health measures that will prevent, control or end the propagation of certain diseases. Because epidemiologists usually work with data involving large numbers of people, one of their main tools is statistics.

A bit of history

In 1854, a cholera epidemic was ravaging London, England. Using a map of the city, Dr. John Snow examined the frequency of cases, and noticed that the centre of distribution of the disease was located next to a water pump. After eliminating other possible causes, he was able to show that the problem was created by the contaminated pump, and he was able to put an end to the epidemic. Because of this accomplishment, Dr. Snow is recognized as the founder of epidemiology.

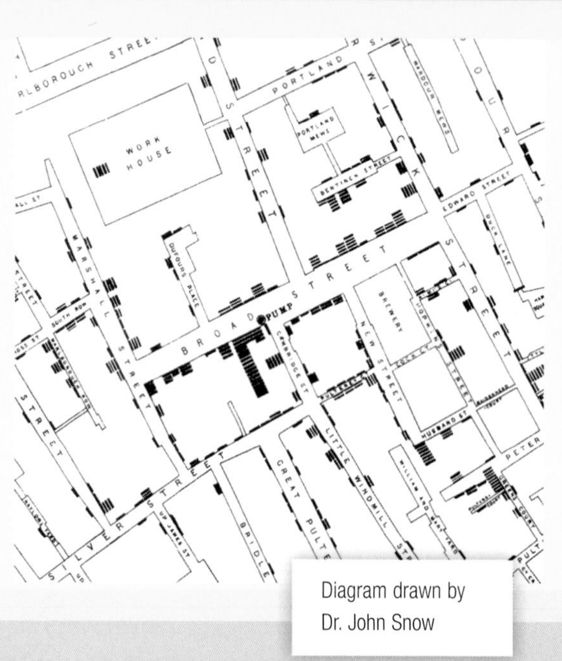

Diagram drawn by Dr. John Snow

Statistics in medicine

Sir Richard Doll (1912-2005)

At the beginning of the 20th century, doctors who used statistics in their area of research often had their results contested. Dr. Richard Doll is the first to have used this method successfully. In 1956, together with other researchers, he studied the first data to come out of a vast research project that involved 40 000 doctors and that lasted 50 years. He concluded that there was a very strong correlation between smoking and lung cancer. At that time, no one suspected that smoking could cause health problems.

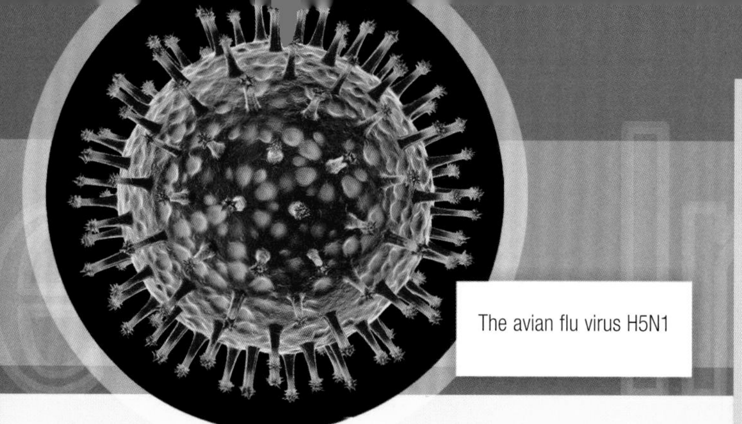

The avian flu virus H5N1

Challenges for the 21st century

The risk of a pandemic has greatly increased with the gradual elimination of borders and the increase in transportation of products and people. This is why organizations like the World Health Organization (WHO) intervene quickly when new diseases (such as the avian flu) appear or when old diseases (such as tuberculosis) reappear. The work of epidemiologists is of major importance; thousands, even millions of lives are saved because of it!

Incidence of the Spanish flu in the US Navy from September to December 1918

Age group	Median age	Number of flu cases per 1000 people
20-24	22	203
25-29	27	191
30-34	32	165
35-39	37	72
40-44	42	62
45-49	47	7
50-54	52	51
55-59	57	59
60-65	62	43

It is estimated that in 1918-1919 the Spanish flu was responsible for up to 40 million deaths.

1. Since Dr. Doll's discovery, many other studies have shown a link between smoking and lung cancer. The scatter plot below shows the relationship between the incidence of lung cancer and the number of packs of cigarettes smoked during a lifetime:

Incidence of lung cancer as related to the mean number of packs of cigarettes smoked in a lifetime

Data from Ontario hospitals (1994-1998)

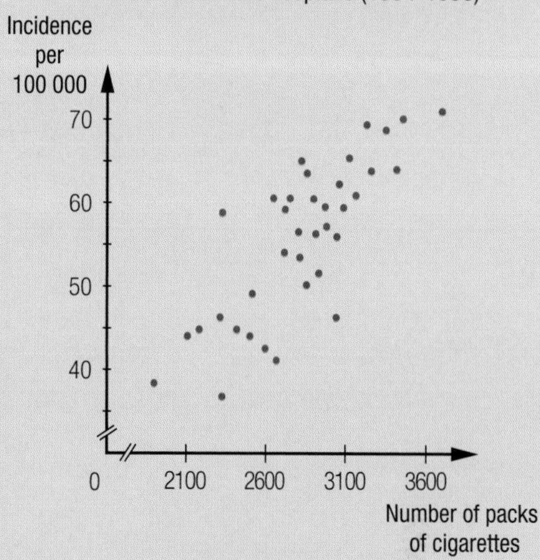

a) Estimate the linear correlation coefficient for this scatter plot.

b) Some people say that the correlation observed between smoking and lung cancer does not mean that there is a cause and effect relationship between these two variables. What do you think of this interpretation?

2. The 1918 Spanish flu pandemic affected millions of people throughout the world. This disease infected mostly young adults, and the highest number of victims was from this age group. Precise statistical data on this topic is scarce. As shown in the table on the left, the US Navy did compile data about personnel affected by the flu.

a) Draw the scatter plot of this data using the median ages and the number of flu cases.

b) Draw the line of best fit for this data and find its equation.

c) Is this line a valid representation of the relationship between the two variables? Justify your answer.

overview

1 The following is a distribution of 25 data values:

X	Y	X	Y	X	Y	X	Y	X	Y
1	29	6	32	11	24	16	16	21	17
2	38	7	23	12	34	17	13	22	18
3	36	8	27	13	18	18	19	23	20
4	31	9	30	14	25	19	15	24	18
5	38	10	31	15	15	20	22	25	16

a) Draw the scatter plot for this distribution and describe the correlation.

b) Estimate the correlation coefficient using the rectangle method.

c) Find the equation of the regression line using the Mayer method and the median-median method. Draw these two lines on the same graph.

d) Using a technological tool, determine the equation of the regression line and draw this line on the same graph.

e) What values of *Y* do these different models predict when *X* is equal to 50, and when *X* is equal to 100?

f) What percentage of error is introduced by using the Mayer line method and the median-median line method compared to the least squares method to find the regression line, when:

1) the value of *X* is 50? 2) the value of *X* is 100?

2 **HEART RATE** A study that involved 40 amateur athletes revealed correlations between various parameters measured.

HRR: Athlete's heart rate at rest
HRA: Heart rate before athlete reaches anaerobic mode
HRM: Maximum heart rate reached by athlete during training

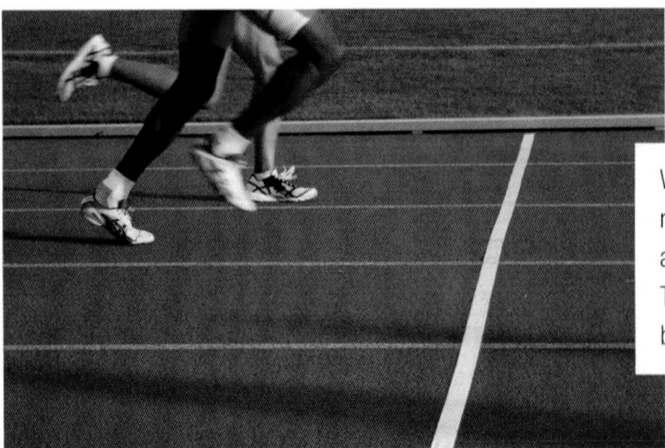

When muscles produce energy from internal resources only and without oxygen intake, they are said to be functioning in anaerobic mode. The energy developed is then at its maximum but of short duration.

The results of the study are as follows:

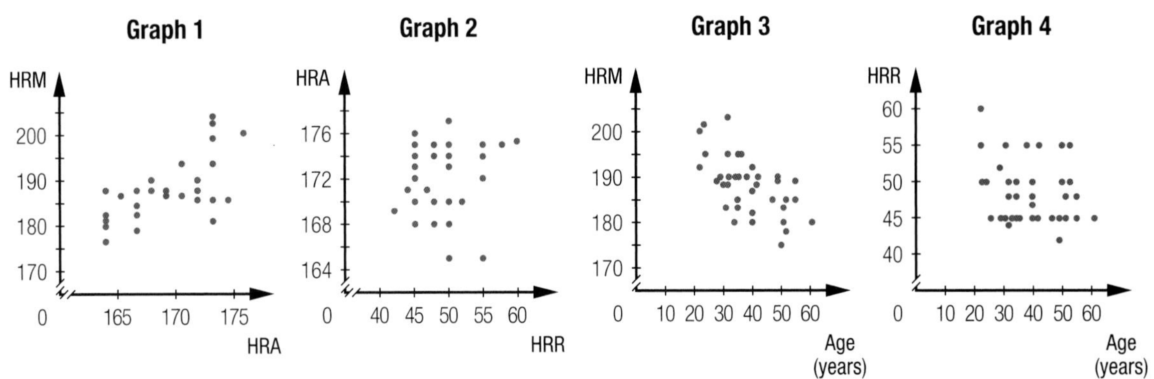

Match each of the following correlation coefficients with one of the scatter plots.

a) -0.31 b) 0.16 c) 0.80 d) -0.67

3 A teacher asked a group of 15 students the following questions:

1. Over the past month, how many times have your parents inquired about your achievement at school?

2. On a scale of 1 to 10, what satisfaction do you get from your schoolwork.

The answers are shown in the table below:

Answers

Number of inquiries by parents	1	2	5	1	3	0	3	1	0	0	2	5	1	2	0
Satisfaction from schoolwork	8	5	5	7	6	6	5	6	7	9	7	3	5	6	7

a) Construct a scatter plot for this data.

b) Describe the correlation between these two variables.

c) Estimate the level of satisfaction for a student whose parents inquire about school achievement twice a week.

d) After analyzing these results, the teacher made a decision. In order to maintain a positive class atmosphere, parents were asked to refrain from pressuring their child(ren). What do you think of the teacher's interpretation?

4 **PROTECTIVE HELMET FOR CYCLISTS** In Switzerland, a widespread campaign is under way to convince people of the importance of wearing a protective helmet when cycling. Below are the results of a 20-year study:

Year	Bicycle accidents relative to the base year 1987 (%)	Cases of cranial trauma relative to base year 1987 (%)	Cyclists wearing helmets (%)
1987	100	100	–
1988	108	98	–
1989	116	79	–
1990	122	70	0.2
1991	141	82	0.4
1992	146	75	1
1993	158	65	2
1994	159	60	3
1995	164	57	6
1996	140	64	7
1997	152	50	7
1998	150	62	14
1999	152	62	18
2000	160	50	20
2001	163	64	20
2002	160	58	24
2003	171	38	17
2004	161	40	33
2005	173	53	35
2006	–	–	39
2007	–	–	38

a) Represent each of the following variables using a scatter plot:
   1) the percentage of bicycle accidents and the percentage of cases of cranial trauma
   2) the percentage of bicycle accidents and the percentage of cyclists wearing a helmet

b) In each case, estimate the correlation coefficient between these variables.

c) Draw the line of best fit for each scatter plot. What is the equation for each of these lines?

d) In each case, suggest an explanation for the relationship that may exist between these variables.

Wearing a protective helmet for cycling is also promoted in Québec. It is estimated that head injuries cause 60% of cycling fatalities. In a fall, the head is the part of the body that is the most exposed to serious injury. When a cyclist wearing a helmet has an accident, the force of impact is absorbed by the surface of the helmet rather than the skull.

e) Below are two more graphs showing data taken from this table:

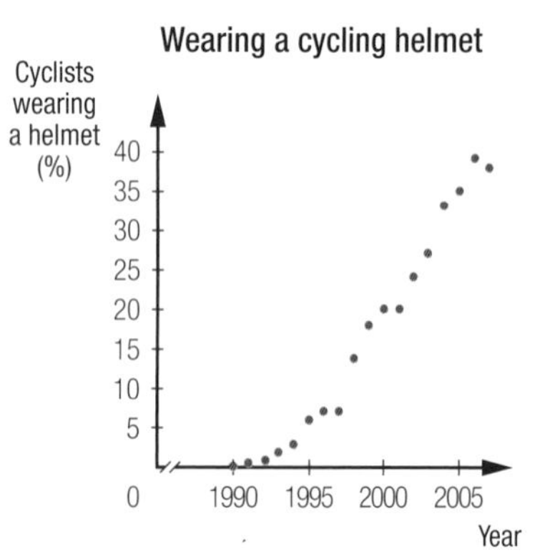

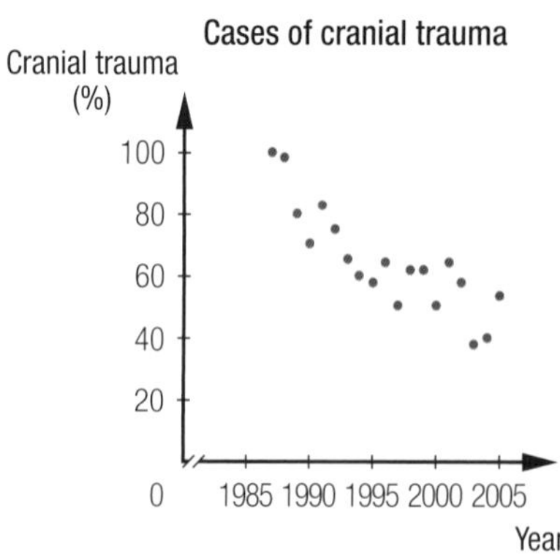

In each case, draw the line of best fit for the scatter plots.
According to these models, what would be the expected percentage of cyclists wearing a helmet and the expected percentage of cases of cranial trauma in Switzerland, in 2015?

5 Simon filled the first two columns of a spreadsheet with random numbers between 0 and 1. He then filled Column **C** by subtracting the value in Column **A** from 1. The results are shown in the adjacent table.

	A	B	C	D
1	0.492391112	0.792623384	0.507608888	
2	0.429213428	0.560222095	0.570786572	
3	0.071560635	0.944068007	0.928439365	
4	0.853032425	0.523994287	0.146967575	
5	0.251015115	0.817546512	0.748984885	
6	0.650084719	0.911948030	0.349915281	
7	0.300147308	0.030566966	0.699852692	
8	0.314222222	0.421067621	0.685777778	
9	0.083022872	0.584224901	0.916977128	
10	0.704904529	0.510038764	0.295095471	
11	0.542043073	0.025635081	0.457956927	
12	0.041695281	0.129730977	0.958304719	
13	0.086645638	0.978238551	0.913354362	
14	0.606820631	0.770273759	0.393179369	
15	0.265992517	0.201505575	0.734007483	

If each student in the class did this experiment, what would the average correlation coefficient be for the values in columns:

a) **A** and **B**?

b) **A** and **C**?

c) **B** and **C**?

Justify your answers.

6 **POLLUTION** Air quality has a great impact on our health. The Province of Ontario studied two factors involved in respiratory diseases. Epidemiologists have determined the correlation between the number of people admitted to hospitals on the day following an increase of pollutants in the air and the quantity of these pollutants.

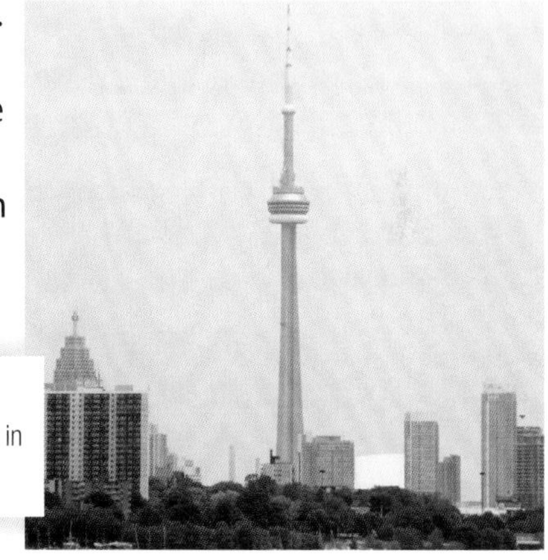

From May to September 2005, Ontario had a record number of smog-alert days, 38 of them in Toronto alone.

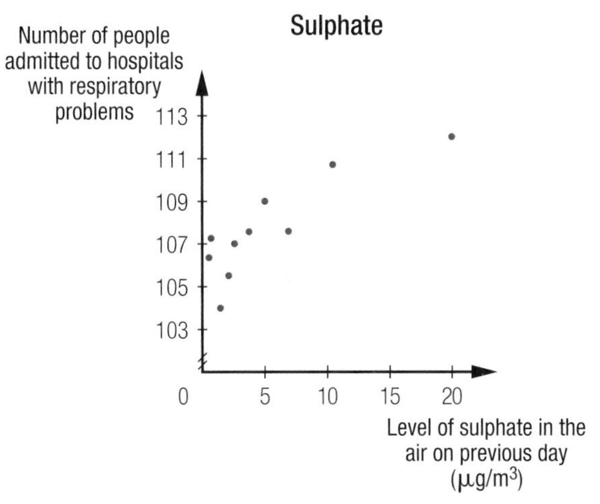

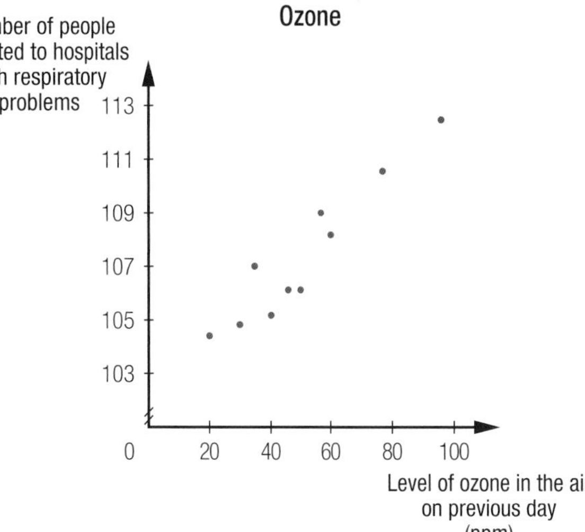

a) Based on this data, which of the two pollutants has the strongest correlation with respiratory problems?

b) A radio announcer warned that an alarming level of ozone in the air is expected today: 160 parts per million (ppm). Based on the data provided, how many cases of respiratory problems should Ontario hospitals expect to treat tomorrow?

7 Fusariose is a disease brought on by a fungus that causes mould to develop on ears of corn. Researchers have isolated a toxin, deoxynivalenol, or DON, which appears to contribute greatly to its spread. This study also shows that hybridization of corn could reduce the occurrence of this disease.

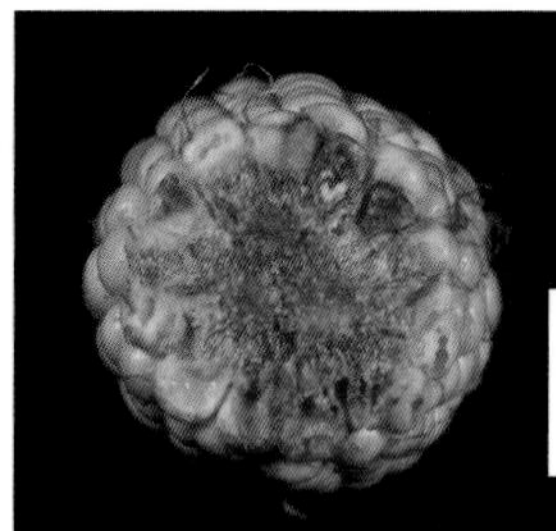

Ear of corn infected with Fusariose

Number of hybridizations	0	0	0	0	1	1	1	1	2	2	2	3	3	4	5
Quantity of DON (µg/kg)	2000	1800	1350	1200	1230	1200	1110	500	1000	650	320	800	550	750	600
Resistance to Fusariose (%)	5	20	35	50	40	45	50	75	50	75	80	60	75	60	70

a) Which of the two variables, number of hybridizations or quantity of DON, is most strongly correlated with resistance to Fusariose? Estimate the linear correlation coefficient using the rectangle method.

Hybridization is crossbreeding, by natural or artificial means, between two varieties or species.

b) With this study in mind, what advice should an agronomist give a corn farmer? Justify your answer.

 **8** **EYE SENSITIVITY** The senses become less acute with age. One factor that influences our vision is sensitivity to light. Approximately 20 subjects underwent testing, and the measurements recorded are presented in the scatter plot below. The median-median line was drawn using the orange median points.

a) Estimate the correlation coefficient between a person's age and sensitivity to light.

b) Is the median-median line an appropriate choice to represent the data from this scatter plot? Justify your answer.

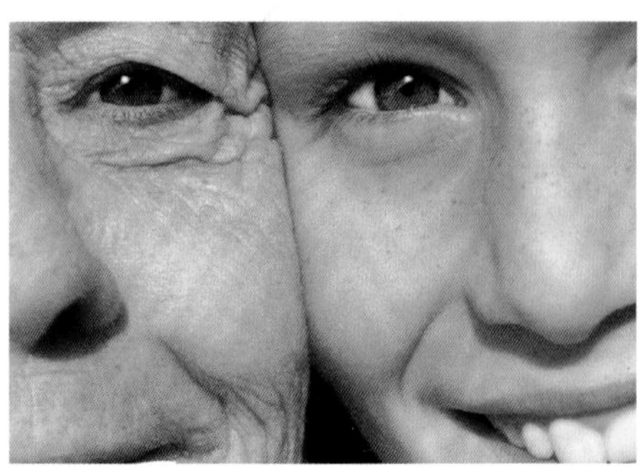

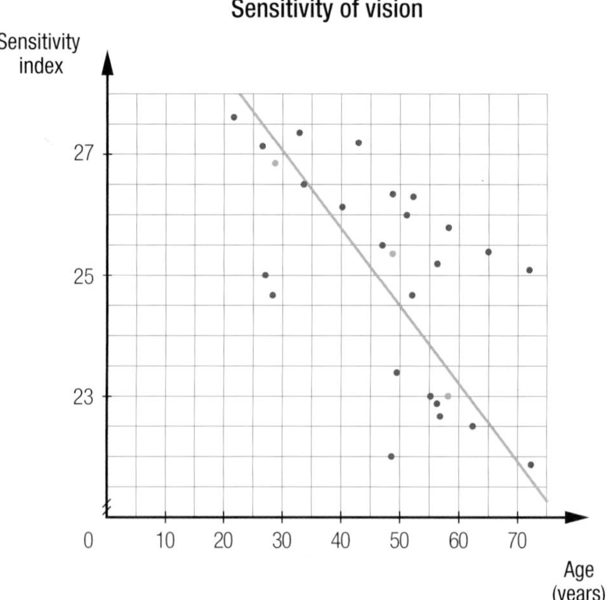

9 **ANTHROPOMETRY** Francis Galton, a statistician and versatile 19th century scientist published a study on the correlation of different body measurements. The following is a reproduction of one of his tables:

Height and cubit

Height in inches	Length, in inches, of the left cubit of 348 men								Total
	Less than 16.5	From 16.5 to 16.9	From 17.0 to 17.4	From 17.5 to 17.9	From 18.0 to 18.4	From 18.5 to 18.9	From 19.0 to 19.4	Over 19.5	
71 and over				1	3	4	15	7	30
70				1	5	13	11		30
69		1	1	2	25	15	6		50
68		1	3	7	14	7	4	2	38
67		1	7	15	28	8	2		61
66		1	7	18	15	6			47
65		4	10	12	8	2			36
64		5	11	2	3				21
Less than 64	9	12	10	3	1				35
Total	9	25	49	61	102	55	38	9	348

a) As precisely as possible, describe the correlation observed. Explain how you proceeded.

b) Would the correlation be different had the measurements been taken in centimetres? Justify your answer.

c) The values in the adjacent table were calculated using Galton's data. Draw the scatter plot for these values and find the equation of the line that best represents these values.

Height and median of cubits

Height in inches	Median value of cubits in inches
70	18.8
69	18.4
68	18.4
67	18.1
66	17.9
65	17.8
64	17.2

10 Isabelle used her computer to record a note played on a flute. Her findings appear on this graph:

a) Describe the correlation between the time and the intensity of the sound produced.

b) On the graph, draw the curve of best fit.

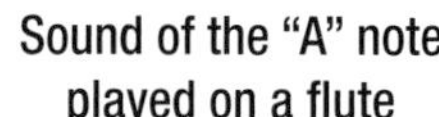

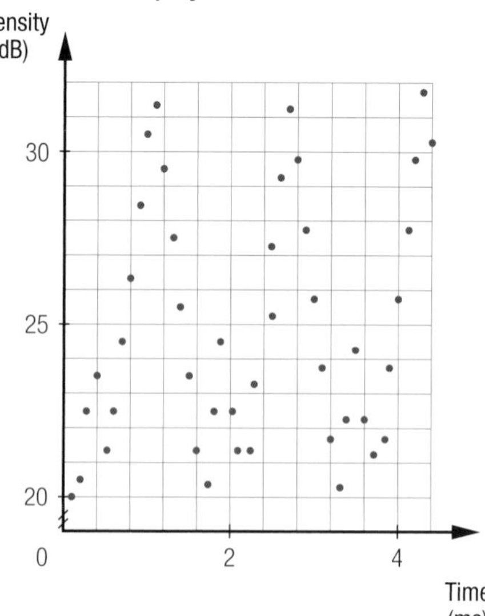

The flute is also called a *traverse flute* because it is played horizontally.

11 **MONKSHOOD** Monkshood, or aconite, is a threatened species in France. The population density of this flower, which is pollinated by bumblebees, decreased substantially after many humid areas dried out. The following information was collected during research conducted by the *Office nationale des forêts* (ONF).

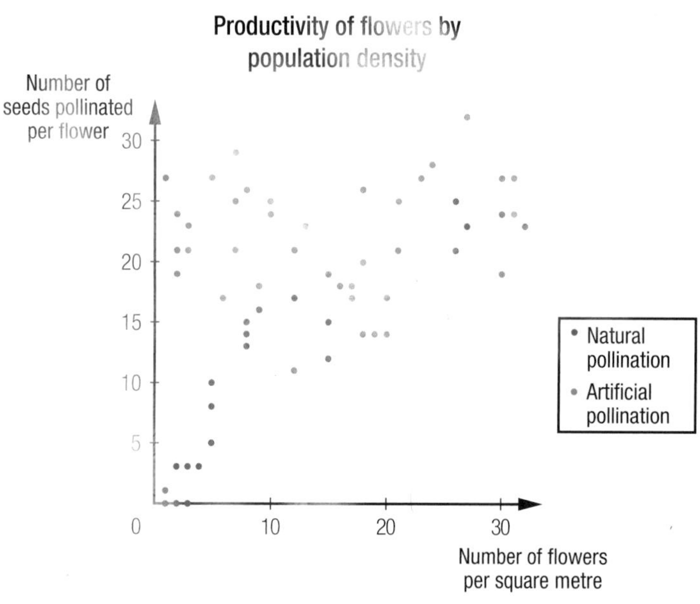

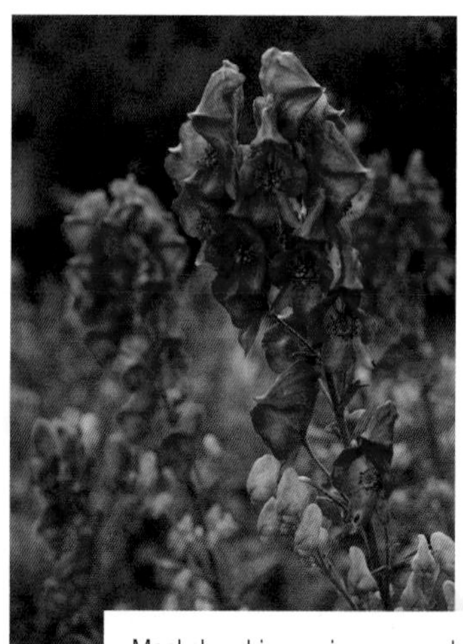

Monkshood is a poisonous and highly toxic plant. One dose of 2 to 4 g of its tuber is deadly for a human being. It must not be picked using bare hands because the poison penetrates the skin. This perennial has been used in pharmacology as an analgesic for neuralgia, toothaches and rheumatism.

Natural pollination

Number of flowers per m^2	Number of seeds pollinated per flower	Number of flowers per m^2	Number of seeds pollinated per flower
1	0	12	17
1	1	15	12
2	0	15	19
2	3	15	15
3	0	16	18
3	3	18	14
4	3	19	14
5	5	20	14
5	8	26	21
5	10	26	25
8	14	27	32
8	13	27	23
8	15	30	24
9	16	30	27
12	11	32	23

Artificial pollination

Number of flowers per m^2	Number of seeds pollinated per flower	Number of flowers per m^2	Number of seeds pollinated per flower
1	27	12	21
2	24	13	23
2	21	17	17
2	19	17	18
3	23	18	26
3	21	18	20
5	27	20	17
6	17	21	25
7	21	21	21
7	25	23	27
7	29	24	28
8	26	27	23
9	18	30	19
10	24	31	27
10	25	31	24

a) Describe the correlation between the number of seeds pollinated for each flower and the density of flowers per square metre. Justify your answer.

b) By identifying the method of pollination, biologists discovered two distinct subgroups. What did they discover by using this procedure?

c) Could you work directly from the graph to estimate the correlation coefficient of each subgroup using the rectangle method? Why?

d) Find the equation of the line of best fit for each subgroup and draw the lines on a graph.

e) According to these equations, how many seeds would be pollinated for each flower in each subgroup if the density is 10 flowers per square metre?

f) At what density does it become unnecessary to intervene in the pollination process?

bank of problems

12 **ADOPTION** This table indicates the number of children from different countries of origin who were adopted in Québec and in the rest of Canada. The linear correlation coefficient between these two variables is approximatively 0.9. Considering this strong correlation, one journalist said that there was no fundamental difference between the adoption situation in Québec and in the rest of Canada. Is this a valid conclusion? What do you think? Justify your answer.

Adoption

	Number of children adopted	
Country of origin	in Québec	in the rest of Canada
China	216	392
Columbia	26	5
Ethiopia	0	61
Haiti	71	52
India	0	36
Philippines	12	41
Russia	5	90
South Korea	52	50
Taiwan	9	3
Thailand	9	12
Ukraine	0	23
United States	5	91
Vietnam	28	6

13 **ATHENS 2004** The results of 12 male gymnasts who participated in the 2004 Olympics in Athens are as follows:

Gymnastics

		Floor exercises	Pommel horse	Rings	Vault	Parallel bars	High bar	Total
BONDARENKO Alexei	RUS	9.600	9.150	9.600	9.400	9.450	9.600	56.800
YERIMBETOV Yernar	KAZ	9.312	8.962	9.537	9.625	9.225	9.737	56.398
VARGAS Luis	PUR	8.337	9.612	9.500	9.462	9.562	9.662	56.135
MYEZYENTSEV Ruslan	UKR	9.512	8.975	9.387	9.437	9.637	9.112	56.060
CARANOBE Benoit	FRA	9.112	9.400	9.575	9.187	9.087	9.612	55.973
VIHROVS Igors	LAT	9.687	8.862	9.187	9.700	9.000	9.437	55.873
GOFMAN Pavel	ISR	9.100	9.262	9.425	9.112	9.725	9.062	55.686
LOPEZ RIOS Eric	CUB	9.137	8.600	9.500	9.700	9.675	8.837	55.449
PFEIFER Sergei	GER	9.312	9.025	9.587	9.087	9.162	9.212	55.385
GIORGADZE Ilia	GEO	8.737	9.587	9.487	9.337	9.662	8.462	55.272
HAMBUECHEN Fabian	GER	9.475	8.287	8.512	9.412	9.387	9.750	54.823
SCHWEIZER Andreas	SUI	8.450	9.062	9.675	9.225	9.450	8.750	54.612

Using a technological tool, process this data and reorganize the six events into two categories requiring the same skills. Explain your choice mathematically.

14 **TIME, FATIGUE AND HAPPINESS** While conducting a study, a British economist asked a number of people to record their state of fatigue and their state of happiness at every hour of the day, for one week. They used a scale from 0 to 4 where 4 meant either very tired or very happy. Below is the mean of the results that were obtained:

Evolution of fatigue and happiness in one day

Time	Fatigue	Happiness	Time	Fatigue	Happiness
8:00 a.m.	1.7	0.5	3:00 p.m.	2.3	1.2
9:00 a.m.	1.3	1.3	4:00 p.m.	2.4	1.1
10:00 a.m.	1.4	1.0	5:00 p.m.	2.6	2.2
11:00 a.m.	0.9	1.2	6:00 p.m.	2.5	2.3
12:00 p.m.	0.6	2.9	7:00 p.m.	2.7	2.5
1:00 p.m.	0.7	2.5	8:00 p.m.	3.5	2.9
2:00 p.m.	1.7	1.1	9:00 p.m.	3.7	4.0

Considering this data, which variable is most strongly related to happiness: the number of hours since the day began or the state of fatigue? Justify your answer.

15 **LIFE EXPECTANCY** As a demographer, Natasha is interested in the evolution of life expectancy of men and women in Canada. Using data made available twice yearly, she has observed that the diffrence between the two has been diminishing over recent decades.

Life expectancy

Year	Life expectancy of men	Life expectancy of women	Year	Life expectancy of men	Life expectancy of women	Year	Life expectancy of men	Life expectancy of women
1960	68.3	74.2	1976	70.3	77.6	1992	74.8	80.8
1962	68.5	74.4	1978	70.9	78.3	1994	74.9	80.9
1964	68.6	75.1	1980	71.6	78.7	1996	75.5	81.2
1966	68.8	75.4	1982	72.3	79.2	1998	76.0	81.5
1968	69.1	75.8	1984	73.0	79.8	2000	76.6	81.9
1970	69.3	76.3	1986	73.2	79.8	2002	77.2	82.2
1972	69.5	76.6	1988	73.6	80.2	2004	77.8	82.7
1974	69.7	76.9	1990	74.3	80.7			

If this trend continues, in what year will life expectancy for Canadian men and women be equal?

In Canada, half of the increase in life expectancy for the period preceding 1980 is due to the decrease in infant mortality. Recent gains are due to a decrease in the death rate of the elderly.

16 **INNOVATION AND HUMAN DEVELOPMENT** Azhar and Natanéli each used a different set of sample countries to analyze the correlation between the innovative power of a country, measured by its innovation index, and its index of human development (IHD). Below are the results of their study:

Azhar's sample

Country	Innovation index	IHD
Sweden	0.98	0.951
Finland	0.98	0.947
United States	0.93	0.948
Denmark	0.93	0.943
Norway	0.92	0.965
Australia	0.92	0.957
Belgium	0.91	0.945
Canada	0.91	0.950
United Kingdom	0.91	0.940
Netherlands	0.89	0.947
Japan	0.89	0.949
Switzerland	0.88	0.947

Natanéli's sample

Country	Innovation index	IHD
United States	0.93	0.948
Australia	0.92	0.957
Ireland	0.84	0.956
Italy	0.78	0.940
Bulgaria	0.63	0.816
Kuwait	0.48	0.871
China	0.35	0.768
India	0.29	0.611
Kenya	0.26	0.491
Guatemala	0.14	0.673
Malawi	0.11	0.400
Ethiopia	0.05	0.371

Do you agree with either of these conclusions? Explain your answer.

17 Xavier and Tania are analyzing a group of students' marks in different subject areas. After having noticed a correlation near zero between marks in Mathematics and Physical Education and Health, and between Physical Education and Health and English Language Arts, they wonder if the same correlation holds true between Mathematics and English Language Arts.

XAVIER: Given that the first two correlations are zero, I'm sure that the third is also zero.

TANIA: Really? I don't think that is necessarily the case.

Who is right? Justify your answer.

 **18** To anaesthetize a patient for an operation, there is a choice of two types of drugs: Anaesthetic **A** or Anaesthetic **B**. Anaesthetic **A** costs $17.10 more for each operation than Anaesthetic **B**. However, the recovery time of the patient must also be taken into account. A survey was made of a sample group of patients who had undergone an operation. Below are the results:

Anaesthetic A

Duration of the operation (min)	80	90	95	105	105	130	165	170	180	210	250	310	390	420	490
Recovery time (min)	44	28	30	24	35	26	19	20	29	28	27	36	21	28	36

Anaesthetic B

Duration of the operation (min)	105	105	110	125	130	150	155	210	270	275	330	350	380	400	420
Recovery time (min)	50	28	18	40	50	40	60	90	40	50	85	62	75	101	75

If time spent in the recovery room costs $72 for each hour, how long must an operation take for Anaesthetic **A** to become more cost efficient than Anaesthetic **B**?

 **19** The two scatter plots below represent the same data: the height and mass of different people. In each case the regression line is shown. In addition, the spreadsheet has provided the equation of this line and the square of the linear correlation coefficient.

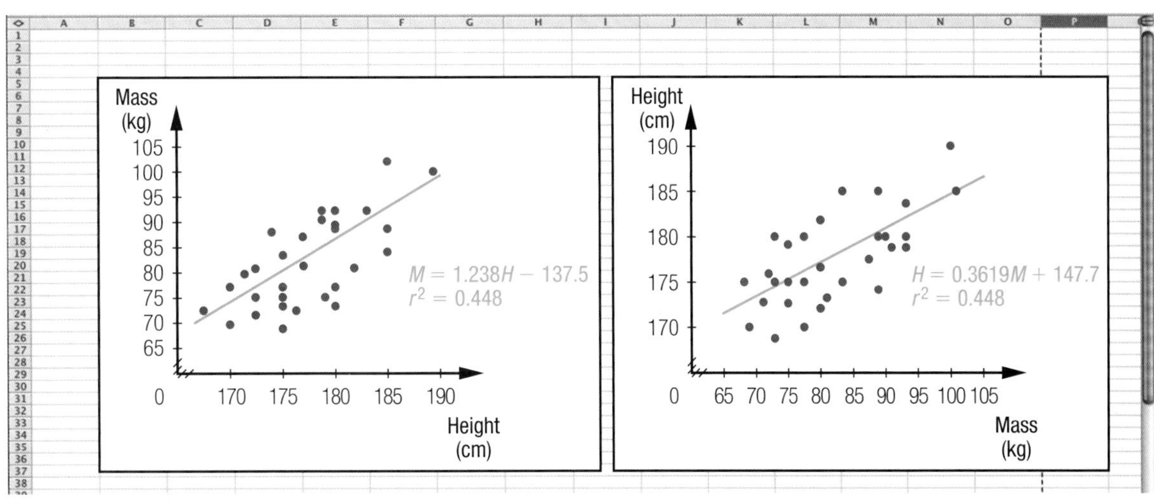

The two lines are different because they pass through different points. However, the linear correlation coefficient is the same in both cases.

Does a relationship exist between the rates of change of the two lines and the value of r^2?

Using a technological tool, study other examples of distributions and formulate a conjecture based on your observations. Provide at least one argument for your conjecture.

VISION 2

Modelling with the help of functions

Mathematical modelling is at the heart of all scientific research, and the concept of a function is a fundamental tool. Using the rule of a function to describe reality helps you better understand a situation and predict its development. But reality is sometimes difficult to model. The question always arises: what function is best suited to represent a specific situation?

In "Vision 2," you will analyze the relationship between variables. As a result, considering the properties of different functions, you will be able to decide which type of function is best suited to represent a situation. Two specific models will be studied: the second-degree polynomial function and the step function.

Arithmetic and algebra	Geometry	Statistics
• Analyzing situations • Modelling with real functions • Properties of functions • The second-degree polynomial function and the step function • Representation • Interpreting parameters • Finding the rule		• Scatter plots

REVISION 2

PRIOR LEARNING 1 Woman power!

Maryse Turcotte is a weightlifter of international calibre. When competing, her movements must conform to strict rules. The clean and jerk, for example, requires that movements be executed in two phases. She must first lift the barbell to shoulder level (the clean phase) and then, after a pause, in one single movement lift it to the top of her extended arms (the jerk phase).

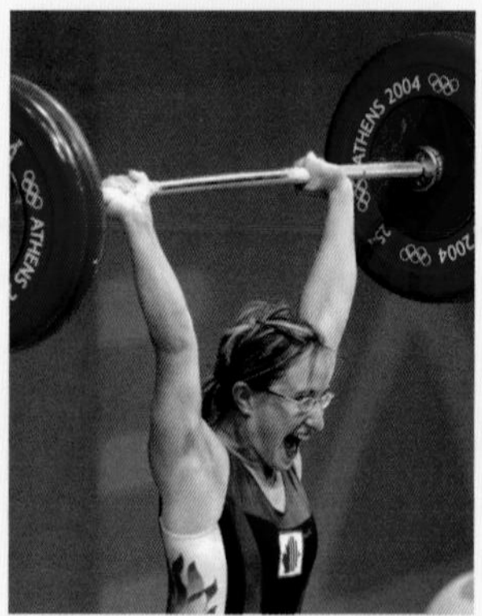

The diagrams illustrate the two phases and show elapsed time in seconds. The weightlifter in the diagrams below represents Maryse Turcotte who is able to lift a bar to a maximum height of 1.6 m from the ground.

Clean

Jerk

a. Draw a graph showing the distance from the bar to the ground as a function of elapsed time.

b. In this situation, what are the values of:

1) the independent variable?
2) the dependent variable?

c. During which time intervals is the distance between the barbell and the ground:

1) increasing?
2) decreasing?
3) constant?

d. What is the value of the y-intercept?

e. How many zeros are there?

PRIOR LEARNING 2 Simple machines for strong men

Strongman wheelbarrow contests are very spectacular because the lever effect makes it possible for contestants to lift enormous masses. The lever effect depends on the length of each of the two "arms of the lever."

Hugo Girard, Canadian Strongman Champion from 1999 to 2004 and World Champion in 2002.

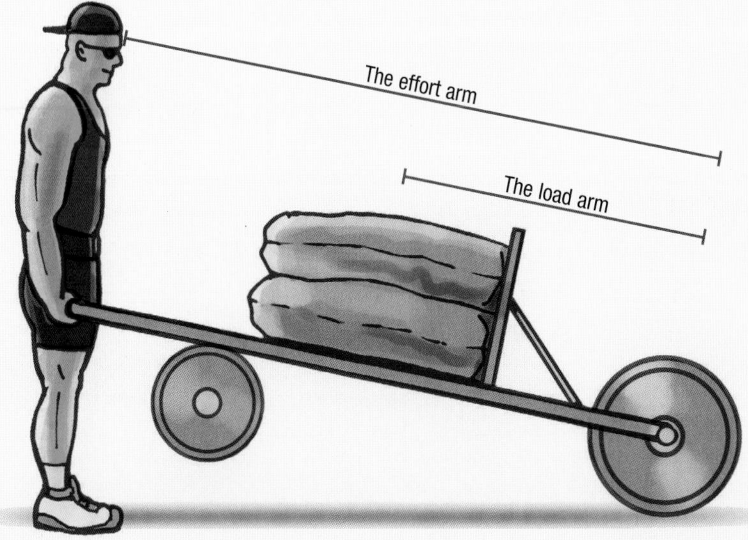

The force required, in newtons, to hold the wheelbarrow when it contains a 500 kg mass, depends on the length of these lever arms. Data for this situation, disregarding the mass of the wheelbarrow, is shown in the following tables:

One newton (N) is the force required to accelerate a 1 kg mass 1 m/s^2.

Force required for different load arms (Effort arm = 2 m)

Load arm (m)	Force required (N)
0.6	1470
0.8	1960
1.0	2450
1.4	3430

Force required for different effort arms (Load arm = 1m)

Effort arm (m)	Force required (N)
1.4	3500
2.0	2450
2.5	1960
2.8	1750

a. Does this data suggest that these are proportional situations? Justify your answer.

b. Which function can model each of these situations? How do these functions differ from one another?

c. At a competition, a strongman has the choice between lengthening the effort arm by 25% or shortening the load arm by 25%. Which is the best option? Justify your answer.

knowledge summary

PROPERTIES OF A FUNCTION WITHIN A CONTEXT

The properties of a function can easily be described from its graphical representation.

E.g. The adjacent graph depicts the quantity of water in a tank as a function of time.

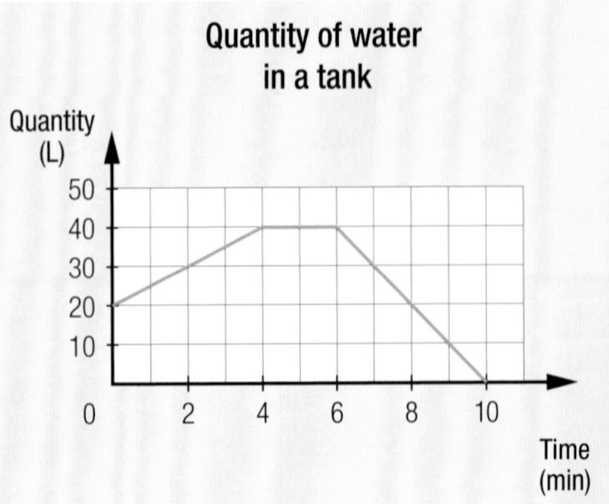

The table below summarizes several **properties of any function** *f*, the examples refer to the graph above.

Property	Example
• The **domain** is the set of values that the independent variable *x* may take on. • The **range** is the set of values that the dependent variable *y* (or *f(x)*) takes on.	In this situation, the domain refers to elapsed time, in minutes. The domain is [0,10]. The range refers to quantities of water in litres. The range is [0,40].
Over an interval of the domain, you can recognize from its graph, that the function is: • **constant** if it is represented by a horizontal line, that is, a line parallel to the *x*-axis • **increasing** if it is represented by a line that, from left to right, is ascending or horizontal • **decreasing** if it is represented by a line that, from left to right, is descending or horizontal	The quantity of water in the tank is increasing for the first 6 minutes. It is decreasing as of the 4th minute. It is constant between 4 and 6 minutes.
The **minimum** and the **maximum (extreme values or extrema)** of the function are respectively the smallest and the largest values of the dependent variable *y* (or *f*(*x*)).	The minimum quantity of water is 0 L and the maximum quantity is 40 L.
• The ***y*-intercept (initial value)**, if it exists, is the *y*-value of the intersection point of the curve with the *y*-axis. • An ***x*-intercept (zero of the function)**, if one or more exist, is the *x*-value of the intersection point of the curve with the *x*-axis.	The *y*-intercept is 20 because the tank initially contained 20 L of water. There is one *x*-intercept. Its value is 10. The tank is empty after 10 minutes.

PROPORTIONAL SITUATIONS

Two related variables are:

- **directly proportional** if multiplying one variable by a number implies that the other variable is multiplied by the same number
- **inversely proportional** if multiplying one variable by a number implies that the other variable is divided by the same number

Direct variation and **inverse variation** functions are used to model these two types of proportionality.

	Direct variation	Inverse variation
E.g.	Consider the perimeter of an equilateral triangle for different lengths of the base.	Consider the height of a rectangle with an area of 30 cm^2 for different lengths of the base.
Analysis of the proportionality	An equilateral triangle with a base twice as long will have a perimeter twice as long.	If the base of the rectangle is doubled, then its height must be divided by 2 for the area to remain the same.
Table of values	Base (cm) / Perimeter (cm): 2 / 6; 4 / 12; 6 / 18; 30 / 90 (Base: × 2, × 1.5, × 5; Perimeter: × 2, × 1.5, × 5)	Base (cm) / Height (cm): 2 / 15; 4 / 7.5; 6 / 5; 30 / 1 (Base: × 2, × 1.5, × 5; Height: ÷ 2, ÷ 1.5, ÷ 5)
Equation	$P = 3b$ where P is the perimeter of the triangle, and b is the length of its base.	$h = \frac{30}{b}$ where h is the height of the rectangle, and b is the length of its base.
Graphical representation	Perimeter (cm): 0, 10, 20, 30, 40, 50, 60; Base (cm): 5, 10, 15, 20, 25, 30	Height (cm): 0, 10, 20, 30; Base (cm): 10, 20, 30

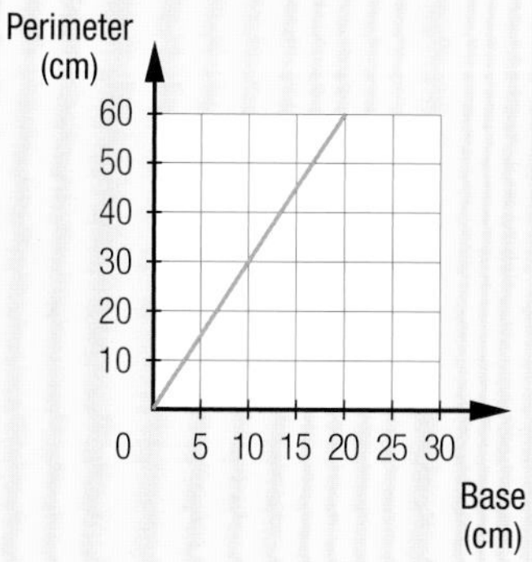

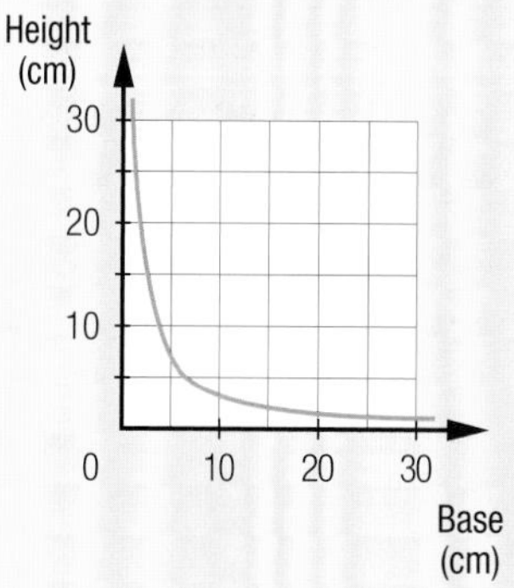

knowledge in action

1 Two people are walking towards each other on a sidewalk. At a certain point, one person stops at a bus stop while the other continues walking. The adjacent graph shows the distance between these two people until the arrival of the bus.

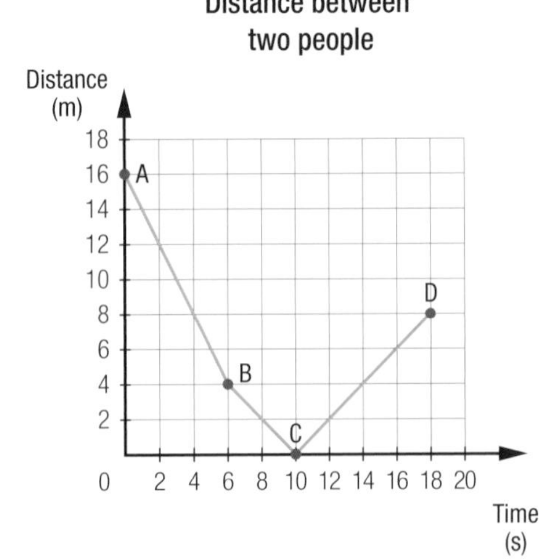

a) Which of the points A, B, C or D corresponds to the moment when one of the people stopped walking? Justify your answer.

b) What are the values of the independent variable and of the dependant variable?

c) At what moment do these two people pass one another?

d) Over which time interval is the distance increasing?

e) What does the y-intercept represent in this context?

2 The power output of an automobile is generally expressed in horsepower (hp). Power output is not constant. It depends, among other things, on motor speed which is measured in revolutions per minute (rpm). The graph of this function, for a particular automobile, appears below.

a) What is the maximum power output of this vehicle?

b) At what motor speed is the maximum power output attained?

c) Determine the domain and the range of this function.

d) Determine when this function is increasing and when this function is decreasing.

e) Interpret the zero of this function.

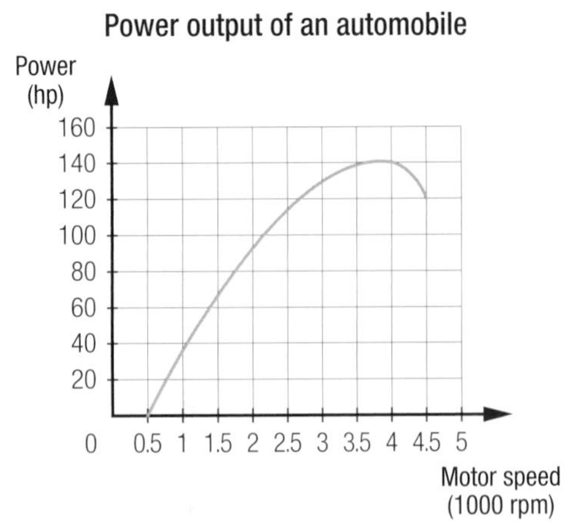

3 The theoretical speed of a runner based on the time she needs to complete a stride is as follows:

Theoretical speed of a runner

Duration of stride (s)	0.18	0.20	0.24	0.30
Speed (m/s)	6.0	5.4	4.5	3.6

a) Is the speed proportional to the duration of the stride?

b) Calculate the number of strides per second as listed in the table of values.

c) Is the number of strides per second proportional to speed? Justify your answer.

d) Find an equation that represents the situations described in **a)** and **c)**.

4 During an experiment, a gas contained in a cylinder is compressed by placing a weight on a piston. The following are observations of the height of the column of air in relation to the total mass of the piston and of the weight combined:

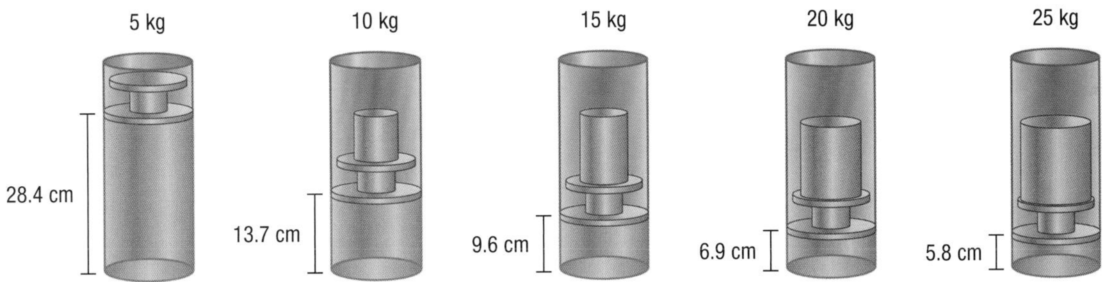

a) Draw the scatter plot that represents this data.

b) What type of function is best suited to represent this situation?

c) Calculate the product of the mass and the height for each ordered pair of the scatter plot.

d) Estimate the height of the column of air if the total mass is 30 kg.

e) What must the total mass be for the height of the column of air to measure 1 mm?

f) Is it possible for the piston to touch the bottom? Justify your answer.

5 To estimate the value of π, Gaby measured the diameter and the circumference of various circular objects with the help of a measuring tape. Using only the data collected, determine the equation that best represents the relation between diameter and circumference.

Measurements of circular objects

	Chip	Glass	CD/DVD	Plate	Drum
Diameter (cm)	2.3	6.2	12.1	26.0	38.2
Circumference (cm)	7.1	19.5	37.9	81.6	119.7

SECTION 2.1 Several models

This section is related to LES 4.

PROBLEM Understanding the human body

A physiology teacher presents different situations to her students.

❶ In swimming, inhalation occurs rapidly to fully inflate the lungs while exhalation is done gradually underwater.

❷ During the first two years after having stopped physical activity, a significant reduction in cardiac volume is observed. Over time, all that had been gained will slowly be lost.

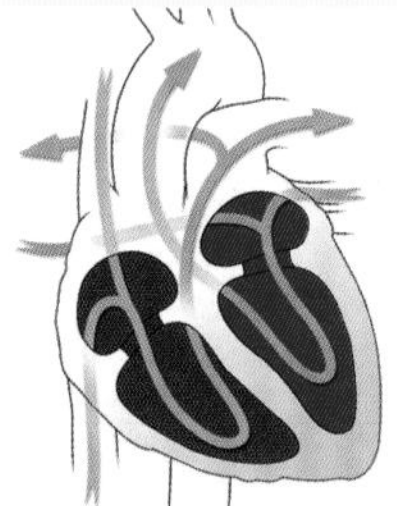

❸ To determine your maximum theoretical heart rate, subtract your age from 220.

❹ A spirometer is an instrument used for measuring the volume of air a person can exhale. During the test, exhalation must be as rapid as possible.

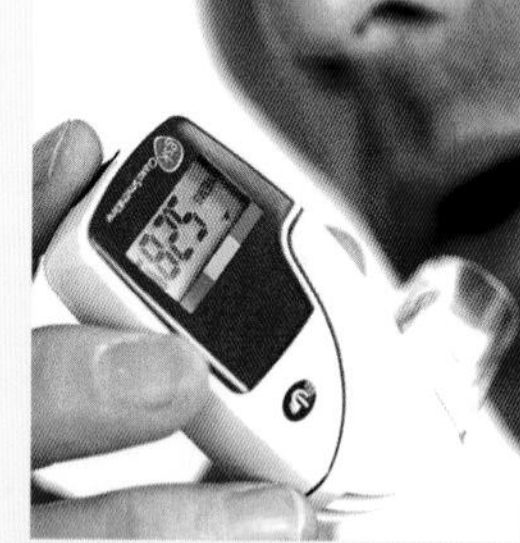

Associate each of the four statements above with one of the graphical models below. Justify each association.

Ⓐ

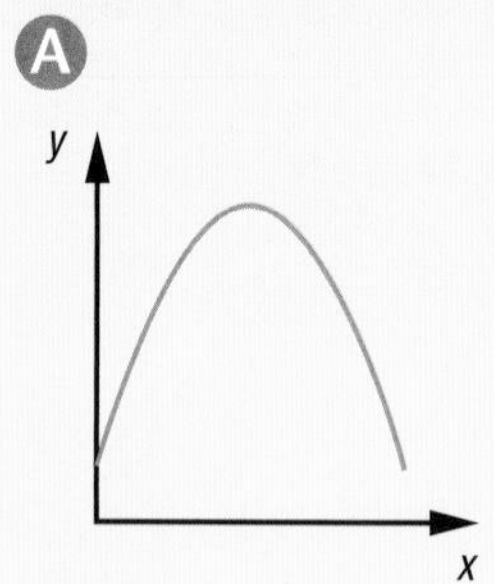

Ⓑ

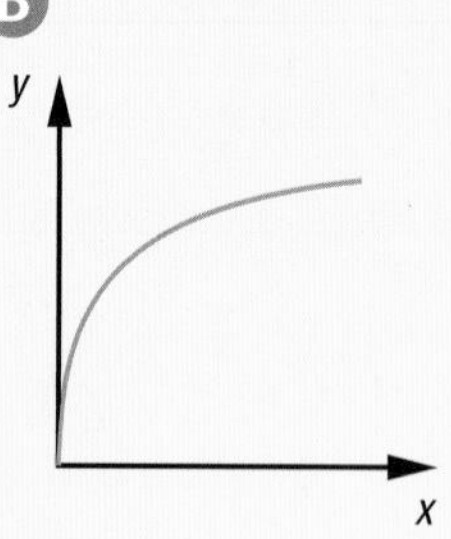

Ⓒ

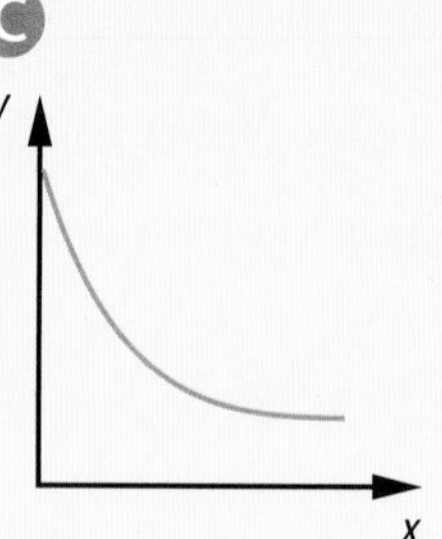

Ⓓ

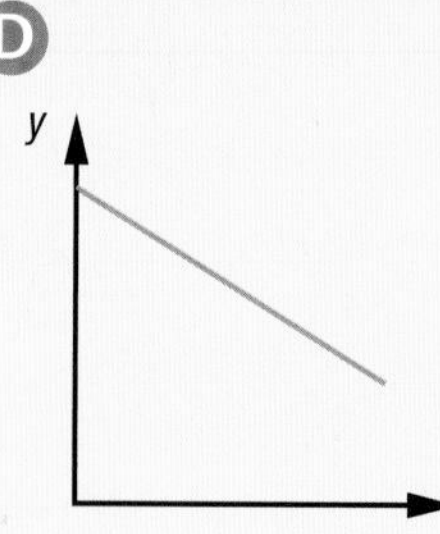

Ⓔ

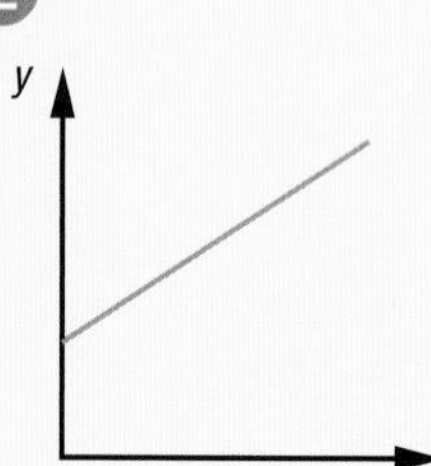

Ⓕ

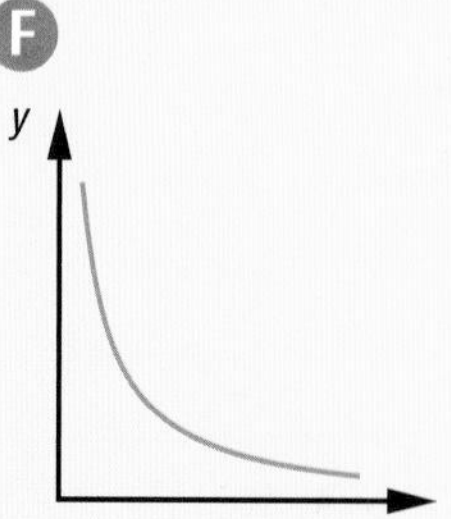

Ⓖ

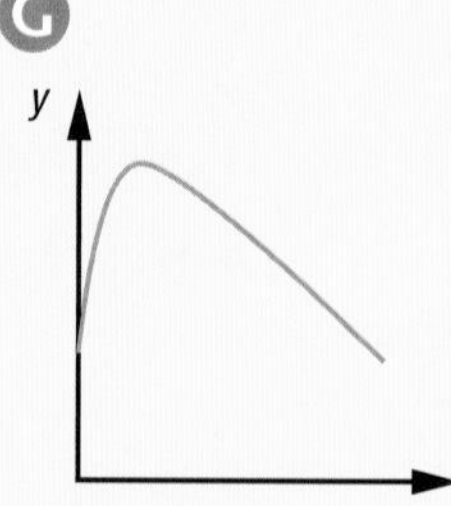

Ⓗ

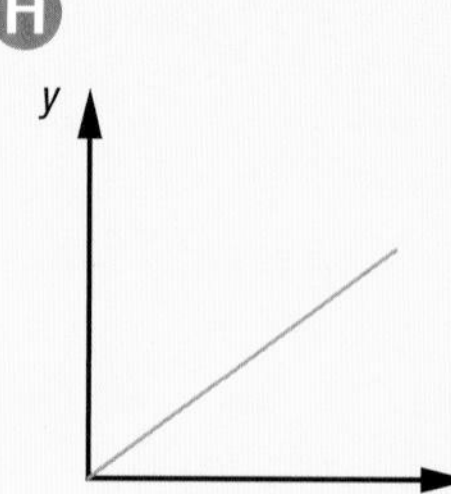

ACTIVITY 1 Practical models

Mathematical models can be useful for representing everyday situations. Consider the following situations.

Temperature measured on the Fahrenheit scale F can be converted into the Celsius scale C using this equation:

$$C = \frac{5}{9}(F - 32)$$

A driver drives 72 km while maintaining a constant speed.

The speed V (in km/h) that is maintained can be represented as a function of the duration t (in h) of the drive:

$$V(t) = \frac{72}{t}$$

The probability P of obtaining heads on repeated throws of a coin can be expressed as a function of the number x of throws:

$$P(x) = \left(\frac{1}{2}\right)^x$$

Leah has set the cruise control at 90 km/h. A stationary traffic radar is located 360 m away. The distance d (in m) from car to radar, as a function of time t (in s), can be represented by:

$d(\text{t}) = 360 - 25t$,

before passing the radar

and

$d(\text{t}) = 25t - 360$,

after passing the radar.

The area A of a cube can be represented as a function of the length of one of its edges s:

$$A = 6s^2$$

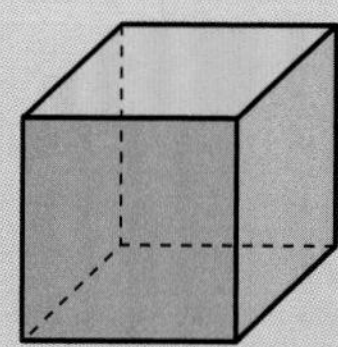

The entry speed V (in m/s) of an Acapulco cliff diver can be expressed as a function of his initial distance above water level h_0 (in m):

$$V = \sqrt{19.6h_0}$$

a. Represent each situation using a graph to show the relation between the variables involved.

b. Compare the properties of each function and determine the differences between them.

A table of values is another way of representing a situation.

ACTIVITY 2 A poor model

Atmospheric pollution has important effects on the environment and on our health. Pollutants emitted by cars and trucks are among the main sources of this pollution. However, some vehicles pollute more than others.

The impact of air pollution on athletes was a major concern for the 2008 Beijing Olympic organizing committee.

The black exhaust emitted by tractor-trailers contains many pollutants. The quantity of pollutants emitted varies according to the speed of the vehicle, as shown below.

Pollution caused by tractor-trailers

Speed (km/h)	40	45	50	55	60	65	70
Quantity of pollutants emitted per 100 km (g)	485	463	440	430	420	402	395

a. Draw the scatter plot that represents this data.

b. Which one of the following equations best represents the function associated with this situation? Justify your answer using the properties of these functions.

First-degree polynomial function

$y = 600 - 3x$

Inverse variation function

$y = \frac{23\ 500}{x}$

Second-degree polynomial function

$y = \frac{1}{10}(x - 70)^2 + 400$

c. According to the model chosen in **b.**, what is the quantity of pollutants emitted in the form of black exhaust by a tractor-trailer travelling a distance of 100 km at a speed of:

1) 10 km/h?
2) 30 km/h?
3) 60 km/h?
4) 100 km/h?
5) 120 km/h?

Techno math

A graphing calculator allows you to graph functions and to determine their properties.

This screen allows you to enter the rule of one or more functions where x is the variable associated with the horizontal axis and y is the variable associated with the vertical axis.

Screen 1

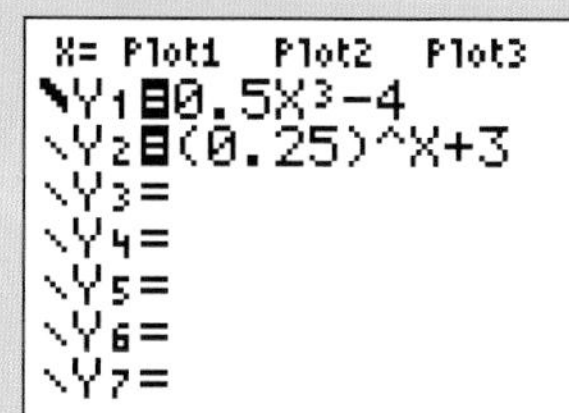

Screen 2

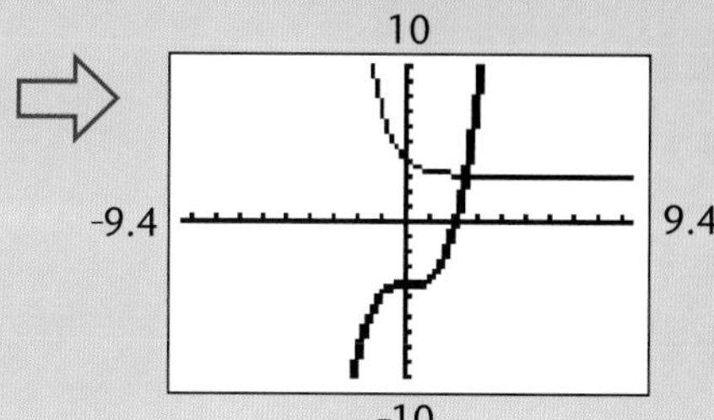

This screen displays different calculations that can be executed.

Screen 3

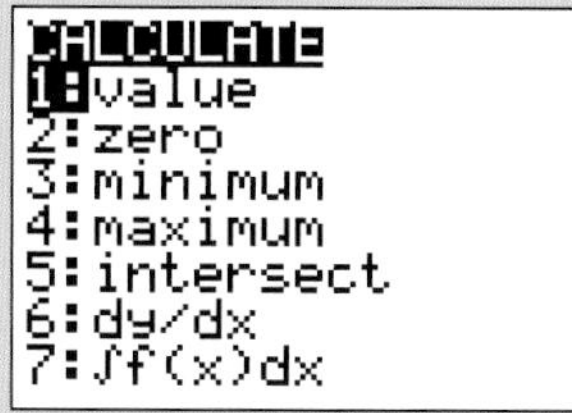

Exploration 1: The y-intercept

By setting the value of x to 0, the corresponding value of y can be determined.

Screen 4

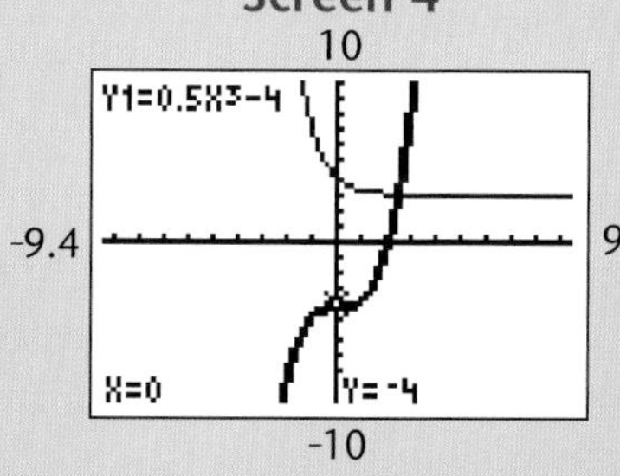

Screen 5

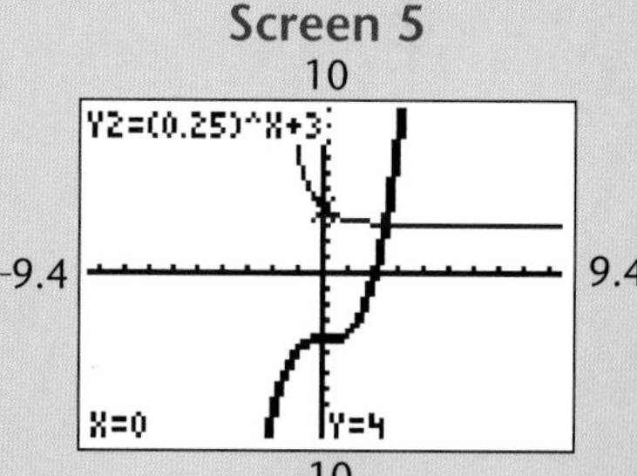

Exploration 2: The zero(s)

By setting an upper and a lower limit, and then positioning the cursor near the zero, its coordinates will be determined.

Screen 6

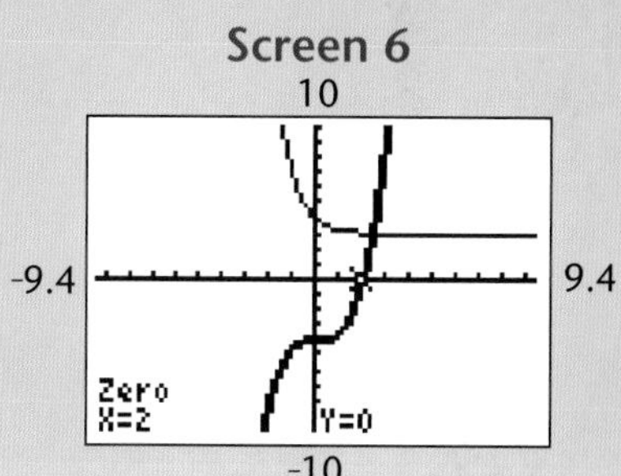

a. What is the y-intercept of the function displayed on:

1) Screen **4**?   2) Screen **5**?

b. What is the value of the zero of the function displayed on Screen **6**?

c. Using a graphing calculator, enter the rules shown on the adjacent screen and for each function determine:

1) the y-intercept

2) the zero(s)

Plot1 Plot2 Plot3
Y1=-X³+3+4
Y2=√(X+8)-2
Y3=X²+2.5X-4
Y4=
Y5=
Y6=
Y7=

A CLOSER LOOK AT SEVERAL MODELS

Many types of functions can be used to model a situation that may or may not be represented by a scatter plot.

- Some functions, such as zero-degree polynomial functions and first-degree polynomial functions are graphically represented by straight lines.

E.g.

1) **Zero-degree polynomial function (the constant function)**

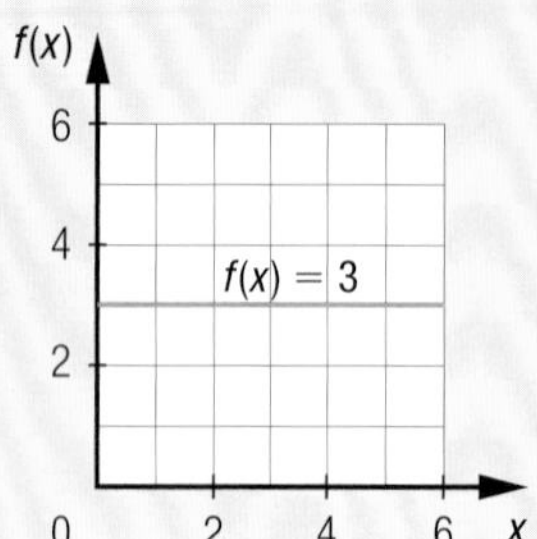

2) **First-degree polynomial function (the linear function)**

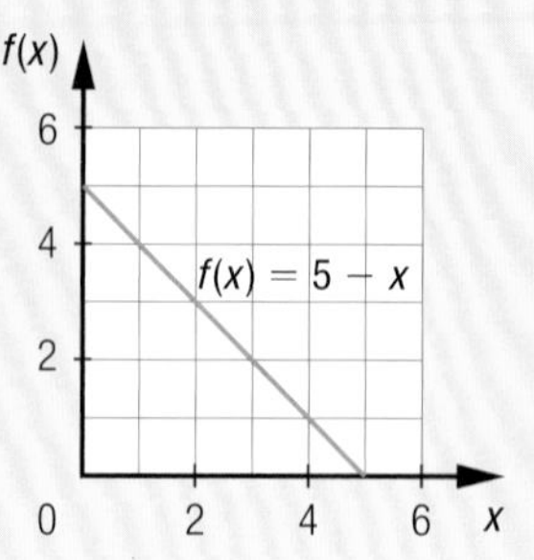

- Other functions such as the second-degree polynomial function and the inverse variation function are graphically represented by curves.

E.g.

1) **Second-degree polynomial function (the quadratic function)**

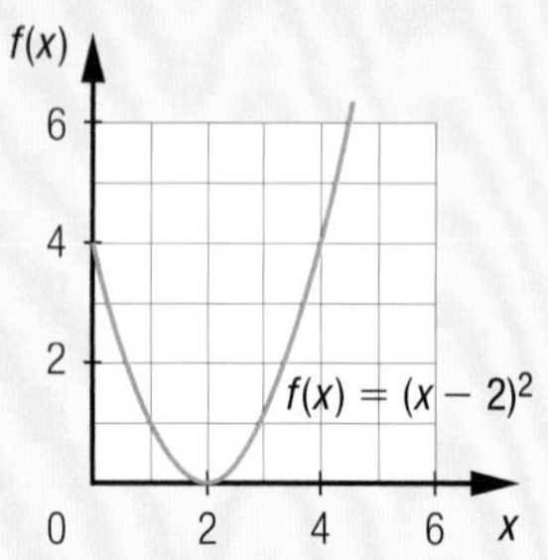

2) **Inverse variation function**

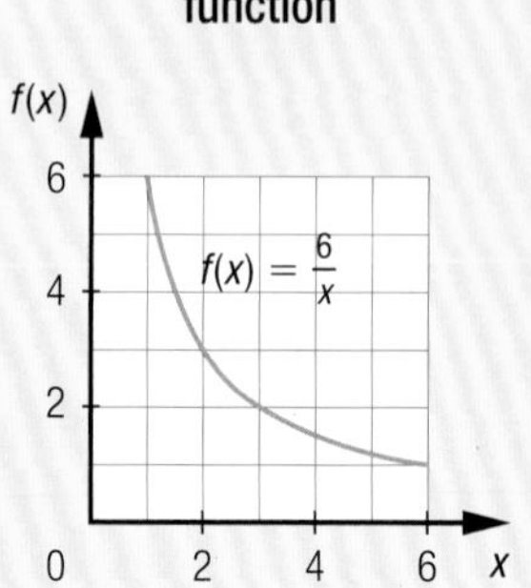

Many other functions (the square root, exponential or polynomial of a degree greater than 2, for example) can be used to model a situation.

- It is possible to combine different models to define a **piecewise function**.

E.g.

$$f(x) = \begin{cases} 4 - (x - 2)^2 & \text{if } x \in [0, 2[\\ 4 & \text{if } x \in [2, 4[\\ -x + 8 & \text{if } x \in [4, 8] \end{cases}$$

CHOOSING A MODEL

Various factors must be considered before choosing a suitable model for the analysis of a situation, and include the shape of the scatter plot and regularities observed in the fluctuations of variables (proportional situations, rate of change, etc.). A comparitive analysis of the **properties of functions** allows you to choose among different possible models.

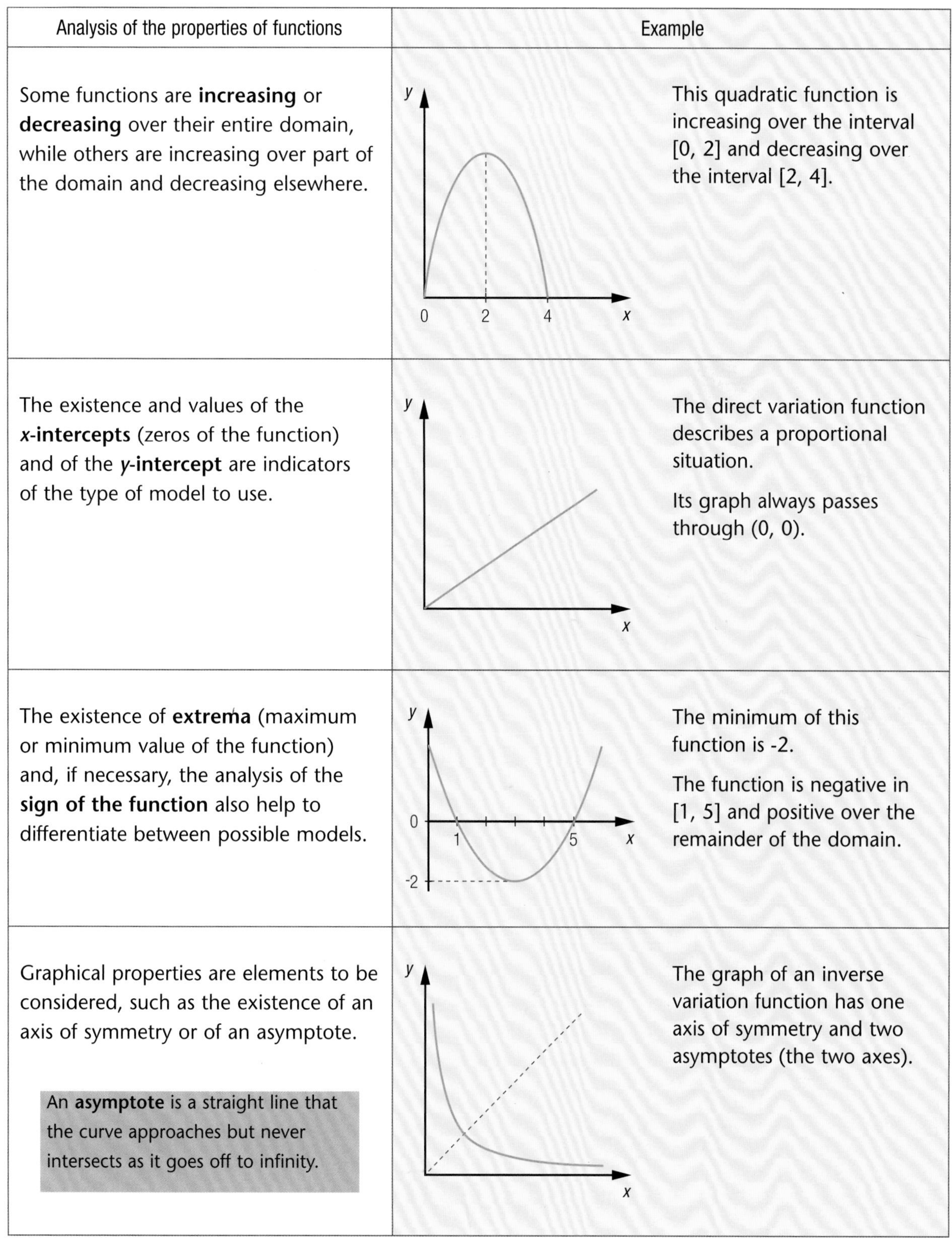

Analysis of the properties of functions	Example
Some functions are **increasing** or **decreasing** over their entire domain, while others are increasing over part of the domain and decreasing elsewhere.	This quadratic function is increasing over the interval [0, 2] and decreasing over the interval [2, 4].
The existence and values of the ***x*-intercepts** (zeros of the function) and of the ***y*-intercept** are indicators of the type of model to use.	The direct variation function describes a proportional situation. Its graph always passes through (0, 0).
The existence of **extrema** (maximum or minimum value of the function) and, if necessary, the analysis of the **sign of the function** also help to differentiate between possible models.	The minimum of this function is -2. The function is negative in [1, 5] and positive over the remainder of the domain.
Graphical properties are elements to be considered, such as the existence of an axis of symmetry or of an asymptote. An **asymptote** is a straight line that the curve approaches but never intersects as it goes off to infinity.	The graph of an inverse variation function has one axis of symmetry and two asymptotes (the two axes).

practice 2.1

1 Three polynomial functions are displayed on a calculator.

$f(x) = -2$ $\quad$ $g(x) = 2x - 3$ $\quad$ $h(x) = (x - 1)^2 - 4$

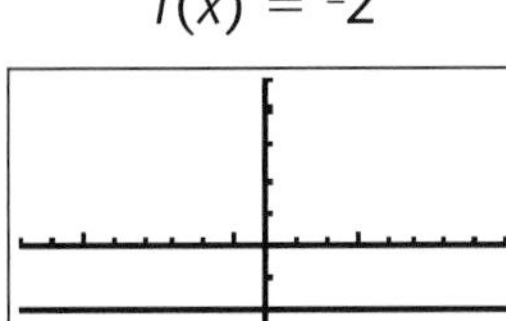

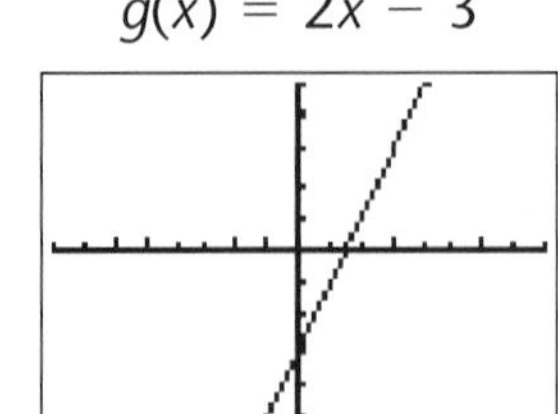

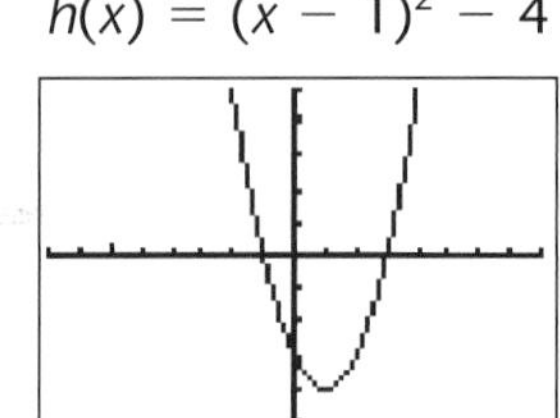

For each of these functions, determine the following properties, if applicable:

a) the domain and the range

b) the interval over which the function is decreasing

c) the y-intercept

d) the zero(s) of the function

e) the minimum and the maximum

f) the interval over which the function is negative

2 Consider the following rules of functions:

$f_1(x) = 2x$ $\quad$ $f_2(x) = 2$ $\quad$ $f_3(x) = x^2$ $\quad$ $f_4(x) = 2^x$

a) Represent these functions using a table of values for when x is equal to 0, 1, 2, 3 and 4.

b) Represent these functions graphically on the same Cartesian plane.

c) Find the range of these functions if the domain is restricted to [0, 10].

d) Which of these functions are strictly increasing?

e) Which of these functions have a zero?

f) Find the y-intercept of each function.

g) In each of the following intervals, which function has the greatest value?

1)]0, 1[$\quad$ 2)]1, 2[$\quad$ 3)]2, 4[$\quad$ 4)]4, 10[

A function is strictly increasing if it is increasing over its entire domain without ever being constant.

3 Assuming that the variable x represents only positive values, draw the graph of the two functions below, compare their properties (domain, range, increasing, decreasing, etc.) and identify their differences.

$$f(x) = \frac{10}{x} \qquad g(x) = \frac{(x - 10)^2}{10}$$

4 **SPORTS PHYSIOLOGY** To become a high-level athlete many things must be considered, including the body's reaction to effort. Consider the graph below which is based on studies in the physiology of sport and exercise.

VO_2 is the abbreviation for the volume of oxygen absorbed by a person.

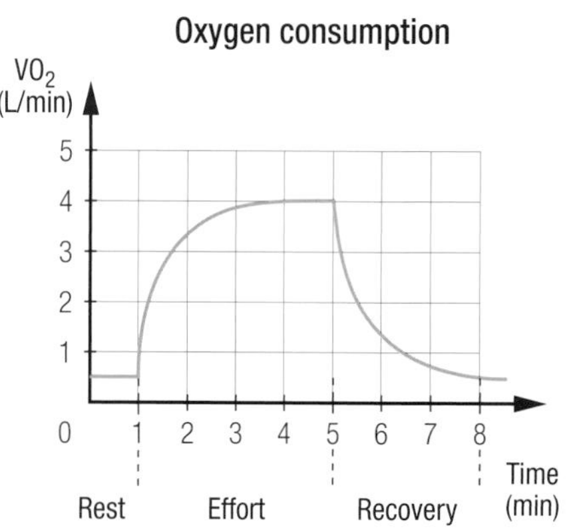

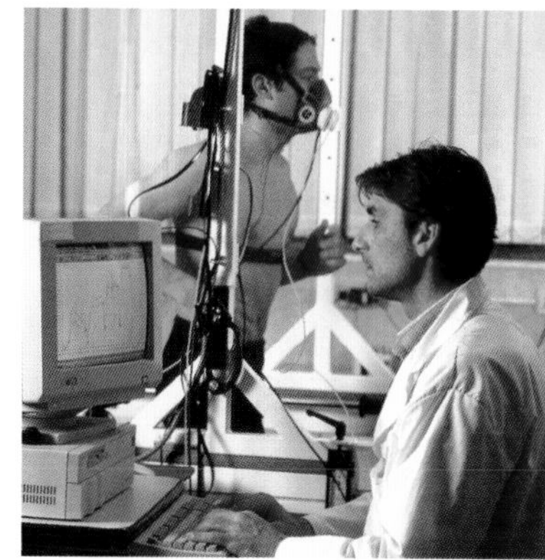

This situation is represented by a piecewise function.

a) In what way are the parts for effort and recovery similar? In what way do they differ?

b) What does the maximum of the function represent in this situation? What does the minimum represent?

5 In swimming, as in many high-level sports, an athlete's success relies on good technique. The position of a swimmer's hands, including their height above water in the early moments of a race, plays an important role. A sports analyst recorded the following data.

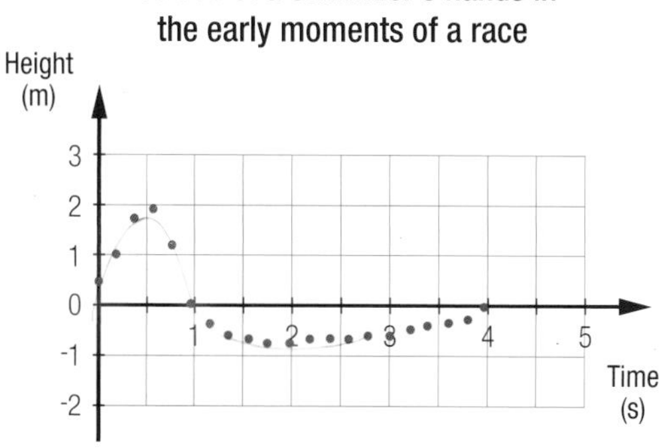

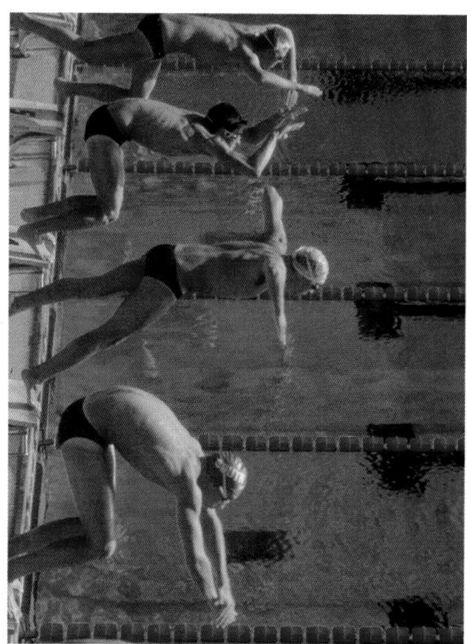

a) In your own words, describe the model that would best fit this scatter plot.

b) Compare this model with the model used in the preceding exercise. What are their similarities and differences?

6 A trainer measured the oxygen consumption and the heart rate of a 20-year-old woman while she was exercising. Measurements were taken before and after she had done 10 weeks of aerobic training. Each scatter plot was modelled using a first-degree polynomial function.

Before training

Heart rate (beats/min)

$y = 172x - 82$

Oxygen consumption (L/min)

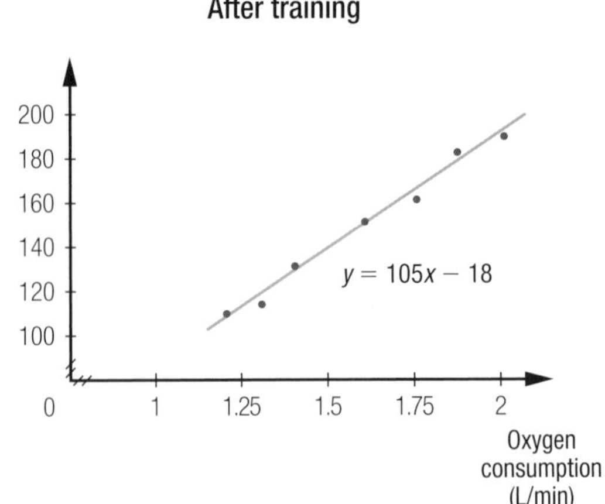

a) Considering that this woman's heart rate cannot exceed 200 beats/min and that her minimum oxygen consumption, at rest, is 1 L/min, find the domain and the range of these two functions.

During intense physical activity, the oxygen level in your body increases. A higher comsumption of oxygen causes a faster heart rate.

b) Based on this data, explain in your own words, the effect of training on heart rate and on oxygen consumption.

7 Simon is inflating balloons that will be used as decorations for his girlfriend's birthday party. After inflating a balloon with a single breath, he then lets it deflate. While doing so, Simon makes the following observations about the volume of air that the balloon contained.

- The volume of air increases during the first 6 seconds.
- During the first 2 seconds, the volume of air in the balloon increases more and more quickly. In the last 4 seconds the volume of air continues to increase but more slowly.

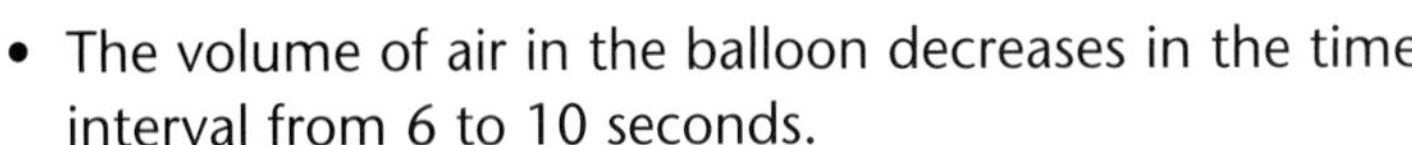

- The volume of air in the balloon decreases in the time interval from 6 to 10 seconds.
- The maximum volume of air in the balloon is 4 L.

Determine the graphical model that best represents the function associated with this situation.

8 Jennifer snowshoes along the *Sentiers des Caps* in the Charlevoix region. One day, with the temperature at 0°C, she brought along hot chocolate. At the same time as she placed her cup on a table, a strong gust of wind blew one of her gloves down a cliff.

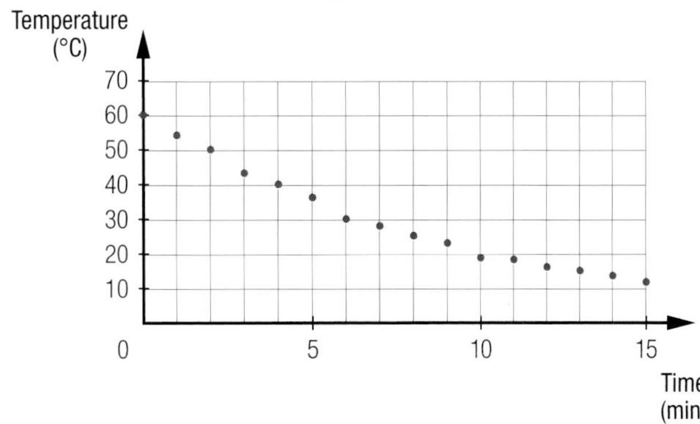

She retrieved her glove and, on her way back, wondered if her hot chocolate was still hot.

Which of the following equations best represents the function associated with this situation? Justify your answer using the properties of these functions.

A $y = 60(0.9)^x$ **B** $y = 60 - 3.5x$

9 Consider the following three situations.

Situation 1

A marble, initially launched using an elastic, rolls along a table. Observations are made about the distance travelled as a function of time.

Situation 2

A marble, initially placed at the top, rolls down an inclined plane. Observations are made about the distance travelled on the inclined plane as a function of time.

Situation 3

A moving object travels at a constant speed towards a wall. Observations are made about its distance from the wall as a function of time.

For each situation, sketch a graphical model that represents the relation described. Explain your choice of graph using properties of the specified function.

10 The scatter plot below shows the relation between the radius of a ball as a function of its area. A curve has been drawn to model the situation.

Measurement of the radius of various balls

Radius (cm)
6
5
4
3
2
1
0
100 200 300 400
Area (cm^2)

a) What are the properties of the function represented by this curve?

b) Express, in your own words, the meaning of each property in this specific context.

c) Do you think that the curve will eventually approach an asymptote? Explain your answer.

11 Michael places a jug of water in the freezer and records the water temperature every minute. He notices that the temperature can go below 0°C without the water freezing. This phenomena is known as supercooling.

Data recorded by Michael

Elapsed time (min)	0	1	2	3	4	5	6	7	8	9	10	11	12
Temperature (°C)	15.0	11.0	8.0	5.5	3.0	1.0	-0.5	-2.0	-3.0	-4.0	0.0	0.0	0.0

a) Draw the scatter plot that represents Michael's data.

b) Draw the curve that best fits the scatter plot. Be sure that this curve is really that of a function.

c) Assuming that the domain of this function is restricted to the interval [0, 12], determine:

1) the range of the function

2) the increasing and decreasing intervals

3) the zero(s) of the function

4) the interval where the function is negative

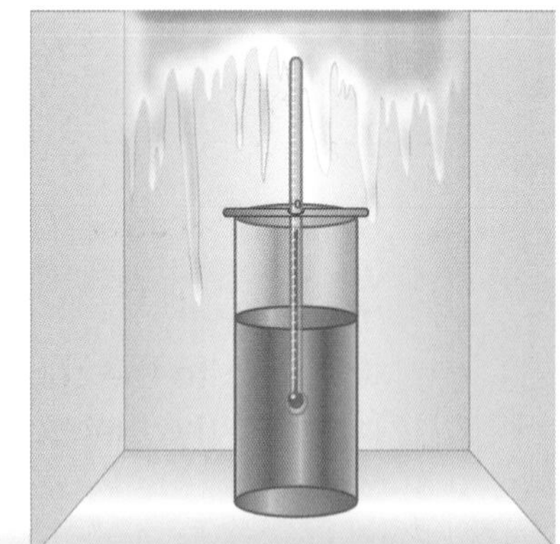

Matter is in a state of supercooling if it remains liquid after its temperature has dropped below its freezing point. However, the slightest disturbance can cause it to solidify instantly.

12 ANALYSIS OF A MOVEMENT The adjacent table of values shows the acceleration of a person's hand for the first tenth of a second from the moment he decides to grab an object.

Analysis of movement

Time (ms)	Acceleration (mm/s²)
5	16
10	24
15	27
20	24
25	20
30	14
35	4
40	-5
45	-10
50	-11
55	-11
60	-12
65	-12
70	-13
75	-13
80	-12
85	-10
90	-10
95	-10
100	-11

a) In your own words, explain the meaning of the negative accelerations recorded in the table.

b) Draw the scatter plot that represents this data.

c) This situation can be modelled by a piecewise function. What type of function seems appropriate for each part? Graph these functions on the scatter plot.

d) What does the zero of the function mean in this context?

13 THE STRENGTH OF AN ANGLE The force produced by the biceps depends on the angle formed by the forearm and the upper arm. The illustration below shows the percentage of the maximum force generated by biceps at different angles:

a) Draw the scatter plot that represents this data.

b) Draw the curve of best fit.

c) Referring to the context, determine the domain and range of the function represented by the curve you have drawn.

d) Estimate the percentage of the maximum force produced by the biceps when the angle with the forearm is:

1) 90° 2) 45°

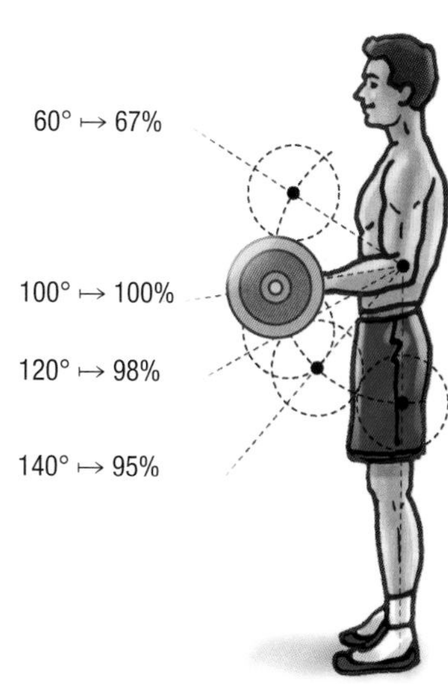

SECTION 2.2 The quadratic model

This section is related to LES 5.

PROBLEM Full speed ahead

Speed skiing and skydiving are the fastest non-motorized sports.

The basis of speed skiing is that the skier's aerodynamic position minimizes air resistance. Wind-tunnel tests have been used to improve the aerodynamics of both the skier and the equipment.

In 2006, Swedish skier Sanna Tidstrand was recorded as the fastest woman in the world. Her record of 242.59 km/h was established in des Arcs, France. In the male category, the Italian speed skier Simone Origone clocked 251.40 km/h.

The launching area consists of the first 300 metres of the slope. To determine the skier's speed, measurements are taken at 300 and 400 metres. The mean speed between these points is then calculated.

Modelling the launch of the descent of a skier

Elapsed time (s)	0.5	1.0	1.5	2.0	2.5	3.0
Distance travelled (m)	0.7	2.8	6.3	11.2	17.5	25.2

Based on the model described by the table of values, what speed will this skier achieve?

ACTIVITY 1 The hammer throw

The hammer throw is a sport that requires both strength and technique. The speed at which the ball is launched after the swing is one of the factors that will determine the distance it travels. During the swing, which consists of several rotations, the athlete gradually increases the speed of the ball. As its speed increases, the force needed to hold on to the ball also increases. Sensors were used to measure the speed of the ball and the corresponding force (in newtons) achieved by the athlete at different times during the swing.

Measurements taken during the hammer throw

Speed of ball (m/s)	Force exerted to hold on to the ball (N)
2	70
4	50
9	280
9	500
17	980
19	1150
25	2000
26	2300
29	3200
30	3000

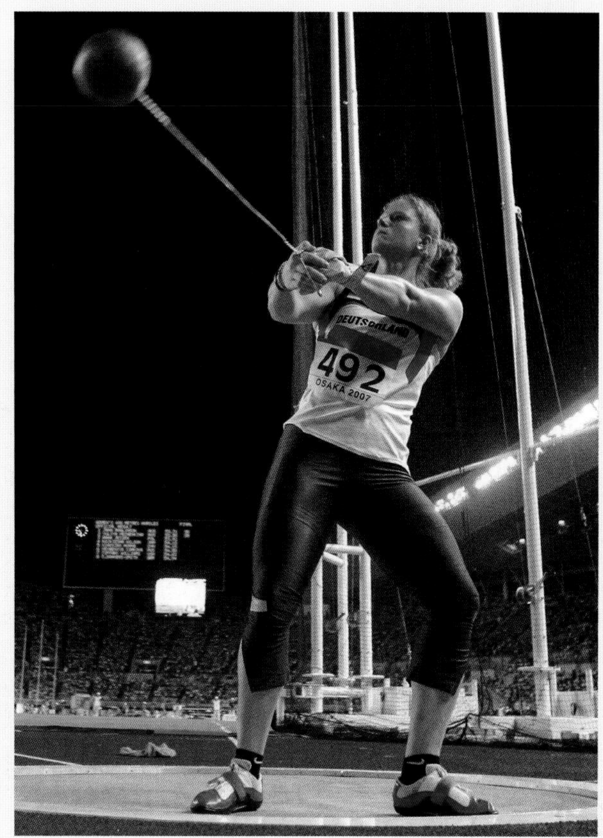

a. Graph the following relations using a scatter plot:

1) force as a function of speed
2) force as a function of speed squared

b. Is the relation between the speed of the ball and the force exerted a proportional situation?

c. What is the rule of the function that models this relation between speed and force?

d. The best female hammer throwers are able to swing their ball so that it reaches a speed of 115 km/h. Estimate the force she exerts when the ball is rotating at this speed.

ACTIVITY 2 Controlled transformation

Marco displayed the graphs of functions $f(x) = x^2$ and $g(x) = \frac{1}{4}x^2 - 1$ on his graphing calculator. He observed that both curves have an axis of symmetry, which is the y-axis.

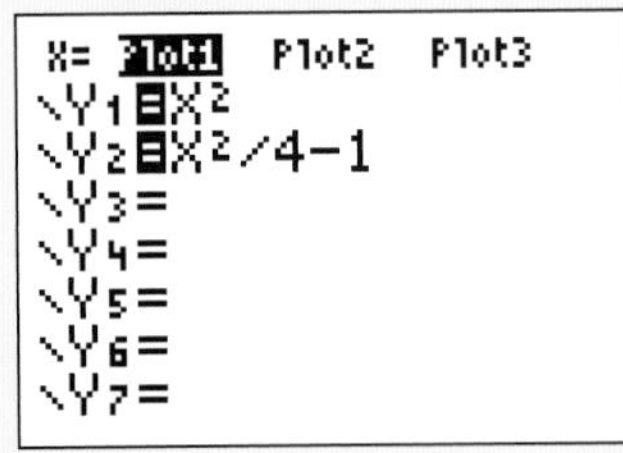

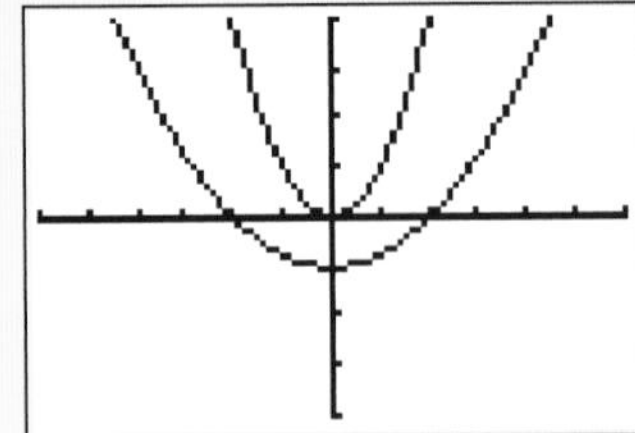

The vertex is the intersection point of the curve and the axis of symmetry.

a. What are the coordinates of the vertex of each curve displayed?

b. How do the graphs of these two functions differ from one another? In what ways are they similar?

Function g is a member of the family of functions whose equations are of the form $y = ax^2 + k$, where the parameters **a** and **k** are positive or negative real numbers. Each parameter effects the graph of the function.

c. Formulate a conjecture concerning the role of the parameters **a** and **k** on the graphical representation of a quadratic function.

d. Find at least one reason that makes your conjecture plausible.

Having analyzed a few examples in this form, Marco comes to the conclusion that the value of parameter **a** can be determined graphically by simply observing the position of the vertex and the position of the point whose x-value is 1 on the graph.

e. Do you think that he is right? If so, formulate a conjecture for this statement. If not, explain why you disagree with him and suggest another way of finding the value of the parameter **a**.

f. Using the information that you have discovered, find the rule of the function represented by the following graph where each division of the scale is one unit. Explain your reasoning.

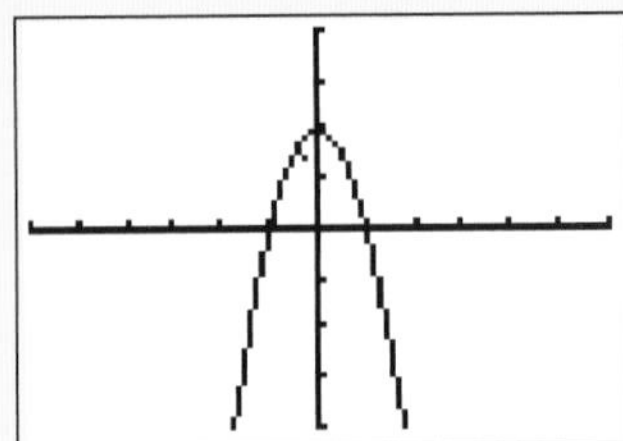

ACTIVITY 3 Good reflexes

The first few moments of a runner's acceleration phase were modelled with the function $d(t) = 3.5t^2$, where $d(t)$ is the distance covered (in m) and t is the elapsed time (in s). The following graph represents this function:

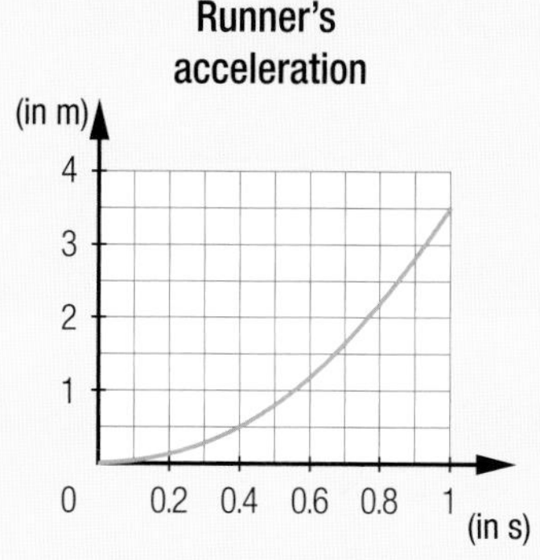

The mean reaction time to an acoustic signal is 235 ms. The best athletes manage to reduce this to 145 ms. In competition, a false start is called if an athlete leaves within 100 ms of the starting shot. The athlete is considered to have caused a false start because no one can react in less than 100 ms.

It is assumed in the situation above that the runner begins acceleration exactly at the sound of the starter's pistol. However, in reality this is never the case. There is, at the very least, a time lag between the shot and the runner's reaction. The following graphs describe one runner's acceleration phase taking into account the exact start time.

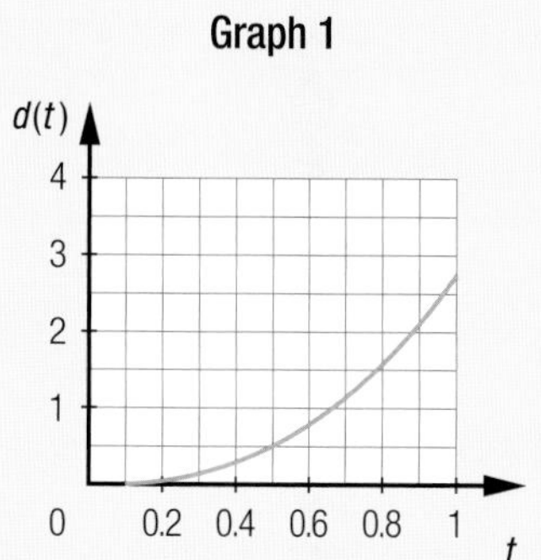

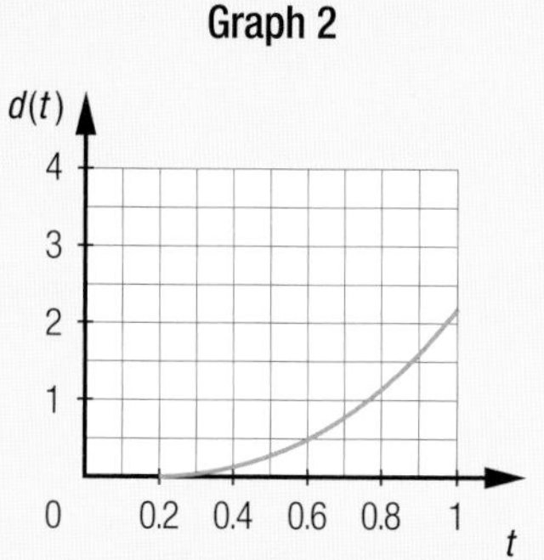

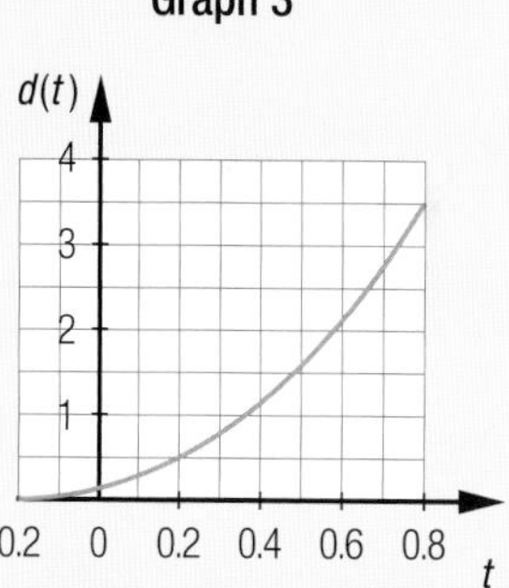

a. Why does a negative value for time appear in Graph 3?

b. Each of these graphs can be obtained by applying a geometric transformation to the initial graph of the function d. Describe these geometric transformations.

c. For each graph, find the equation that best represents the distance run as a function of time elapsed after the starting shot.

d. The runner's reaction time is usually 0.15 s. What distance would be gained during the first second if the reaction time was improved by 0.05 s?

Techno math

A graphing calculator allows you to simultaneously display the curves of several polynomial functions in the same Cartesian plane. The effects of the parameters **a**, **h** and **k** on the graph of a function whose rule in standard form is $f(x) = \text{a}(x - \text{h})^2 + \text{k}$ can be observed in the following exploration:

Screen 1

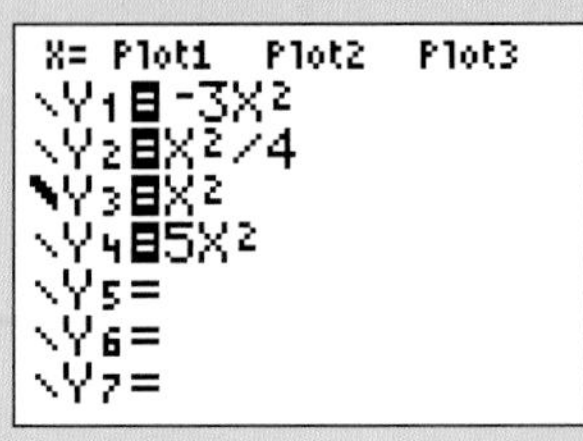

Screen 2

8

-12 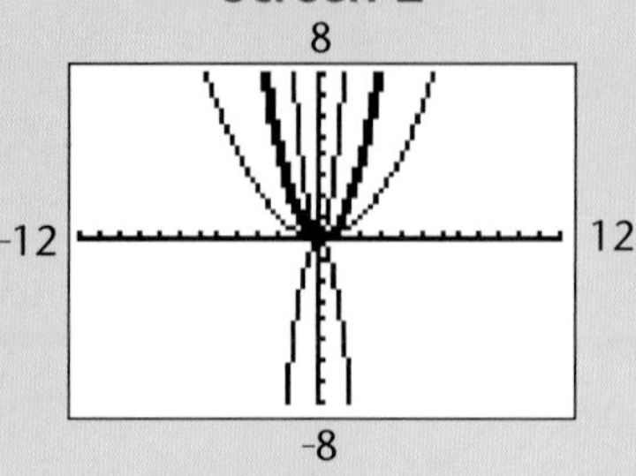 12

-8

Screen 3

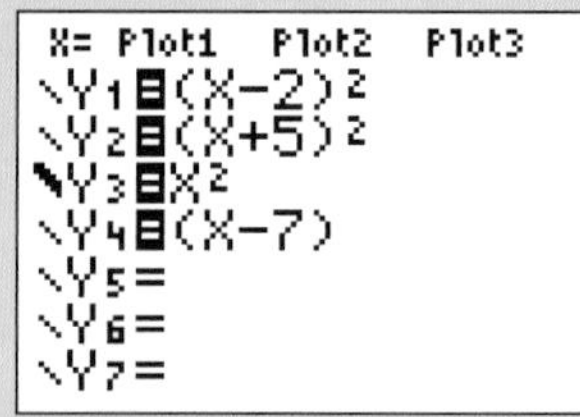

Screen 4

8

-12 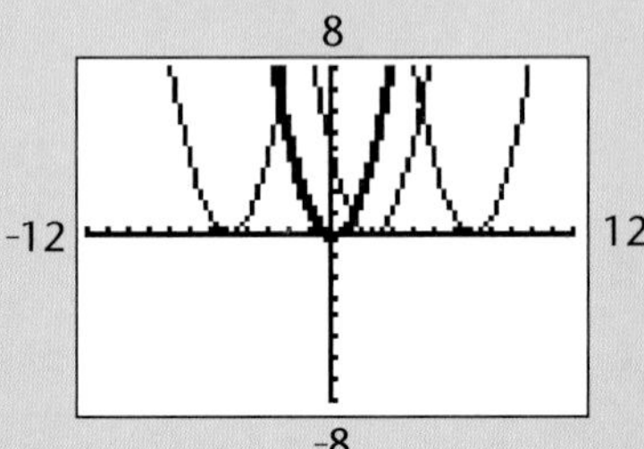 12

-8

Screen 5

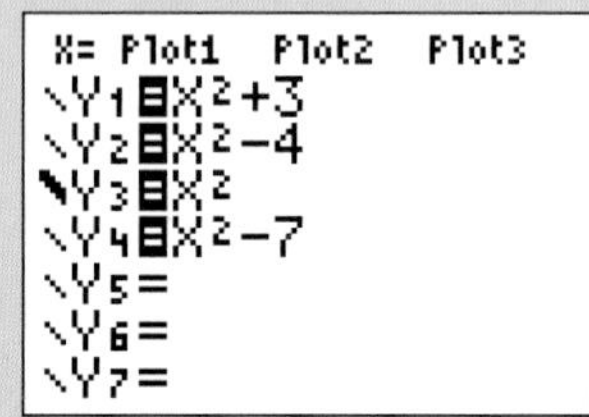

Screen 6

8

-12 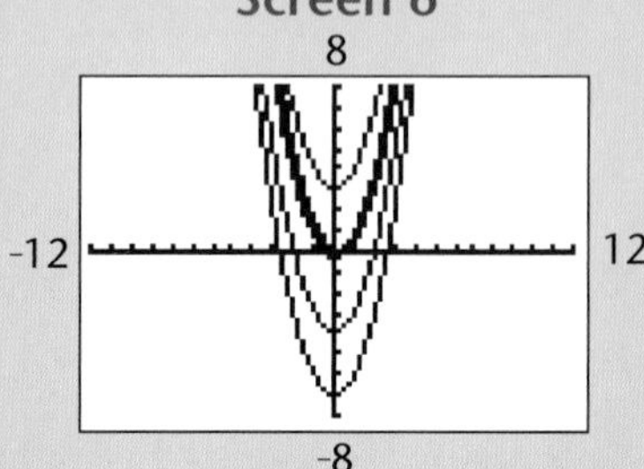 12

-8

a. Indicate which parameter has changed in:

1) Screen **1**? 2) Screen **3**? 3) Screen **5**?

b. What distinguishes the second-degree polynomial functions in:

1) Screen **2**? 2) Screen **4**? 3) Screen **6**?

c. What is the effect on the graph of a second-degree polynomial function, written in standard form, when:

1) the value of **a** is increasingly distant from zero?
2) the value of **h** is increasingly distant from zero?
3) the value of **k** is increasingly distant from zero?

d. Consider the adjacent equations.

1) Display the graphs of the functions shown on the adjacent screen and describe the differences observed when comparing the two second-degree polynomial functions.
2) Find the *y*-intercept and the zeros of the function Y_2.

Plot1 Plot2 Plot3
\Y1 = X²
\Y2 = 0.25(X-2)²-4
\Y3 =
\Y4 =
\Y5 =
\Y6 =

MODELLING WITH A QUADRATIC FUNCTION

The rule of the basic quadratic function is in the form: $f(x) = x^2$.

Verbal description

The value of the independent variable can be any real number. The dependent variable however, because it is the square of a number, must necessarily be positive. The graph of this function is a curve called a **parabola** that has one **axis of symmetry** (the y-axis) and a **vertex** at (0, 0).

Table of values

x	$f(x)$
-3	9
-2	4
-1	1
0	0
1	1
2	4
3	9

Graph

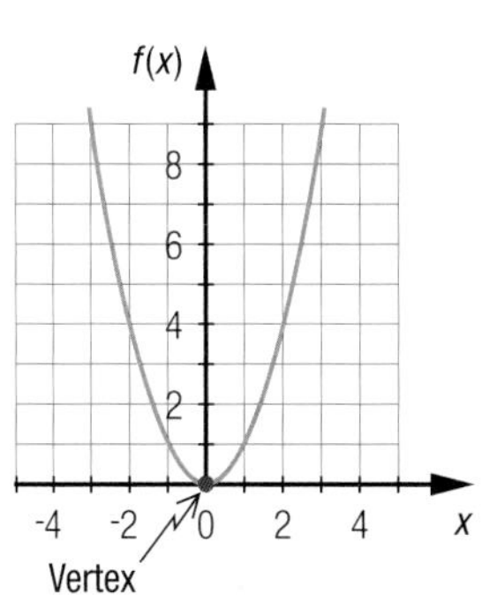

The transformed quadratic function

The rule of the transformed quadratic function in **standard form** can be expressed in the form: $f(x) = a(x - h)^2 + k$, where **a** $\neq 0$.

The parameters **a**, **h** and **k** are real numbers. Each of these parameters plays a role in the graphical representation of the function. In each of the following graphs, the orange-coloured curve is the graph of the basic function $f(x) = x^2$.

- An increase (decrease) in the value of parameter **a** results in a vertical stretch (compression) of the curve.
- Changing the sign of parameter **a** results in a reflection of the curve over the x-axis.
- Parameters **h** and **k** determine a horizontal translation of **h** units and a vertical translation of **k** units.

E.g.

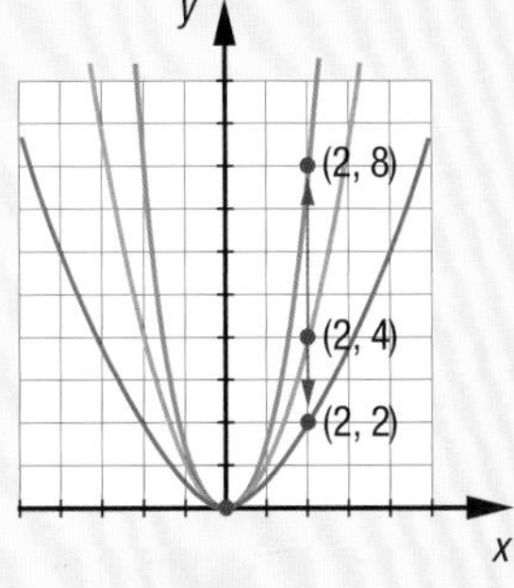

$f_1(x) = 2x^2$

$f_2(x) = \frac{x^2}{2}$

E.g.

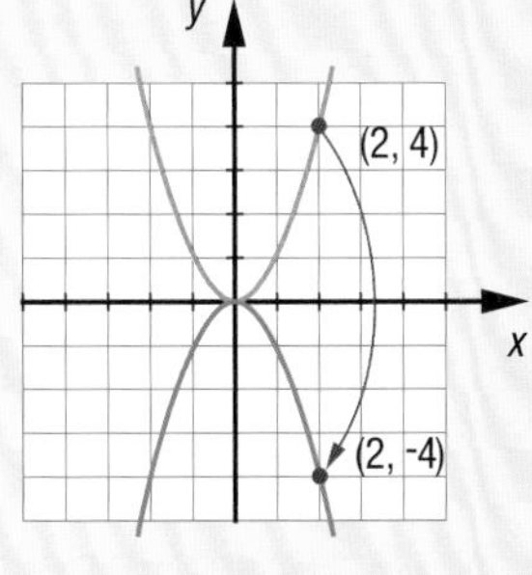

$f_3(x) = -x^2$

E.g.

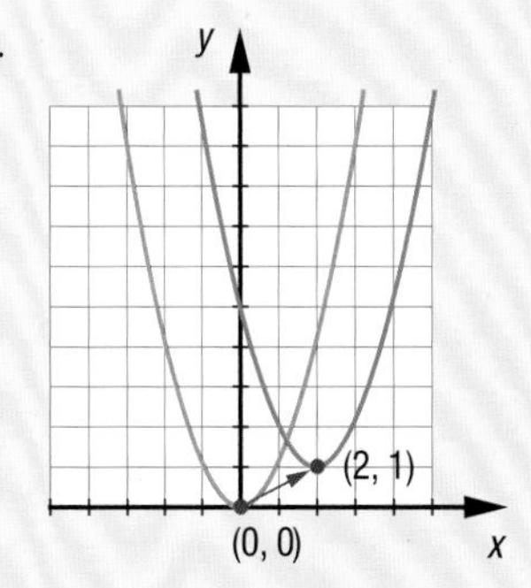

$f_4(x) = (x - 2)^2 + 1$

The coordinates (h, k) define the vertex of the parabola.

Properties of a quadratic function

The properties of a quadratic function depend on the values of the parameters **a**, **h** and **k**. The graph of the function helps us determine these properties.

E.g. The properties of the function: $f(x) = -\frac{5}{4}(x + 1)^2 + 5$

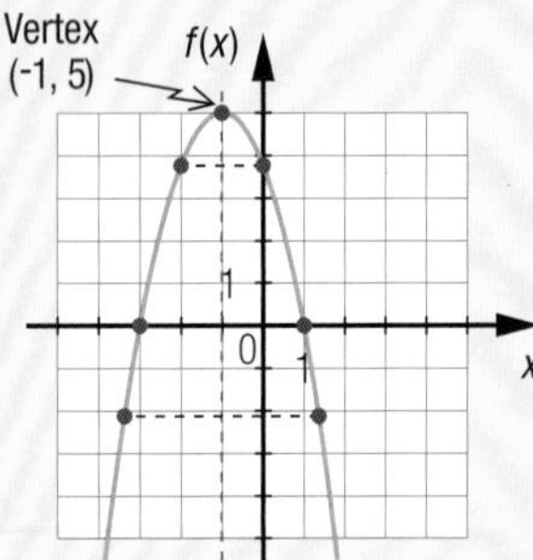

The vertical axis of symmetry intersects the x-axis at -1. This axis makes it possible to locate points on the graph using reflection.

- The domain of f: $\mathbb{R}$.
- The range of f: $]-\infty, 5]$.
- The function is increasing over the interval $]-\infty, -1]$ and decreasing over the interval $[-1, +\infty[$.
- The y-intercept is 3.75 because $f(0) = -\frac{5}{4}(0 + 1)^2 + 5 = 3.75$.
- The zeros of the function are -3 and 1.
- The function is positive in the interval $[-3, 1]$ and negative in the interval $]-\infty, -3] \cup [1, +\infty[$.

Proportionally squared situations

A variable y is **directly proportional to the square** of x, if $y = ax^2$. In science, many situations can be modelled by this type of function.

E.g. The power (in watts) of a light bulb was measured for different intensities of current (in amperes) and the corresponding scatter plot was created.

Intensity (A)	Power (W)
0.1	3
0.2	9
0.3	27
0.4	44
0.5	70
0.6	90

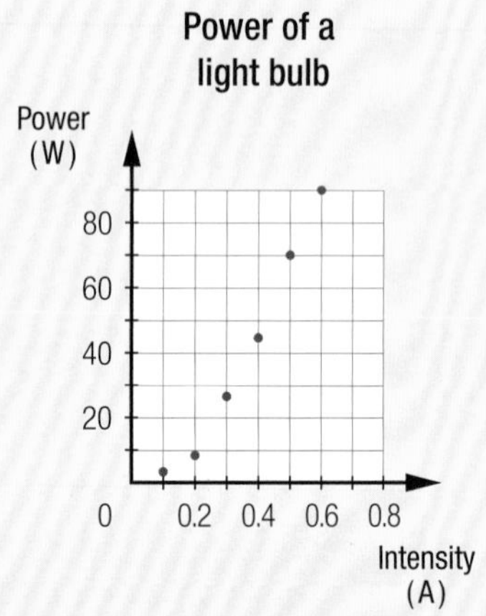

1. The shape of the scatter plot suggests the use of a quadratic function. Moreover, if the intensity is 0 then the power will be 0. Thus, the model $P = aI^2$, where P is the power and I is the intensity, seems appropriate in this situation.

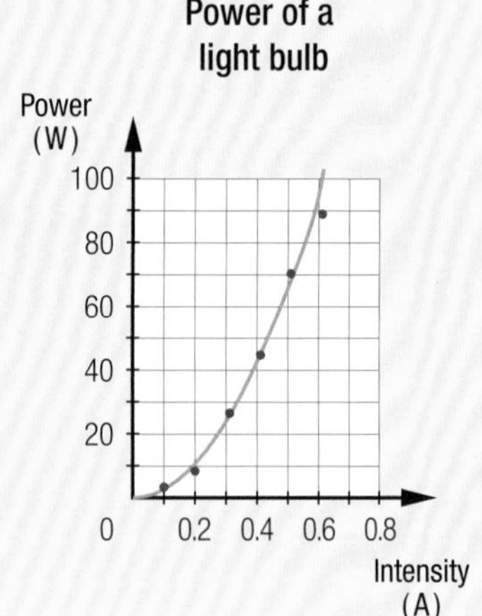

2. To find the value of parameter **a**, calculate the mean of the ratios $\frac{P}{I^2}$ for each entry in the table of values. The result is approximately 272 which is obtained from the expression $(300 + 225 + 300 + 275 + 280 + 250) \div 6$.

   Thus, the equation is $P = 272I^2$.

practice 2.2

1 Consider these three quadratic functions:

① $f(x) = {}^-4(x + 5)^2$ ② $g(x) = {}^-0.5x^2 + 8$ ③ $h(x) = 3(x - 5)^2 - 12$

Draw the graph of these functions and determine the following properties:

a) the domain
b) the range
c) the coordinates of the vertex
d) the y-intercept
e) the extrema of the function
f) the zero(s)
g) the increasing interval
h) the decreasing interval
i) the intervals over which the function is positive
j) the intervals over which the function is negative

2 Four quadratic functions of the form $f(x) = a(x - h)^2 + k$ are graphed in the same Cartesian plane.

a) For which functions is parameter **k** negative?
b) For which functions is parameter **h** positive?
c) For which functions do the following parameters have the same value?
   1) parameter **a**
   2) parameter **h**
   3) parameter **k**
d) Which function is defined by the rule $y = \frac{5}{9}(x - 1)^2 - 2$?

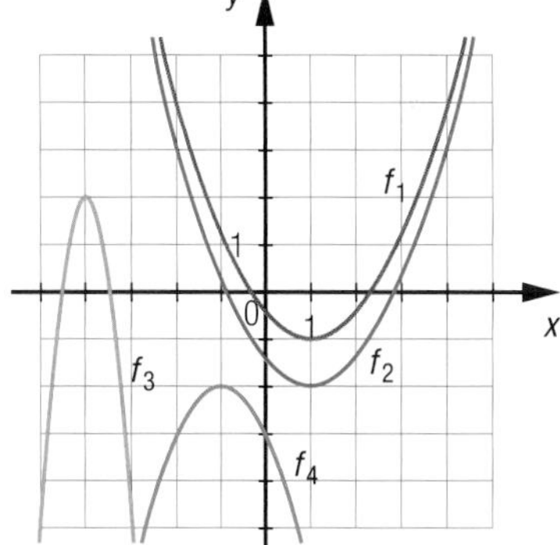

3 The relation between the area of a polygon (a square, a regular hexagon and a regular octagon) and the length of its sides is represented graphically.

a) Match each curve to the polygon it represents.
b) Using the graph, estimate the area of these three polygons if the sides are 1 cm in length.
c) Express the area of these polygons as a function of the length of their sides.

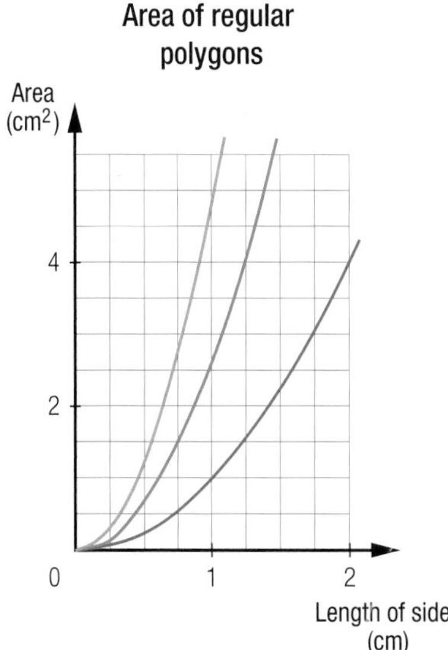

4 The area of a circle can be expressed as a function of its radius: $A(r) = \pi r^2$.

a) From the adjacent table of values, calculate the differences between the successive values of the area. Next, calculate the differences between the successive results just calculated. What do you observe?

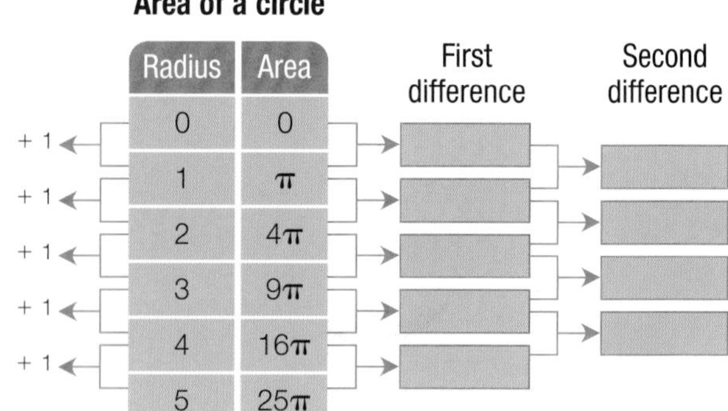

b) What relation is there between the value of the second difference and parameter **a** of the function?

c) Is this relation applicable to all quadratic functions? Check and see if this is the case for the following functions by creating their table of values.

1) $f(x) = (x + 2)^2$ 2) $g(x) = 2x^2 + 5$ 3) $h(x) = -3x^2$

d) Determine the value of parameter **a** of the functions whose tables of values are:

1)

x	y
0	-6
1	6
2	10
3	6
4	-6

2)

x	y
1	1
2	10
3	25
4	46
5	73

3)

x	y
2	2
3	4.5
4	8
5	12.5
6	18

e) Refer to the table of values in **d)**. The independent variable x always varies by one unit. Is this condition essential to determine the value of parameter **a** of the function? Justify your answer.

5 Martha throws a ball vertically in the air and catches it 2 s later. The ball rises to an elevation of 4.9 m.

a) Represent the situation graphically. Explain your choice of model.

b) Find the equation associated with your model.

c) How high did the ball rise after 0.25 s?

6 The user guide for a chest expander provides the following information.

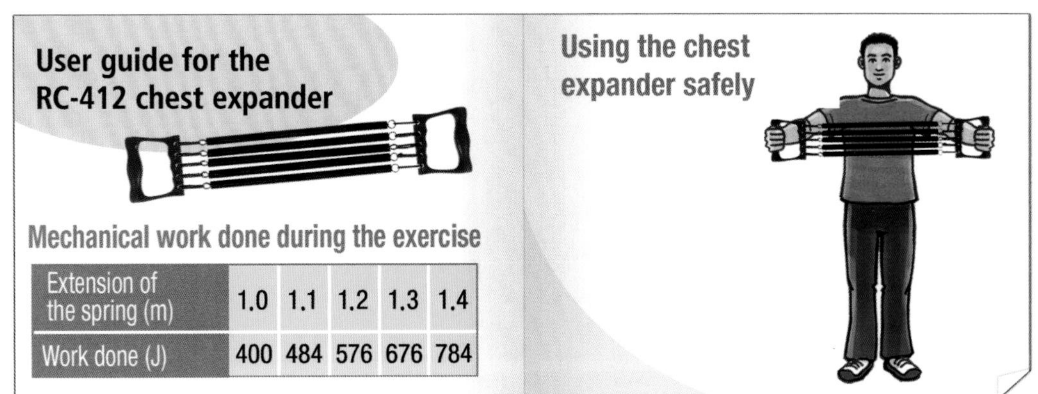

Extension of the spring (m)	1.0	1.1	1.2	1.3	1.4
Work done (J)	400	484	576	676	784

One joule (J) is the energy required to displace an object over a distance of 1 m while applying a force of 1 N.

a) Construct the graph representing the work done (in joules) as a function of the extension (in metres).

b) Find the equation associated with this graph.

c) In practice, it is easier to measure the total length of the expander than it is to measure its extension. Find another equation that expresses the work done as a function of total length, if the expander's initial length is 30 cm.

7 Draw the scatter plot corresponding to the table of values below and model the data using a quadratic function. Assume that Y is directly proportional to the square of X. Draw the graph associated with this model.

X	2	3	4	5	6	7	8	9	10	11
Y	10	30	45	80	90	140	175	205	270	350

8 During a fireworks display, the elevation of a particular firework was measured from the time of launch until the moment of its explosion 5 s later. The scatter plot below presents the data collected. The data in the scatter plot can be modelled by a quadratic function whose rule is $h(t) = {}^{-}5(t - 4.3)^2 + 93$.

a) Draw the graph of this function.

Answer the following questions with the help of that model.

b) At what elevation did the firework explode?

c) What was the maximum elevation reached by the firework? At what moment was the maximum elevation reached?

d) What does the y-intercept of this function represent?

e) At what moment would the firework have fallen to the ground had it not exploded? Estimate this using the graph drawn in **a)**.

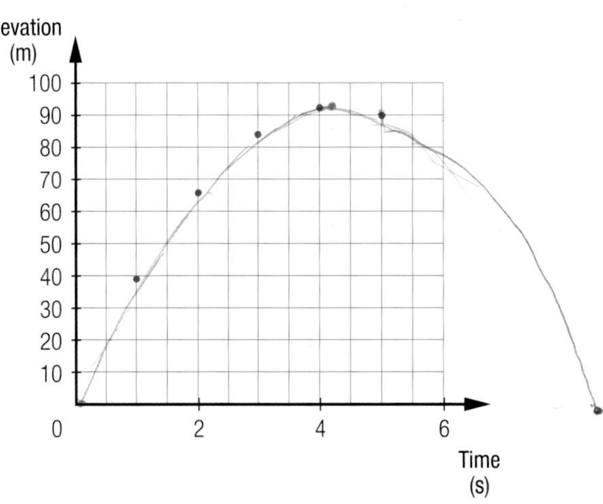

9 **FASTER AND FARTHER** For each of the following situations, determine the model that best represents the data and justify your answer. Answer the question asked for each situation.

Situation 1 Improvement of running time after a 2-unit increase of blood volume.

Distance run (km)	0.4	3.0	5.0	6.5	8.5	9.0	10.5	11.0
Improvement of running time (s)	1	12	22	27	50	52	65	75

a) If the blood volume of a runner in a 42.195 km marathon were to be increased by 2 units, what improvement in performance (in s) would be observed?

Blood doping consists of using any of a variety of prohibited methods or substances to boost the number of red blood cells. Blood doping endangers the athlete's health by creating a higher risk of serious afflictions including cerebral or pulmonary embolism and heart attack.

Situation 2 Distance travelled by a golf ball as a function of the speed of the club head.

Speed of the club head (m/s)	20.2	34.7	36.1	44.4	50.0	58.3	63.9	66.7
Distance travelled by the ball (m)	80	140	170	220	210	300	300	340

b) Jack Hamm broke the previous record for hitting a golf ball the greatest distance when his travelled 418.78 m. At what speed was the head of Jack Hamm's club moving when he established his record?

"Momentum" is the mass of an object multiplied by its speed. Momentum is conserved in the collisions between two bodies. Because the club is heavier than the ball, the ball will take off at a greater speed than the club was moving when it hit the ball.

10 A company produces resistance-training parachutes for runners. In the instruction booklet, the following rule is given to calculate the force of resistance (in newtons) as a function of the runner's speed (in metres per second): $F = 55v^2$.

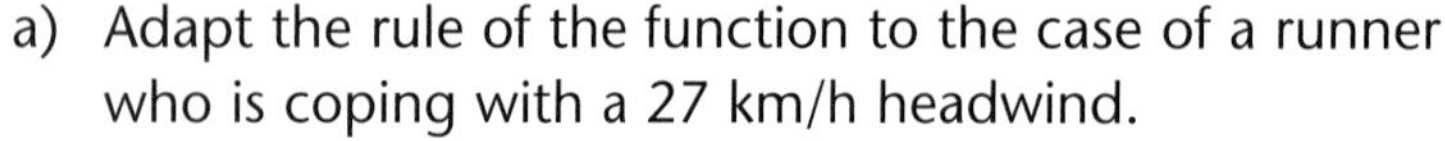

a) Adapt the rule of the function to the case of a runner who is coping with a 27 km/h headwind.

b) Adapt the rule of the function to the case of a person who is running with an 18 km/h wind at his/her back.

c) Which properties of the function are modified when wind speed is taken into account?

11 A drop of water falls in the middle of a circular aquarium whose diameter is 20 cm. As a result, a circular wave spreads out across its surface.

a) Determine the equation for the surface area that has been disturbed as a function of the distance travelled by the wave.

b) Find the domain and the range of this function.

c) Determine the equation that expresses the surface area of water which is not affected as a function of the distance travelled by the wave.

d) Find the domain and the range of this new function.

12 The stopping distance of a car is determined by its speed. For an average reaction time, this situation can be modelled by the equation $d(v) = 0.005(v + 36)^2 - 6.48$ where v is the speed of the car when the brakes are applied (in km/h) and $d(v)$ is the stopping distance (in m).

a) Represent this function using a table of values and a graph.

b) In your own words, describe the change in the stopping distance as the speed changes.

c) Find the domain and the range of this function.

d) Is the vertex of the parabola representing this function located at (0, 0)? Justify your answer.

13 An 8-kg ball is rolled on a horizontal plane surface with an initial speed of 5 m/s. If there were no friction, the ball would roll along at a constant speed without ever stopping. However, contact with the air and with the surface slows it down. Gradually it loses its kinetic energy.
It is possible to deduce the amount of energy lost to friction at any instant because the speed of the ball is known.
The following relation is used to accomplish this:

> Kinetic energy is associated with a body in motion. This energy is a function of mass and speed.

$E = 100 - 4v^2$, where v is the speed of the ball (in m/s) and E is the energy lost (in J).

a) In this context, what are the possible values for the variables v and E?

b) Draw the graph of this function.

c) For this context, what is represented by:

1) the zero of this function?

2) the y-intercept?

d) Choose which case requires the least energy: reducing the speed of the ball from 5 m/s to 4 m/s or from 4 m/s to 3 m/s. Justify your answer.

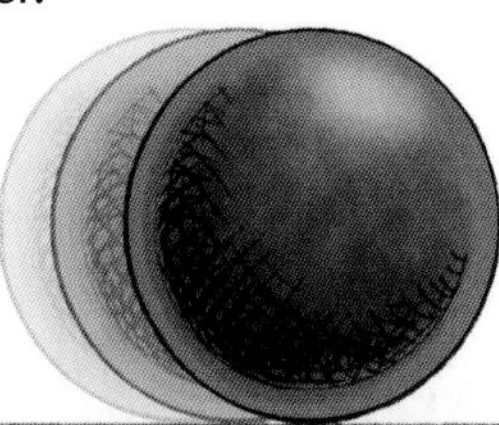

14 Cindy assembled plastic cubes. It was observed that her assemblies were not constructed randomly; rather, they formed a pattern.

a) Determine the rule of the function that would make it possible to calculate:
   1) the number of cubes in the nth assembly
   2) the number of blue cubes in the nth assembly
   3) the number of cubes that are not red in the nth assembly

b) Represent these three functions in the same Cartesian plane.

c) State the geometric transformation that is needed:
   1) to transform the graph of the first function into the graph of the second
   2) to transform the graph of the second function into the graph of the third
   3) to transform the graph of the first function into the graph of the third

d) Draw the first four assemblies of a pattern that could be associated with the function $f(n) = (n + 1)^2 + 3$.

15 In badminton, neither speed nor maximum force produces optimal performance. It is the power of the stroke that needs to be maximized. After an exercise conducted at different speeds, a coach collected data on the power of the athlete's stroke. He modelled the data using a quadratic function.

Determine the rule of this function.

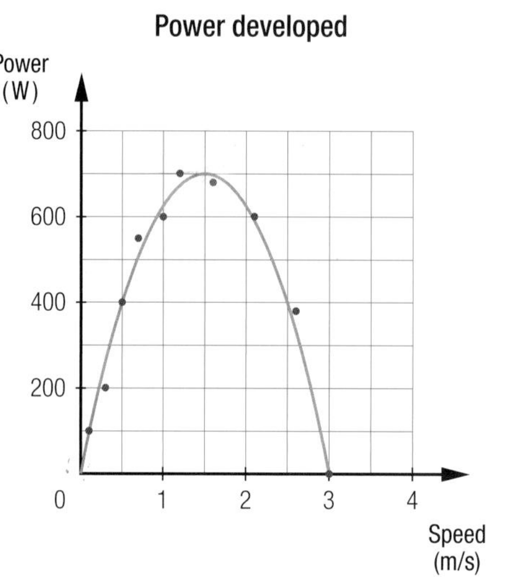

Power is energy expended per unit of time. One watt (W) is 1 joule of energy expended during 1 second. It can also be shown that power is equal to force times speed.

16 A ballistics expert is studying the impact of different bullets fired from a rifle. She is interested in the volume of the hole created in a block of clay as a function of the speed of the bullet. The following is the data she collected:

Impact of bullets

Speed (m/s)	Volume of hole (cm^3)
270	30
310	40
380	60
440	80
510	100
540	120

Most bullet-proof vests worn by members of the police force are made using aramid fibers such as Kevlar. Researchers are looking into replacing these fibres with a natural fibre that is more supple and solid: spider silk (gossamer). A fabric made of spider silk would be more resistant than either steel or Kevlar.

a) Draw the scatter plot that represents this data.

b) If the speed of the bullet approaches 0 m/s, what can be said about the volume of the hole created in the block of clay?

c) Is the size of the hole proportional to the speed of the bullet? If not, is it proportional to the square of the speed? Justify your answer.

d) To determine the equation of the model, the expert draws a scatter plot representing the volume of the hole as a function of the speed squared. Considering the context, draw this scatter plot and draw the line of best fit.

e) What size of hole would a rifle bullet produce when travelling at a speed of 800 m/s?

17 A team consisting of four teenagers is competing in an 80 m relay race. Other than the first runner, no runner can start to run before being tagged by the preceding runner. To model this situation, assume that all the runners maintain the same constant acceleration over their 20 m stretch. With this in mind, a piecewise function can be used to model the distance covered by the team (in m) in relation to elapsed time (in s) since the beginning of the race. The rule of this function while the first runner is in action is $d(t) = 1.25t^2$.

a) When will the second runner start running? What about the third and fourth runners?

b) Determine the rule for *d(t)* when the second runner begins.

c) Determine the rule for *d(t)* for each of the last two runners.

d) Represent this function with a graph.

e) Explain the properties of this function: domain, image, increasing intervals, decreasing intervals, etc.

f) According to this model, what is the average speed maintained by this team?

SECTION 2.3 The step function

This section is related to LES 6.

PROBLEM Two friends, two programs

Annie and Samantha are two friends who train at the same gym. They both start their exercise routine on the treadmill. They have programmed their treadmill for a 15-minute session.

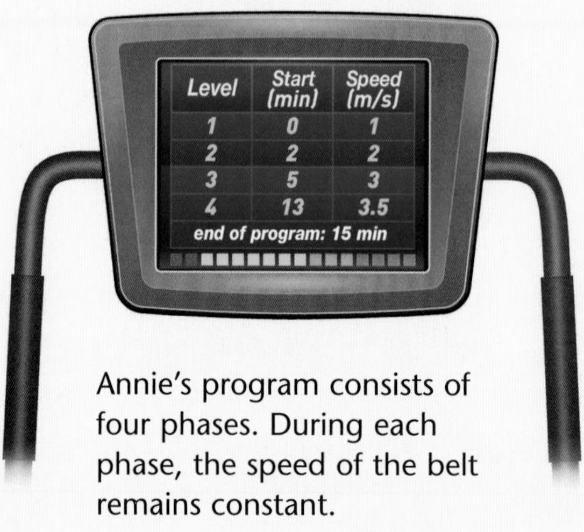

Level	Start (min)	Speed (m/s)
1	0	1
2	2	2
3	5	3
4	13	3.5
end of program: 15 min		

Annie's program consists of four phases. During each phase, the speed of the belt remains constant.

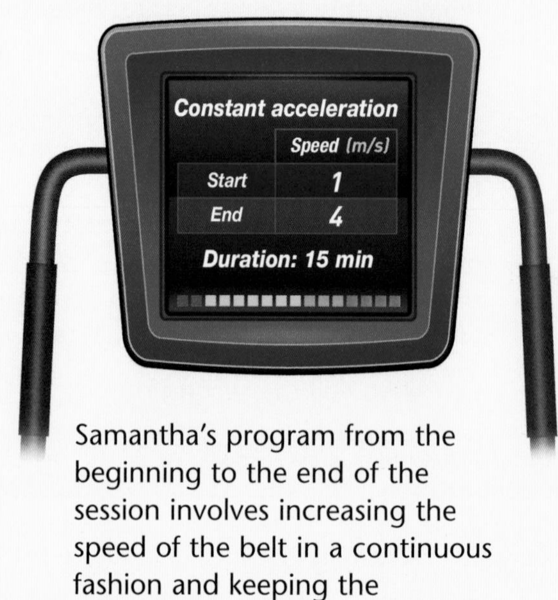

Constant acceleration

	Speed (m/s)
Start	1
End	4

Duration: 15 min

Samantha's program from the beginning to the end of the session involves increasing the speed of the belt in a continuous fashion and keeping the acceleration constant.

Assuming that the two friends started their programs at the same time, at what moments did Annie run faster than Samantha?

ACTIVITY 1 The cost of waiting

Louise takes a taxi. Along the way, she asks the driver to stop at the bank and wait for her. The driver tells her that the meter will be running while she is gone. While the taxi waits, the fare will increase in \$0.10 increments five times each minute.

A taximeter shows the amount due based on the base fare, the number of kilometres travelled, the wait time and the period of the day during which the taxi is hired.

Part 1: The rule

a. Calculate the cost of stopping at the bank, if Louise returns to the taxi after:

1) 1.5 min 2) 2.4 min 3) $3\frac{3}{4}$ min 4) 5 min 20 s

Explain your reasoning.

If t is the wait time (in min), then the total cost (in \$) is expressed by the rule $C(t) = 0.1[5t]$.

In this rule the expression $[5t]$ is read "the greatest integer less than or equal to $5t$."

b. What do you think this new symbol with square brackets means?

Give numerical examples to illustrate your explanation. Compare your answers with those of your peers.

Part 2: The graph

c. Determine the values of $C(t)$ for:

1) $t = 0$ 2) $t = 0.1$ 3) $t = 0.19$ 4) $t = 0.199$ 5) $t = 0.2$

d. Represent this function graphically assuming a wait time between 0 and 1 min.

e. The graph of this function is in the shape of a staircase. What can you say about the length of the step and the length of the riser?

f. How would the situation and the graph differ if the rule of the function was $C(t) = 0.05[10t]$?

ACTIVITY 2 What's the temperature?

An electronic thermometer is programmed so that the temperature is always displayed in whole numbers. If x represents the outside temperature in degrees Celsius, the number displayed is given by the greatest-integer function $f(x) = [x]$. The graph of this function is shown below.

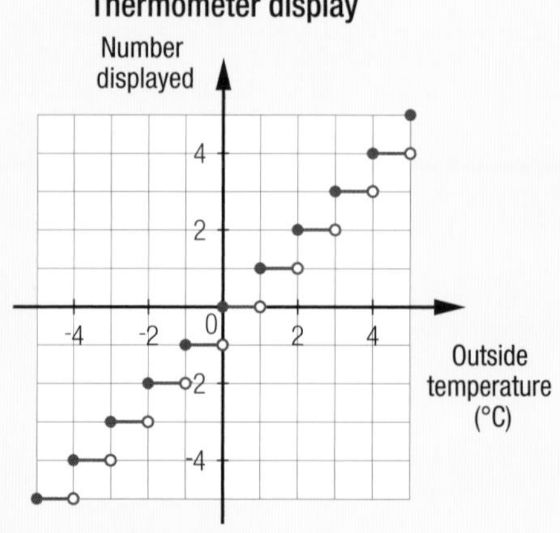

a. Determine the domain and the range of f.

b. What numbers will be displayed for the following outside temperatures?

1) 2.95 °C
2) 12.3 °C
3) $^-$1.27 °C
4) $^-$15.725 °C

To obtain a more precise reading of the temperature, the thermometer can be programmed so that the number displayed is given by the function $g(x) = [x + 0.5]$.

c. With this new function, what numbers will be displayed for the outside temperatures in question **b.**?

d. Explain, in your own words, how function g operates.

e. Draw the graph of this function. What geometric transformation can be used to transform function f into function g?

In science, it is sometimes necessary to measure temperature in Kelvins. An approximation of this measure can be displayed using the function $h(x) = [x + 0.65] + 273$.

f. How does the graph of function h differ from the graphs of functions g and f?

The origin of the Kelvin temperature scale, 0 K, which is equivalent to -273°C, is known as absolute zero. It is the lowest temperature theoretically possible. It would be reached if all molecular movement ceased. Nothing in the universe can reach this temperature.

ACTIVITY 3 A problem that requires some reflection!

The following rules of four functions differ from one another only by the signs involved.

1	2	3	4
$f_1(x) = 2\left[\frac{1}{3}x\right]$	$f_2(x) = -2\left[\frac{1}{3}x\right]$	$f_3(x) = 2\left[-\frac{1}{3}x\right]$	$f_4(x) = -2\left[-\frac{1}{3}x\right]$

a. Associate each function with one of the graphs shown below.

A

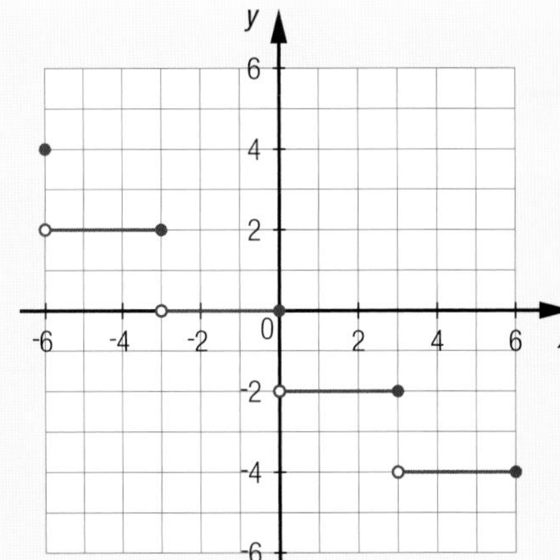

B

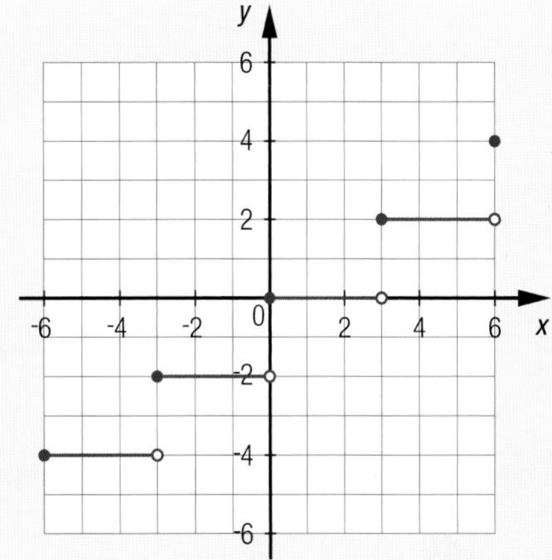

C

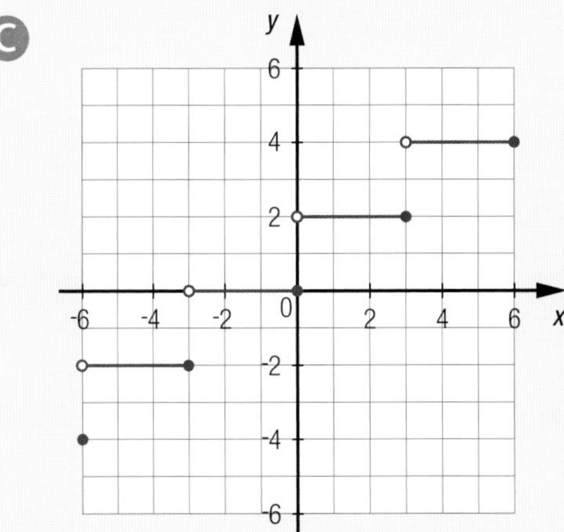

D

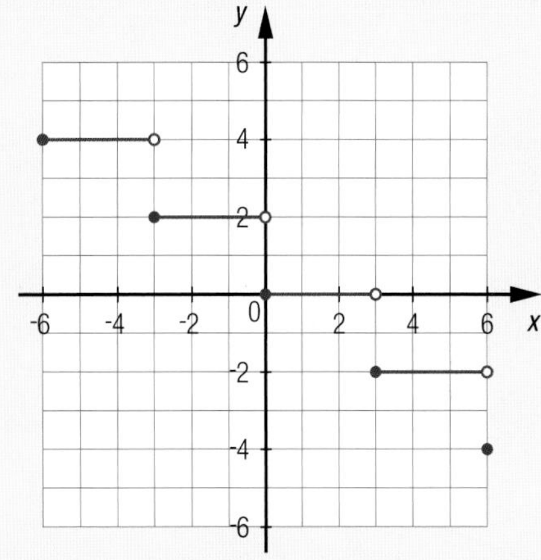

b. Determine the geometric transformation that will transform the graph of f_1 into the graph of each of the following:

1) f_2 2) f_3 3) f_4

c. In the rule for the function in the form $f(x) = \text{a}[\text{b}x]$, what signs must the parameters **a** and **b** have in order for the function to be increasing? Justify your answer.

d. Consider another greatest-integer function: $g(x) = 3 - \left[2\left(x - \frac{1}{2}\right)\right]$. Is this function increasing or decreasing? Justify your answer.

e. In your own words, summarize the role of the parameters **a**, **b**, **h** and **k** in a function of the form $f(x) = \text{a}[\text{b}(x - \text{h})] + \text{k}$.

Techno math

A graphing calculator allows you to simultaneously display the graphs of two functions in the same Cartesian plane. The following exercise will make it possible to observe the effects of the parameters **a**, **b**, **h** and **k** in the graphical representation of a function whose rule, in standard form, is written as $f(x) = a[b(x - h)] + k$.

Screen 1

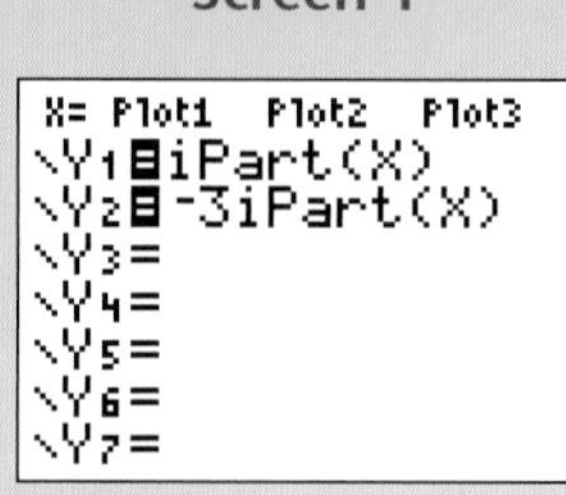

Screen 2

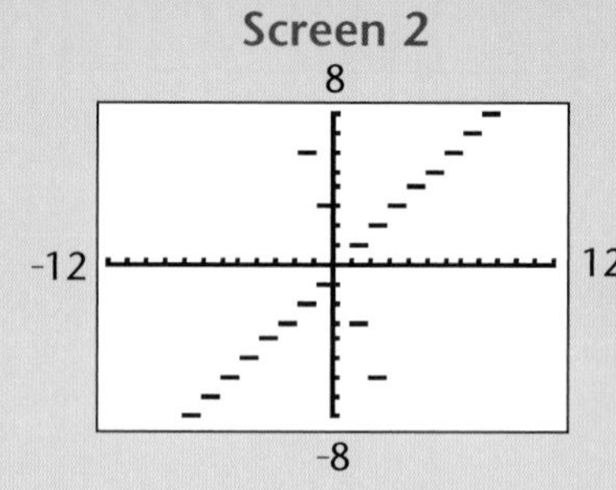

Screen 3

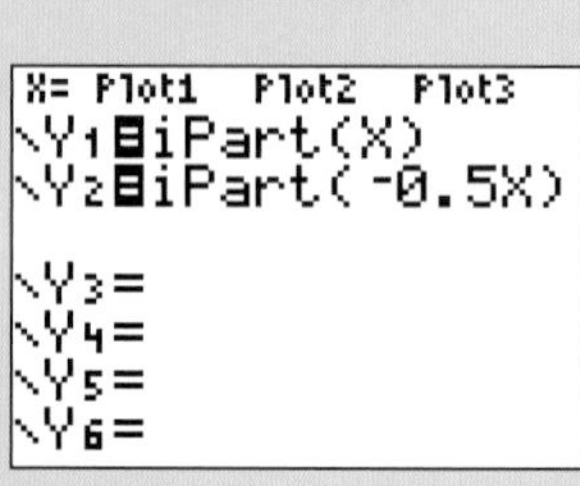

Screen 4

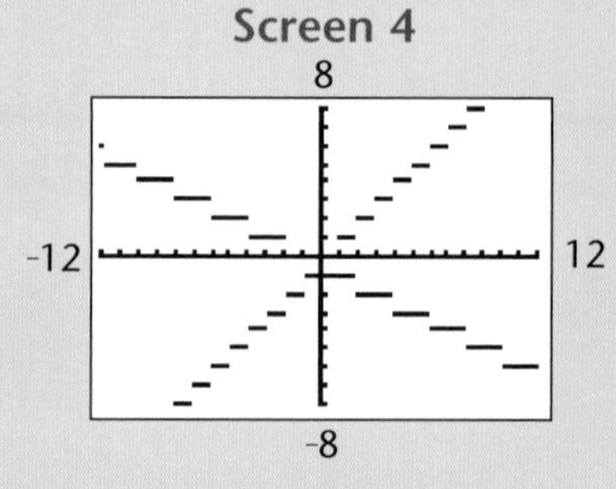

Screen 5

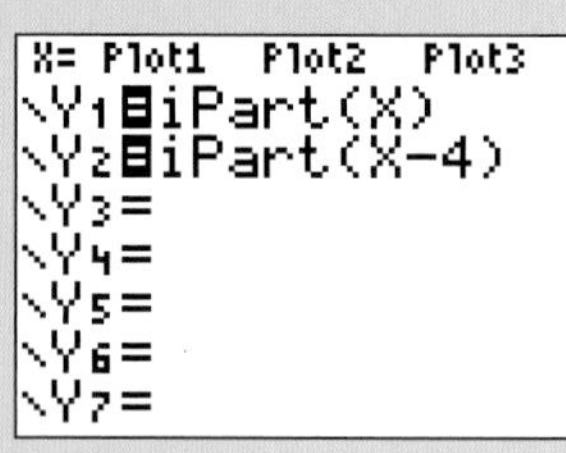

Screen 6

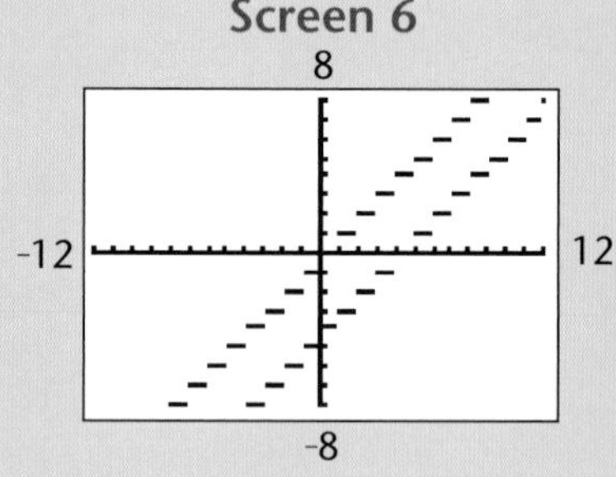

Screen 7

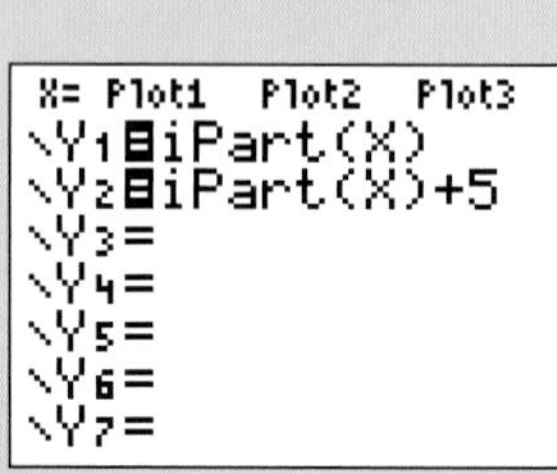

Screen 8

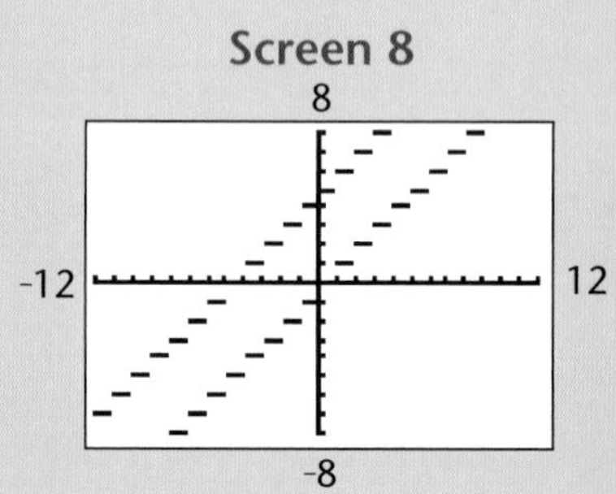

a. Indicate which parameter has been changed on:

1) Screen **1**
2) Screen **3**
3) Screen **5**
4) Screen **7**

b. Indicate how the greatest-integer functions differ on:

1) Screen **2**
2) Screen **4**
3) Screen **6**
4) Screen **8**

c. What is the effect on the graph of a greatest-integer function, written is standard form, when:

1) the value of **a** is increasingly distant from zero?
2) the value of **b** is increasingly distant from zero?
3) the value of **h** is increasingly distant from zero?
4) the value of **k** is increasingly distant from zero?

d. Display the graphs of the functions shown on the adjacent screen and describe the differences observed when comparing these two greatest-integer functions.

```
Plot1 Plot2 Plot3
\Y1 = iPart(X)
\Y2 = -2iPart(0.2X
-4)-5
\Y3=
\Y4=
\Y5=
\Y6=
```

knowledge 2.3

MODELLING WITH THE HELP OF A STEP FUNCTION

A **step function** is a function that is constant over intervals of the independent variable but changes abruptly for certain **critical values** of the independent variable.

The graph of this function consists of horizontal segments. It is important to determine the critical values of the independent variable and to indicate whether or not the extremities of the segments are part of the graph.

E.g.

A technician earns $20/h for an eight-hour workday. When he works overtime, he earns $30/h for each extra hour worked up to 12 hours. After 12 hours, he is paid $40/h. He cannot work more than 16 hours in one day.

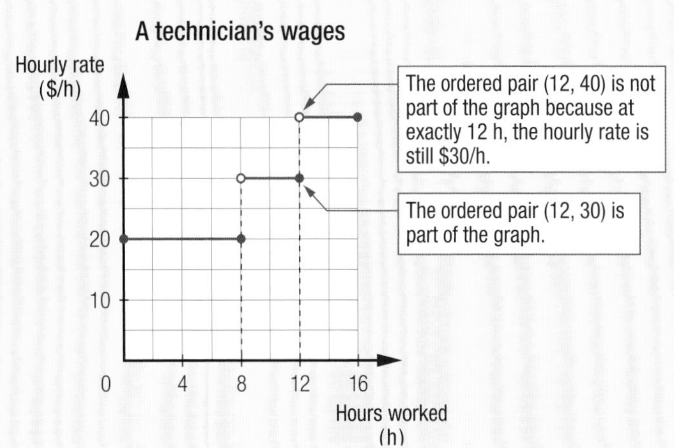

Greatest-integer function

This is a step function whose rule is: $f(x) = [x]$.

The expression $[x]$ is read as "the greatest integer less than or equal to x."

E.g. 1) $[\pi] = 3$ 2) $\left[\frac{7}{4}\right] = \left[1\frac{3}{4}\right] = 1$ 3) $[-2.1] = -3$ 4) $[-2] = -2$

The following are various descriptions of this function:

Verbal description

This is a step function, defined for all real numbers. The critical values are integers. In the interval between two consecutive integers the value of the function is the lower limit.

Table of values

x	$f(x)$
[-3, -2[	-3
[-2, -1[	-2
[-1, 0[	-1
[0, 1[	0
[1, 2[	1
[2, 3[	2

Graph

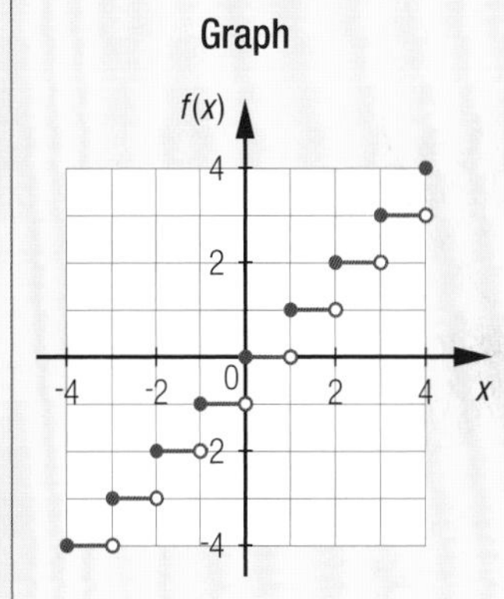

The transformed greatest-integer function

The rule of this function in standard form is: $f(x) = \text{a}[\text{b}(x - \text{h})] + \text{k}$, where **a** $\neq 0$ and **b** $\neq 0$.

The parameters **a, b, h** and **k** are real numbers. Each of these parameters plays a role in the graphical representation of the function.

- The basic function (a = b = 1 ; h = k = 0)

E.g.

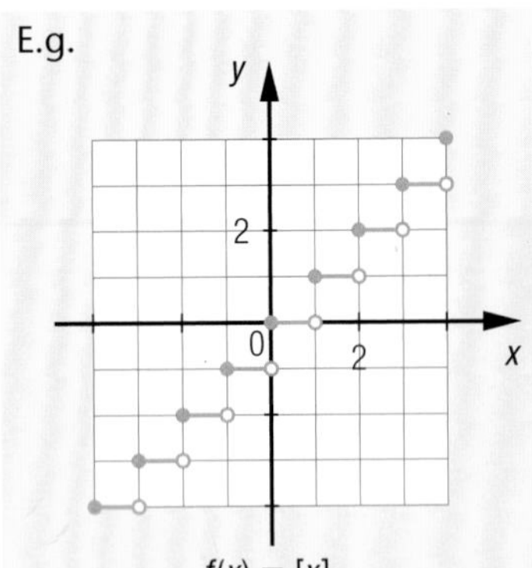

$f(x) = [x]$

- An increase (decrease) in the value of **a** results in a vertical stretch (compression) of the graph.

E.g.

$f_1(x) = 2[x]$

- An increase (decrease) in the value of **b** results in a horizontal compression (stretch) of the graph.

E.g.

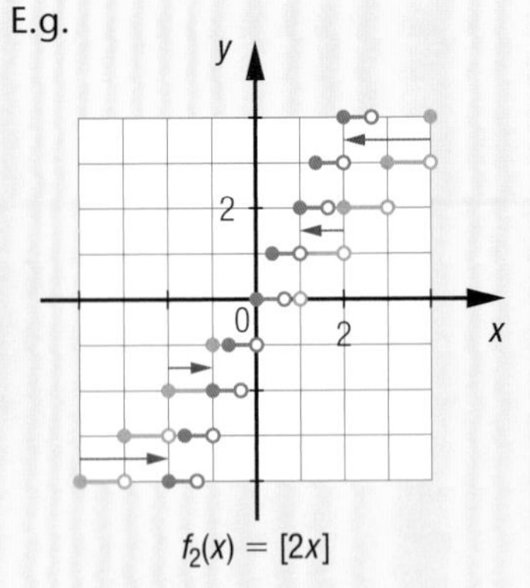

$f_2(x) = [2x]$

- A change of the sign of **a** results in a reflection over the x-axis.

E.g.

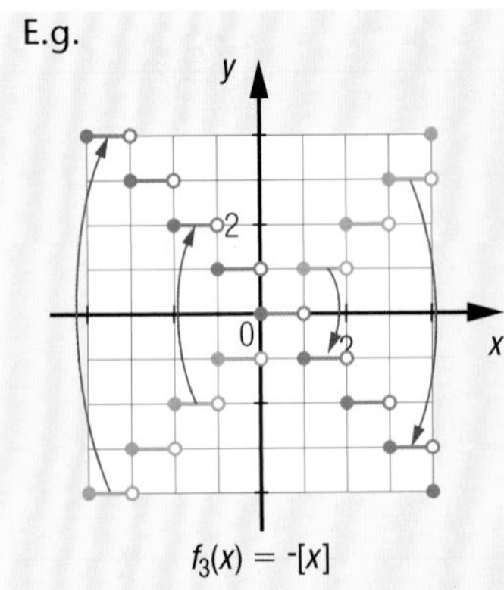

$f_3(x) = \text{-}[x]$

- A change of the sign of **b** results in a reflection over the y-axis.

E.g.

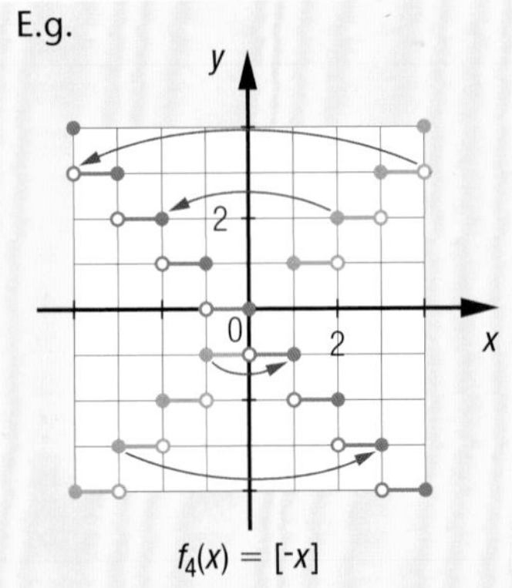

$f_4(x) = [\text{-}x]$

- Parameters **h** and **k** are associated with a horizontal translation of **h** units and a vertical translation of **k** units.

E.g.

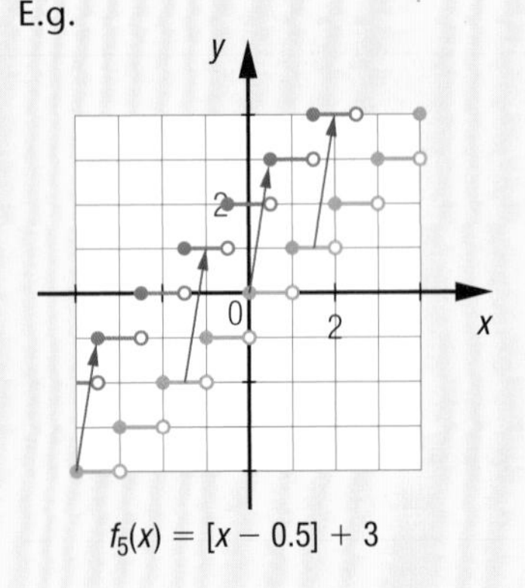

$f_5(x) = [x - 0.5] + 3$

Properties of the greatest-integer function

A unique attribute of step functions is that their range is always a discrete set.

E.g. Below is a list of properties of the function $f(x) = 2[x] - 2$:

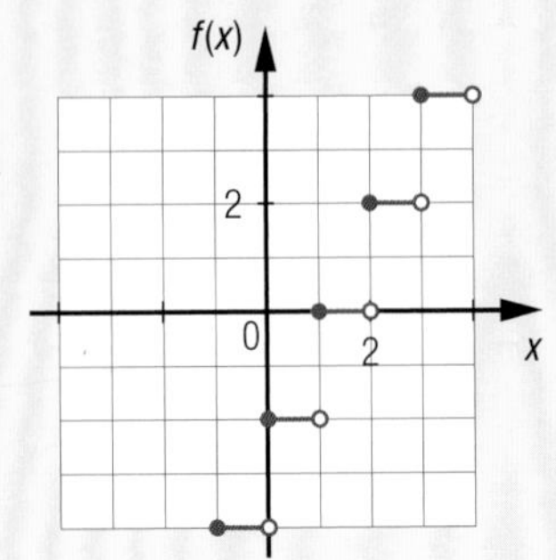

- Domain of f: ℝ.
  Range of f: {..., -4, -2, 0, 2, 4, ...}.
- Function f is an increasing function.
- The y-intercept of f is -2.
- The zeros of f are all the numbers over the interval [1, 2[.
- The function is positive over the interval [1, +∞[and negative over the interval]-∞, 2[.

practice 2.3

1 The graph below indicates the numbers of runners ahead of Alex according to the distance he ran throughout a 100-m race.

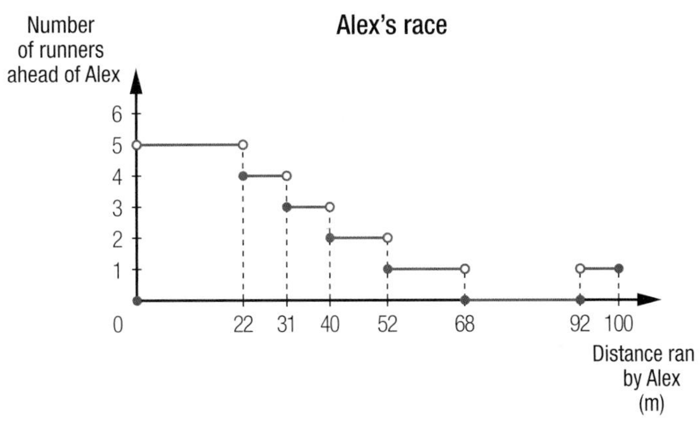

a) In this situation, what do the critical values represent?

b) In what position is Alex in mid-race? At the end of the race?

c) Over what interval is the function decreasing?

d) What are the zeros of this function? What do they represent in this situation?

e) Do you think that Alex got off to a good start in this race? Explain your point of view.

2 Gabriel is late for class. Taking the steps two at a time, he runs up at a constant speed. It takes him exactly 2.4 s to go from the bottom of the staircase (step 0) to the landing at the 16th step. Let *f* be the function that determines the last step reached according to elapsed time.

a) Determine the domain and range of *f*.

b) What are the critical values of this function?

c) Represent this function with:

1) a table of values
2) a graph
3) an equation

d) What was the last step reached after 1 s? After 2 s?

3 Income tax rates are based on the amount of taxable income earned annually. As taxable income increases, so does the tax rate. Typically, a step function can be used to define this relation. As an example, the following is the structure in Québec.

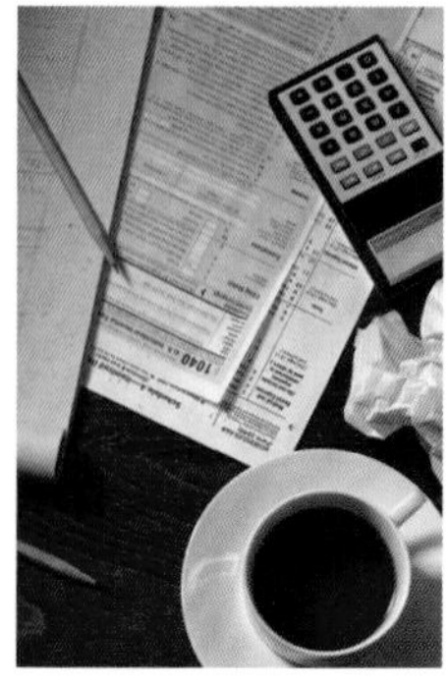

Rate structure

Taxable income		Tax rate
Greater than …	not exceeding…	
$0	$30,000	16%
$30,000	$60,000	20%
$60,000	–	24%

Taxable income is what remains after allowable deductions have been made.

According to the table above, a person earning $80,000 will pay 16% on the first $30,000 of taxable income, 20% on the next $30,000 and finally 24% on the remaining $20,000.

a) Draw the graph of the tax rate as a function of taxable income.

b) Calculate the income tax payable in Québec if the taxable income is $80,000. To what geometric concept does this value correspond in the graph drawn in **a)**?

c) Calculate the income tax payable if taxable income is $10,000, $20,000, $30,000, etc. up until $70,000?

d) Use the values calculated in **c)** to graph the income tax payable as a function of taxable income.

e) What is the rate of change of each of the segments of the graph drawn in **d)**?

4 Matthew is competing in a triathlon. The adjacent graph shows the speed he would like to maintain in each of the three events of the race. The events, in order, are swimming, cycling and running.

a) According to this graph what distance will he cover in each event?

b) After 1 h Mattew will have covered a total of 29.5 km. Will he be ahead or behind his target?

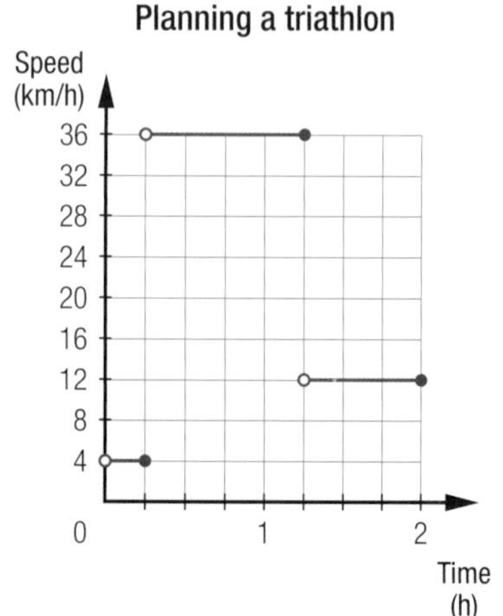

5 Evaluate the value of each of the following expressions.

a) $[\sqrt{3}]$ b) $[-\sqrt{3}]$ c) $[\sqrt{3} + 0.5]$ d) $[10\sqrt{3}]$ e) $0.1[10\sqrt{3} + 0.5]$

6 The following functions are all of the form $f(x) = a[bx]$.

a) $f_1(x) = 2\left[\frac{x}{4}\right]$ b) $f_2(x) = -[0.5x]$ c) $f_3(x) = -3[-x]$ d) $f_4(x) = \left[-\frac{x}{2}\right]$

For each function, do the following:

1) Taking into account the parameters **a** and **b**, find the length of the step and the length of the riser.

2) Determine if the function is increasing or decreasing.

3) Determine if the segments are open at their right extremity (●——○) or at their left extremity (○——●).

4) Draw the graph of the function over the interval [-4, 4].

7 Consider $f(x) = -2\left[\frac{x}{4}\right] + 6$ over the interval [0, 20].

a) Represent this function using a table of values and a graph.

b) Determine the following properties of this function:

1) the range; 2) the minimum; 3) the maximum; 4) the set of zeros.

c) Is this function increasing or decreasing?

d) Analyze the sign of this function.

8 Considering the change in value of the parameters of the following functions, determine the geometric transformations that will transform the graph of the first function into the graph of the second. Use this information to draw the graph of the second function.

a) From $f_1(x) = [x]$ to $f_2(x) = 3[x]$

b) From $f_2(x) = 3[x]$ to $f_3(x) = -3[x]$

c) From $f_3(x) = -3[x]$ to $f_4(x) = -3[0.5x]$

d) From $f_4(x) = -3[0.5x]$ to $f_5(x) = -3[0.5x] + 4$

9 Find the rule of the function represented by each of the following graphs.

a)

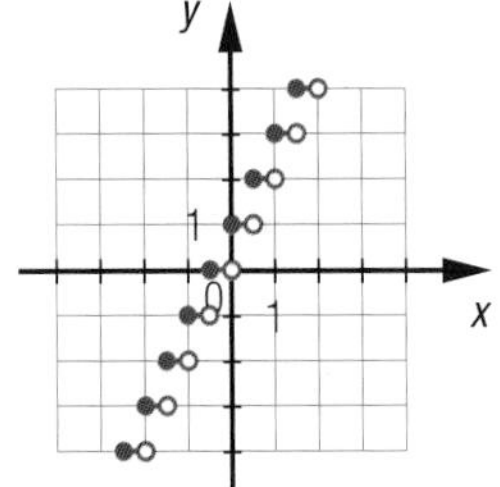

b)

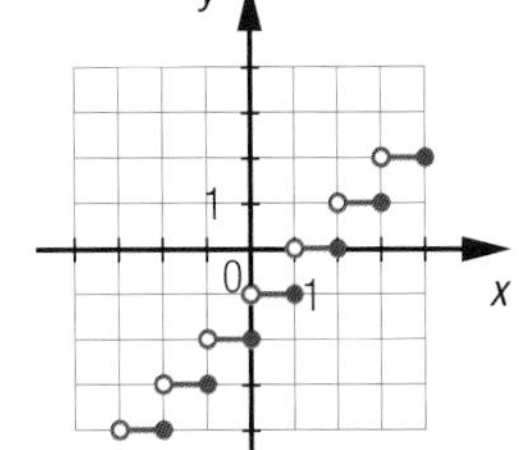

c)

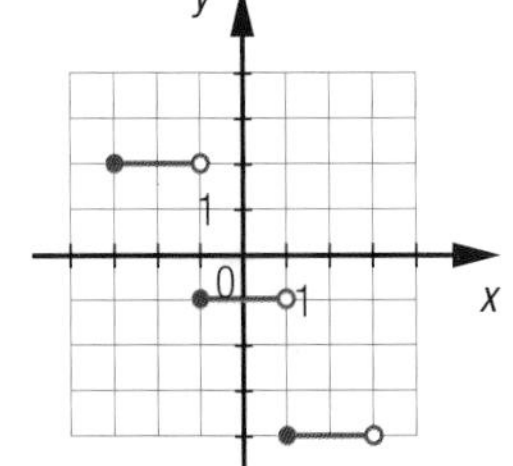

10 In the 1500 m freestyle competition, swimmers must complete 30 lengths of the pool. A swimmer has set his sights on a time of 18 minutes. To do this, assuming his speed is constant, the number of lengths he must have completed after t minutes is given by $L(t) = \left[\frac{5t}{3}\right]$.

a) Find the domain and the range of this function.

b) Graphically represent the first three minutes of the competition.

c) State the number of lengths the swimmer will have completed after:
1) 2 min 2) 10 min 3) 12 min

d) In what time interval will the swimmer have completed 25 lengths?

e) What would the rule of the function be if the race took place in a 25 m pool? How would the graph in **b)** change?

11 Catherine was born on February 29. Find the function that represents the relationship between the number of birthdays she has celebrated and the number of days since her birth.

The very first February 29 was in 1584, the first leap year of the Gregorian calendar enacted in 1582. The previous Julian calendar added an extra day every four years between February 24 and 25.

12 Answer the following questions using, as needed, the greatest-integer symbol "[ ]".

a) How many multiples of 7, less than or equal to each of the following numbers, are there in the set of non-zero natural numbers?
1) 50 2) 100 3) 1000 4) n

b) Find the remainder when each of the following numbers is divided by 7:
1) 50 2) 100 3) 1000 4) n

13 There are different ways of approximating a number to the nearest integer.
E.g.

Number	Truncation	Approximation from below	Approximation from above	Rounding
2.1	2	2	3	2
2.9	2	2	3	3
-2.1	-2	-3	-2	-2
-2.9	-2	-3	-2	-3

a) What method of approximation is used in the greatest-integer function?

b) Graph the results of each of the other methods of approximation for numbers ranging from -3 to 3.

c) Two of the three graphs drawn in **b)** are transformed greatest-integer functions. Find the equation for each of these two graphs.

14 Consider this sequence of operations.

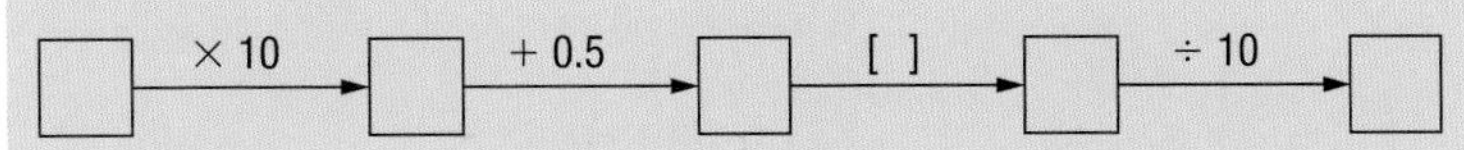

a) What results would you get by starting the sequence with the numbers -2.36 and 4.83?

b) Find the rule of the function that associates the first number of this sequence with the last number.

c) Determine the rule of the function that results in rounding a number to:

1) the nearest hundredth 2) the nearest tenth 3) the nearest 10^n

15 On a commercial street the parking meter rate is $0.25 for each 20 minutes. The meter accepts coins up to a two-hour limit.

a) How much money must be inserted if 45 minutes of parking are required?

b) The amount of money required is a function of the length of time the car is parked. Graph this function.

c) What are the domain and the range of this function?

d) Determine the rule of this function.

In 2007, there were over 16 000 metered parking spaces on the streets of Montréal.

16 A cellular telephone company ad offers a video call service which is billed to the second at the rate of \$0.20 for each minute. This advertisement implies that a video call lasting less than three seconds should be free because the cost of the call is less than \$0.01.

a) Considering that a fraction of a penny is never tallied, calculate the cost of a call lasting:

1) 30 s 2) 40 s 3) 2 min 4) 3 min 10 s

Kristy uses the linear function $C(t) = 0.2\left(\frac{t}{60}\right)$ to model the cost of a call as a function of its duration (in s).

b) What do you think of the function chosen by Kristy? Is this function an adequate model for the situation? Explain your point of view.

c) Graphically represent the real cost of calls lasting less than or equal to 15 s. Using a different colour, graph the line associated with the function determined by Kristy. What do you observe?

d) What is the rule of the function that calculates the precise cost of a call (in \$) based on its duration (in s)?

17 A decimal number consists of two parts: an integer part and a fractional part.
E.g.

$$210.14 = 210 + 0.14$$

Integer part (210) Fractional part (0.14)

Note that the fractional part is equivalent to 210.14 − [210.14].

By generalizing this concept to all numbers, the following function can be defined:

$$\text{Fractional part of } x = x - [x]$$

a) What is the fractional part of each of these numbers?

1) 3.14 2) π 3) 5 4) $\frac{16}{7}$ 5) $-\frac{16}{7}$

b) Is the fractional part of a number always a rational number? Justify your answer.

c) Represent this function graphically.

d) Analyze the sign of this function.

e) What are the zeros of this function?

18 **GAUSS** The symbol "[ ]", used to denote the integer part of a number, was introduced in the 19th century by the mathematician Carl Friedrich Gauss to demonstrate various arithmetic properties.

Porro existente x quantitate quacunque non integra. per signum $[x]$ exprimemus integrum ipsa x proxime minorem, ita ut $x - [x]$ semper fiat quantitas positiva intra limites 0 et 1 sita. Levi iam negotio relationes sequentes evolventur:

I. $[x] + [-x] = -1$.

II. $[x] + h = [x + h]$, quoties h est integer.

III. $[x] + [h - x] = h - 1$.

IV. Si $x - [x]$ est fractio minor quam $\frac{1}{2}$, erit $[2x] - 2[x] = 0$:

si vero $x - [x]$ est major quam $\frac{1}{2}$, erit $[2x] - 2[x] = 1$.

This text was written in Latin, the language of choice in the scientific community for many centuries.

Below is a translation of the passage in which Gauss used this symbol for the first time:

For all non-integer quantities x, we will use $[x]$ to designate the smallest integer which is the nearest to x, so that $x - [x]$ is always a positive quantity between the 0 and 1. We can then deduce the following sequence of relations:

I. $[x] + [-x] = -1$

II. $[x] + h = [x + h]$, every time that h is an integer

III. $[x] + [h - x] = h - 1$

IV. If $x - [x]$ is a fraction less than $\frac{1}{2}$, we then have $[2x] - 2[x] = 0$

if, on the contrary, - $[x]$ is greater than $\frac{1}{2}$, we then have $[2x] - 2[x] = 1$

a) Provide relevant examples to demonstrate these properties.

b) Gauss defined this symbol for non-integer values of x. Which of these four properties are no longer true if x is an integer?

19 Just like a mathematician, Judy formulated a conjecture concerning the greatest-integer. She verified her conjecture using various numbers and she is convinced that it is true.

Judy's conjecture:

For all values of a and b, if $[a] = [b]$ then $[a - b] = 0$.

a) Unfortunately, as formulated, her conjecture is false. Prove it.

b) Modify Judy's conjecture to make it true.

Chronicle of the

past

Isaac Newton

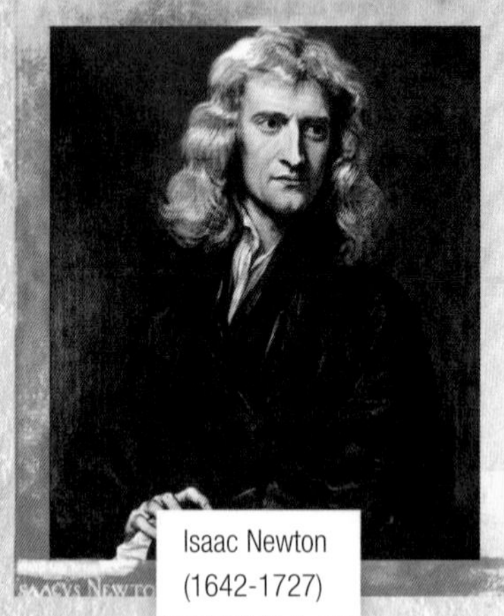
Isaac Newton
(1642-1727)

Childhood

Isaac Newton was born in Woolsthorpe (England) on December 25 in the year 1642 of the Julian calendar which was in use at the time. After his father died, he was raised by his grandparents. He later said that he had had a rather unhappy childhood while in their care. He did not demonstrate any particular talent in school, but an uncle insisted that he attend university. As a result, he entered Cambridge University at age 18 where he discovered a passion for physics and mathematics.

Our current calendar, the Gregorian calendar, was not introduced in England until 1752.

First discoveries

In 1665, a cholera epidemic broke out in London forcing the university to close temporarily. Newton returned to Woolsthorpe where he undertook the study of light. He discovered that white light is a mixture of different colours. In mathematics, he invented the *method of fluxions. Fluxions* are the origin of what is known today as differential calculus, a part of mathematics used to analyze the variation of functions. According to legend, it is at this time that Newton, sitting under an apple tree while gazing up at the moon, noticed a falling apple. He suddenly understood that the force that holds the celestial bodies together is the same as the force that attracts an apple to the earth.

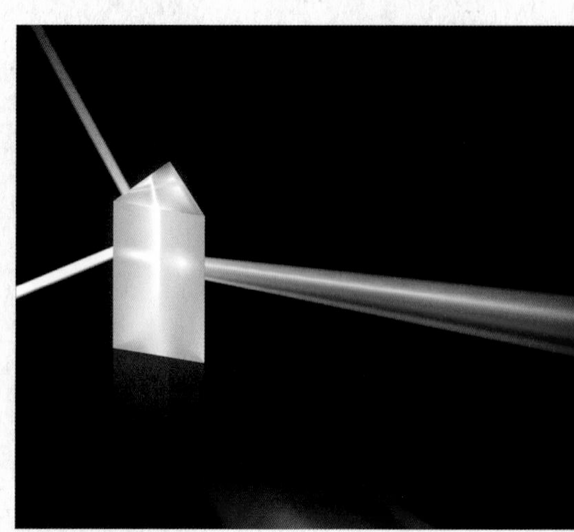

1. According to Newton's terminology, the fluxion of a variable y, written as $\dot{y}$, is the rate of change of this variable in relation to the time elapsed. With the help of the *method of fluxions*, it becomes possible to prove the following property:

If the distance travelled by an object is proportional to the square of the time, $d = at^2$, then the fluxion of d, that is the speed of the object, is expressed by the equation $\dot{d} = 2at$.

a) A ball dropped from a tower will have travelled 4.9 m by the end of the first second of its descent. What is its speed at that precise moment?

b) Determine the distance and the speed travelled by the ball at 2 s and 3 s. Draw the graphs of these two variables as a function of time.

c) The symbol $\ddot{d}$ represents the fluxion of the fluxion $\dot{d}$. What does that correspond to in this situation?

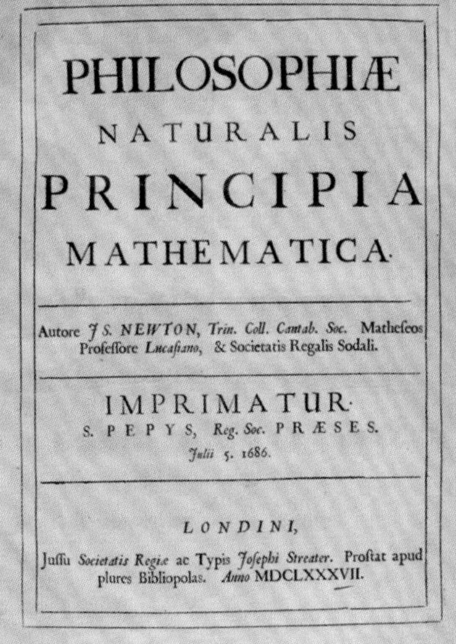

PHILOSOPHIÆ
NATURALIS
PRINCIPIA
MATHEMATICA.

Autore *J S.* NEWTON, *Trin. Coll. Cantab. Soc.* Matheseos Professore *Lucasiano*, & Societatis Regalis Sodali.

IMPRIMATUR.
S. PEPYS, *Reg. Soc.* PRÆSES.
Julii 5. 1686.

LONDINI,

Jussu *Societatis Regiæ* ac Typis *Josephi Streater*. Prostat apud plures Bibliopolas. *Anno* MDCLXXXVII.

Newton's Magnum Opus

Newton became a professor at Cambridge in 1669. He remained there for 25 years. In 1687, he published, in Latin, his most important work, *Philosophiae naturalis principia mathematica*, in which he explains and demonstrates several laws of nature. It defines the relationship between the force exerted on a body and acceleration, the behaviour of objects in motion, the explanation of tides and the famous law of universal gravity which can be expressed as follows: "Two objects attract one another with a force that is directly proportional to their mass and inversely proportional to the square of the distance between them. "

The end of his life

Newton pursued his research on many subjects until the beginning of the 18th century. Ennobled by royalty, famous throughout the world, considered by many, with Archimedes, as one of the greatest geniuses of the history of humanity, he died on March 20, 1727. He is buried in Westminster Abby, alongside Kings of England.

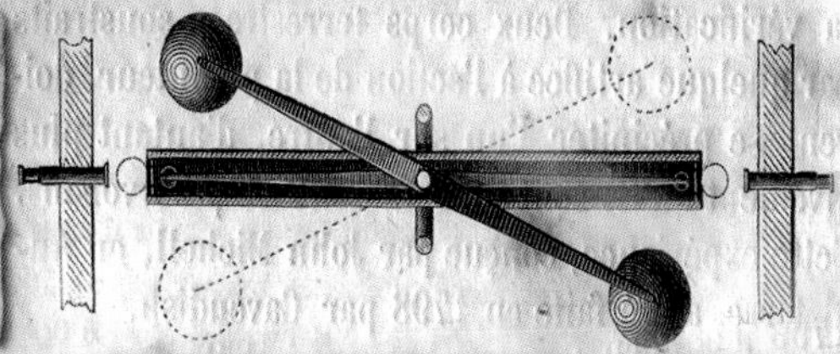

Illustration of Lord Cavendish's device

2. The universal law of gravity can be expressed by an equation.

$$F = G\,\frac{m_1 m_2}{d^2}$$

where F is the gravitational force (in N); m_1 and m_2 are the masses of the bodies (in kg); d is the distance between the centres of gravity of these two bodies (in m); G is a constant (in Nm^2/kg^2)

Newton had discovered that F is proportional to $\frac{m_1 m_2}{d^2}$ but he had no means of determining the precise value of the proportionality constant G. In 1798, Lord Henry Cavendish succeeded in measuring this coefficient in the laboratory using a very sophisticated instrument.

The adjacent table presents data that could be obtained by an instrument similar to the one used by Cavendish.

a) Estimate the value of the coefficient G using this data.

b) Estimate the mass of the Earth, given that the gravitational force exerted on a 10 kg object, at the surface of the Earth, is approximately 98 N.

Resulting forces

m_1	m_2	d	F
0.015	1.5	0.046	7.1×10^{-10}
0.030	1.5	0.046	1.4×10^{-9}
0.030	2.0	0.046	1.7×10^{-9}
0.030	2.0	0.034	3.3×10^{-9}
0.045	2.5	0.040	4.7×10^{-9}

In the workplace

Astrophysicists

A vast field of study

Astrophysics is the study of celestial phenomena. It seeks to explain the origin, the properties and the evolution of the universe. It is a subject that requires a broad mastery of mathematics.

Henrietta Swan Leavitt (1868-1921)

The discovery of galaxies

At the beginning of the 20th century the known universe was limited to our own galaxy: the Milky Way. Henrietta Leavitt, an American astronomer, discovered, classified and studied a group of stars of various luminosity located in the Small Magellanic Cloud, the Cepheids. Based on her work, Edwin Hubble was able to show, in 1925, that the Andromeda nebula was in fact a galaxy distinct from our own.

Luminosity is the measure of total luminous energy emitted by an object every second. Luminosity is generally expressed in solar luminosities whose symbol is $L_{\odot}$. For example, the luminosity of the star Altair is 13 $L_{\odot}$, meaning that its luminosity is 13 times that of our sun.

The expanding universe

In 1929, Hubble tried to measure the speed of galaxies relative to one another. While studying a sample of 46 galaxies, he discovered that the farther away they are from us, the faster they move away. This is Hubble's law. How can this be explained? The simplest hypothesis is to assume that the universe is expanding like a great inflating balloon. Indeed, if we blow into a balloon, we can observe that two points close together on its surface move apart more slowly than two points that are more distant from each other.

Small Magellanic cloud

The Big Bang: An explanation of the expansion of the universe

According to this theory, about 15 billion years ago, all the matter in the universe was concentrated in one, infinitely dense and infinitely small point that expanded to become the universe we know today. However, the future of the universe is still in question. Will it continue to expand or will it collapse as a result of its own mass, as suggested by the *big crunch* theory?

The issues in astrophysics remain as fundamental as the density, the age and the size of the universe. The precision of modern instruments has opened the door to the search for planets outside of our solar system. Who knows? They could be sheltering life.

1. The table below presents some of the measurements Hubble obtained by observing different galaxies.

a) Draw the scatter plot that represents this data.

b) Model the data with the help of a function.

c) Use this model to estimate the speed with which a galaxy located 500 Mpc from our solar system is moving away from us.

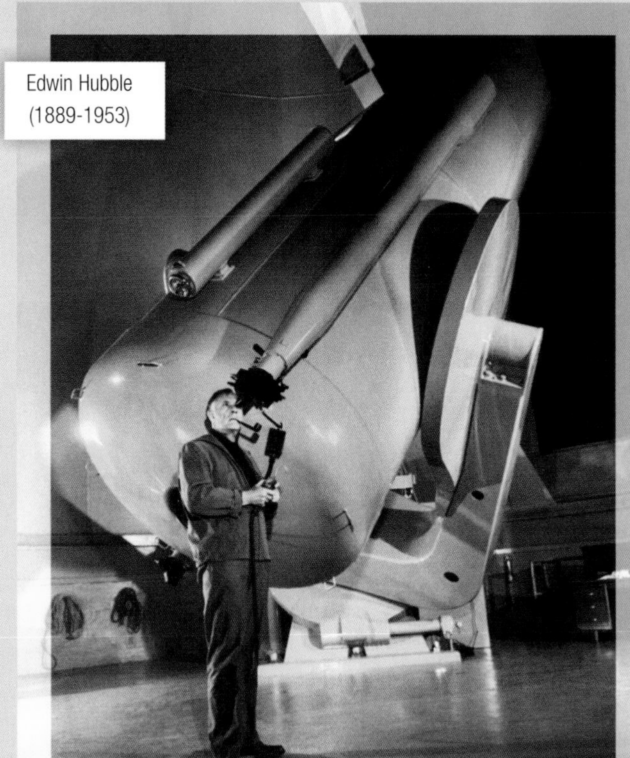

Edwin Hubble (1889-1953)

Distance (Mpc)	Recessional velocity (km/s)
1.0	740
1.4	755
1.6	730
1.9	950
3.4	2120
6.9	4520
7.4	3420
9.1	4800
11.2	5150
13.8	7320
21.6	11 710
32.7	19 510

Mpc means "megaparsec" or 1 million parsecs.
1 parsec = 3.26 light years

2. Viewed from Earth, two stars can have the same intensity without having the same luminosity. A nearby star with low luminosity can have the same intensity as a star far away with stronger luminosity. The table below shows the luminosity/intensity ratio of 10 of the stars closest to Earth.

The *intensity* of a star is the measure of the amount of its light that reaches Earth. The intensity of all stars can be defined as a percentage of the intensity of Sirius, the brightest star in the sky after the sun. The unit of measure is the sirius (sir). The star Betelgeuse, for example, has an intensity of 0.18 sir. This means that it shines, as seen from Earth, with 18% of the intensity of the star Sirius.

a) Draw the scatter plot that represents this data.

b) What function models the data best? Justify your answer.

c) The luminosity of a Cepheid is 20 000 $L_\odot$ and its intensity is 7.8×10^{-9} sir. The radius of our galaxy is 50 000 light years. Does this Cepheid belong to our galaxy, the Milky Way?

Star	Distance (light years)	Luminosity/Intensity ($L_\odot$/sir)
Alpha Centauri A	4.3	8.8
Barnard	5.9	19.3
Wolf 359	7.6	28.9
Lalande 21185	8.1	31.9
Sirius A	8.7	38.0
Luyten 726-8 A	8.9	38.0
Ross 154	9.4	43.3
61 Cygni A	11.2	63.6
Indian Epsilon A	11.2	66.7
Procyon A	11.6	69.2

overview

1 Nicolas and Carla are seated on a bench, 2 m apart. Nicolas gradually moves closer to Carla. Two situations can evolve:

Situation 1	Situation 2
Each minute, Nicolas halves the distance between himself and Carla.	Each minute, Nicolas moves 20 cm towards Carla.

a) For each situation, determine the distance that separates Nicolas from Carla after:
   1) 1 min   2) 2 min   3) 3 min   4) 5 min

b) The first situation can be modelled with a function whose rule is $d(t) = 2\left(\frac{1}{2}\right)^t$ where t is the elapsed time (in min) and $d(t)$ is the distance between them (in m). Draw the graph of this function.

c) Determine a function that can represent the second situation. Find the rule and draw the graph.

d) Compare the two functions and indicate how their properties (domain, range, increasing or decreasing, extrema, intercept, signs) are similar or different.

e) For each of the situations, after how much time will Nicolas and Carla touch?

2 **CEPHEIDS** Cepheid stars are particular in that their magnitude varies periodically. The graph below presents a model of the variation of the magnitude of a Cepheid over time.

a) Describe this function as precisely as possible by analyzing its properties.

b) How many zeros does this function have and what do they represent?

c) How much time separates two instances of maximum magnitude for this star?

d) According to the scatter plot, at what moment did the star appear brightest in the sky?

Magnitude is a measure of the brightness of an object. The astronomer Hipparchus (2nd century BCE) invented a scale in which the brighter the object, the weaker the magnitude. For example, the sun is the brightest object and its magnitude is -26.9 whereas the dimmest objects that can be seen with the naked eye have a magnitude of 6.

Variation of the magnitude of a Cepheid

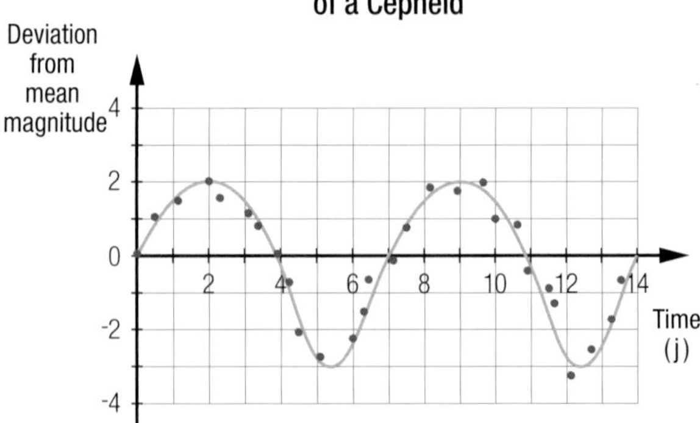

3 Pablo graphed two quadratic functions, f and g.

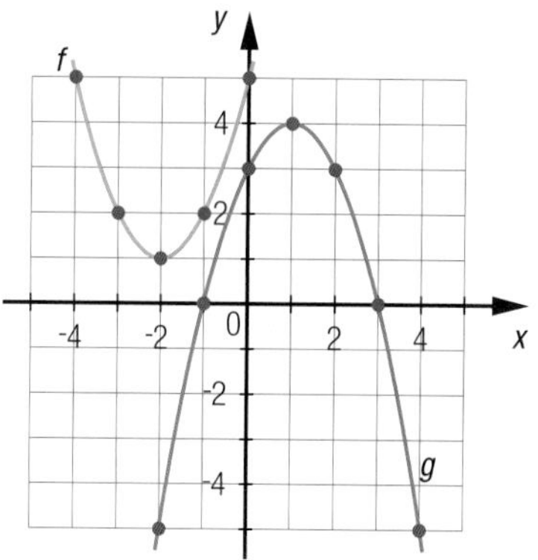

a) Find the equations of each of these functions.

b) For what values of x is the function g greater than the function f?

c) Determine the sequence of geometric transformations that will superimpose parabola f onto parabola g.

d) Is there a link between this sequence of transformations and the parameters of the two functions?

e) Over which interval are the two functions simultaneously increasing?

f) List the differences of the properties for these two functions.

4 For many delivery companies, the mass (in kg) of the parcel determines the cost of delivery (in \$). The following graph shows how STU calculates delivery costs.

a) If the delivery of a parcel costs \$5, what is its mass?

b) Which is more economical: sending two 2 kg parcels or sending a single 4 kg parcel?

c) In the case of a parcel that has a mass of 2 kg or more, the situation is consistent with a transformed greatest-integer function. Find the equation associated with this part of the graph.

d) Determine the delivery costs charged by another company given that the step function associated with the costs is equally increasing and that it has the same range and minimum as the function representing STU's delivery costs.

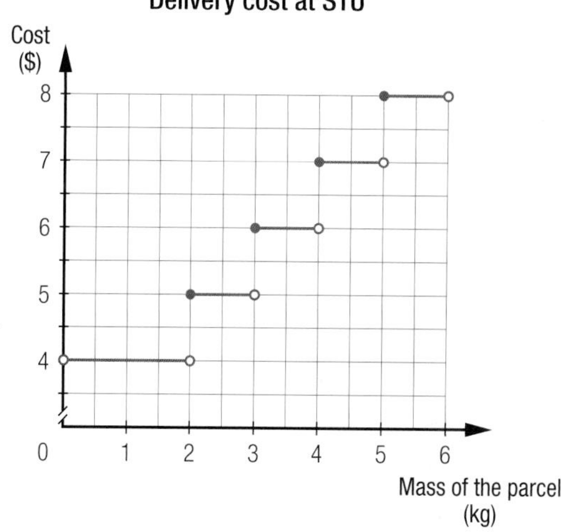

5 **RECOVERY** Competitive endurance sports cause the body to lose a great deal of water and exhaust the sugar reserves of the muscles. For the most part, the mass lost during an event will be regained during the recovery phase in following days. In this phase, the quantities of sugar and of water in the muscles obey the following relations where x represents the number of days since the event.

Sugar: $f(x) = {}^{-}16(x - 5)^2 + 425$
Water: $g(x) = {}^{-}43.2(x - 5)^2 + 1147.5$

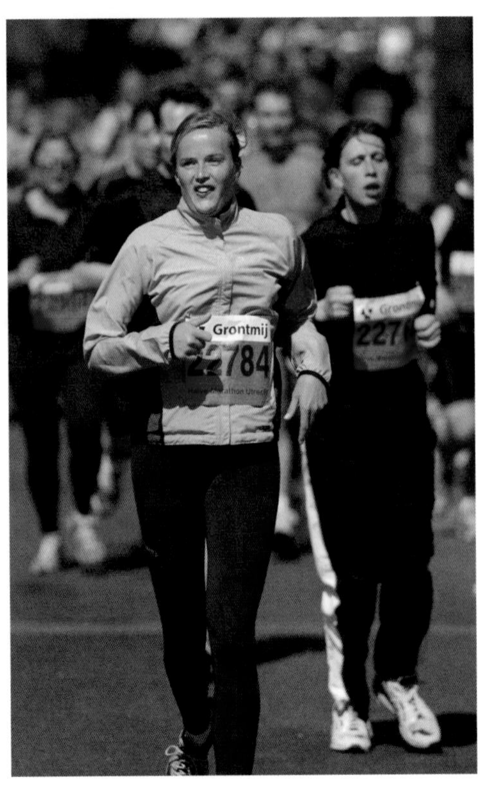

a) Draw the graphs of the functions f and g in the same Cartesian plane.

b) In view of this context, determine the domain and the range of these functions.

c) Compare the following properties of these two functions: increasing, decreasing, y-intercept, zeros, vertex and axis of symmetry.

d) What is the maximum increase in mass that an athlete can hope to gain during the recovery phase?

e) There seems to be a relation between the quantities of sugar and of water stored in the body. Which mathematical model would best represent this relation? Justify your answer.

6 While studying falling objects, Tiffany drops a 150 g marble alongside a metre stick. In order to measure time during the fall, she uses a stroboscope and photographs the experiment in the dark. The stroboscope emits 10 flashes per second:

a) Draw the scatter plot that represents this data.

b) Determine the equation of the model that best represents the data.

c) Estimate the distance travelled by the marble 1 s after it is dropped.

A stroboscope is an instrument that emits brief flashes of light of adjustable and known frequency at regular intervals. This device can make rapidly moving objects appear immobile or slow.

7 Matthew always leaves his house 10 minutes before classes start. He lives nearby, so he walks to school. This morning he met a friend along the way; he stopped to talk to him and, as a result, had to run to be on time. This graph shows the distance travelled by Matthew as a function of time:

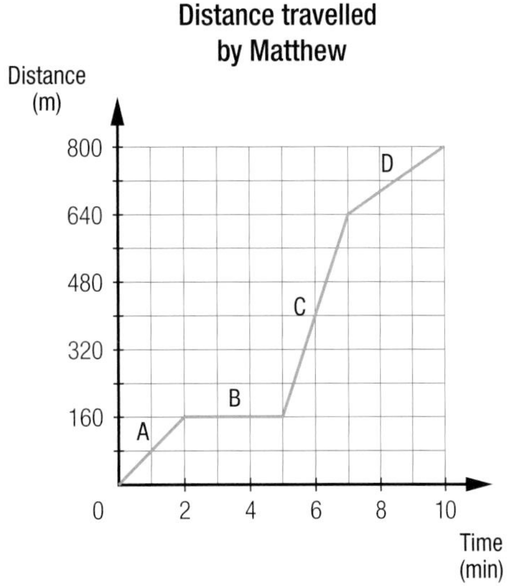

a) Determine the rule of this piecewise function.

b) Construct a table of values specifying Matthew's speed during each of the four parts of his trip.

c) What is the connection between the answer in **a)** and the answer in **b)**?

d) In this situation, what type of function best models the relation between speed and time?

e) Find Matthew's average speed:

1) over the first 400 metres

2) over the last 400 metres

3) during the first 5 minutes

4) during the last 5 minutes

The mean speed during a given period of time is the constant speed required to travel the same distance in the same time.

f) According to **e)**, is the average of the results obtained in **1)** and in **2)** equal to Matthew's average speed over the complete trip? What about the average of the results obtained in **3)** and in **4)**?

8 The quadratic function and the greatest-integer function both served as starting points to define the following functions.

$$f(x) = [x^2] \qquad g(x) = [x]^2$$

a) Construct a table of values for each function and draw their graph over the interval [-3, 3].

b) Compare the properties of these two functions.

c) For what values of x over the interval [-3, 3] is $f(x)$ equal to $g(x)$?

9 **WARM UP** To verify the merit of warming up before any physical activity, a physiologist recorded the performance and the body temperature of a sprinter. These scatter plots display his results:

Effect on athlete's time

Time (s)

14
13.5
13
12.5
12
0
10 20 30 40 50
Duration of warm up (min)

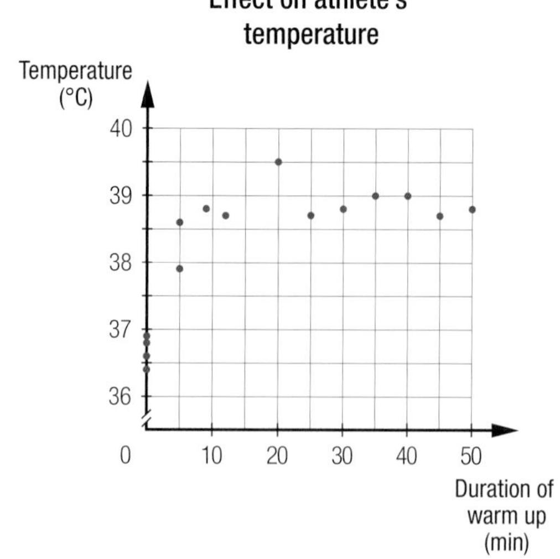

a) What model seems to best fit the data from each graph?

b) Consider the context to decide if these functions can have:

1) a minimum 2) a maximum 3) zeros

Justify your answers.

c) Restricting the domain to the interval [0, 50], determine how much time the athlete should spend warming up to perform at his or her best.

10 The *Enterprise* is a very popular amusement ride that can accommodate up to 20 people at a time. Eight hundred people can go for a ride every hour. Consider the wait time as a function of the number of people ahead of you in the lineup.

a) Determine the best model to represent this function.

b) Draw the graph corresponding to this situation when the lineup varies from 0 to 100 people.

c) What equation is associated with your graph?

d) At the beginning of the day the ride must complete two runs without passengers. Modify the equation found for **c)** to account for the wait time in these circumstances.

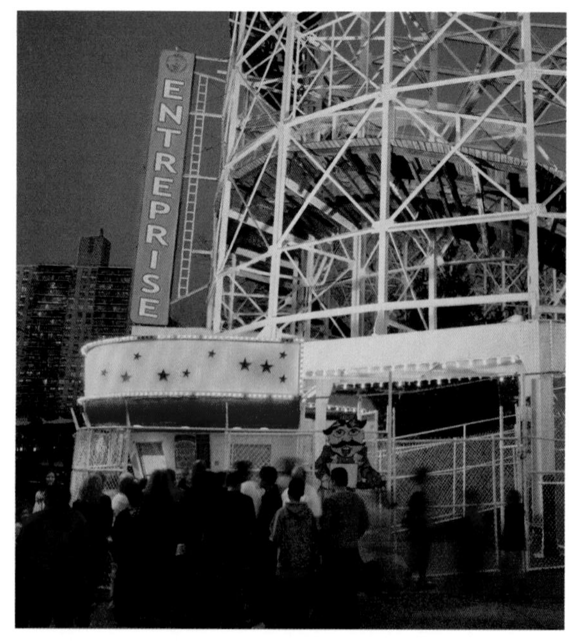

11 Brendan found several values for each of the functions $f(x) = \left[\frac{x}{200}\right]$ and $g(x) = -\left[-\frac{x}{200}\right] - 1$.

x	-5	-1	1	10	50	100	111	250	700
$f(x)$	-1	-1	0	0	0	0	0	1	3
$g(x)$	-1	-1	0	0	0	0	0	1	3

He then formulated the following conjecture: $-\left[-\frac{x}{n}\right] - 1 = \left[\frac{x}{n}\right]$, where n is an integer.

Prove Brendan's conjecture or show that it is false.

12 A car is stopped at a red light. When the light turns green, the car accelerates at constant rate for 10 s. The accompanying graph represents this situation.

a) What is the mean speed of this vehicle during the first 10 seconds?

b) Show, on this graph, the constant function corresponding to the mean speed during the first 10 seconds.

c) Compare the area under the curve of this constant function to the area under the curve of the linear function. What is your conclusion?

The area under the curve is the area of the portion of the plane which is between the curve and the x-axis.

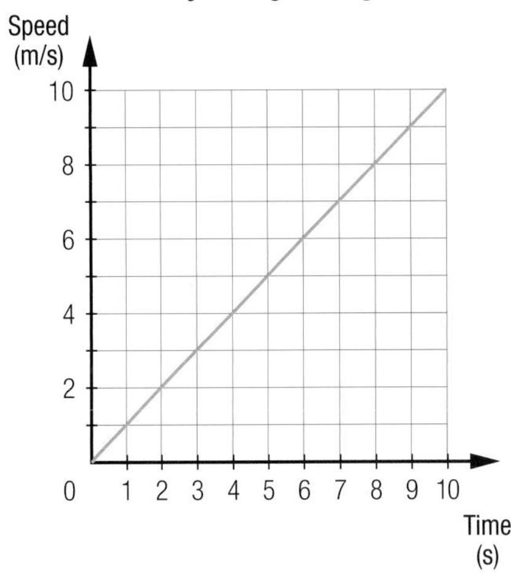

d) What is the mean speed of this vehicle during the first 2 seconds? The first 5 seconds?

e) Use the mean speed to find the distance travelled by the vehicle in 2 s, 5 s and 10 s.

f) In a Cartesian plane, draw a scatter plot of the distance as a function of time and draw the curve of best fit for this scatter plot. Justify your choice.

g) Find the equation for your model.

h) According to this model, what is the total distance travelled by the vehicle 15 s after its departure?

bank of problems

13 **WITHOUT FRICTION** The first magnetically levitating train was put into service in Shanghai.

Below are excerpts from two press releases sent out just after it began operation on January 1, 2004:

Document 1

During this test, the train maintained the same acceleration for 120 s.

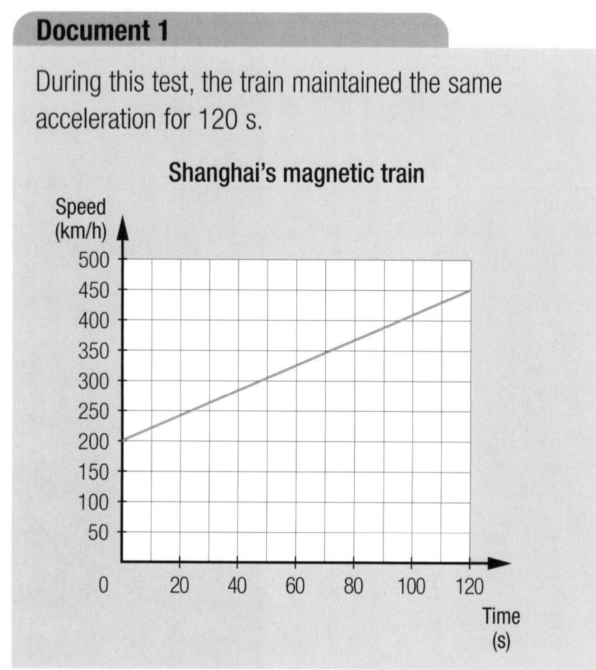

Document 2

The train can accelerate from 0 km/h to the impressive speed of 350 km/h in only 2 min without any discomfort to the passengers because the speed increases at a constant rate.

This information describes two acceleration experiments that lasted 2 minutes each. However, the distance travelled by the train in each experiment was not the same. Approximate the difference between the two distances travelled.

14 Frederica applied to become a contestant on a televised game show. One of the problems submitted to the candidates during the screen test was as follows.

> Complete the sequence:
> 1, 2, 3, 8, 9, 14, 19, 20, 33, __, __

Unfortunately she was unable to answer correctly. Explain how she could have answered the question correctly.

15 It is evident that the quantity of liquid in a prism-shaped or cylindrically-shaped container set on one of its bases is proportional to the height of the liquid. For example, if the water level in the container below is doubled, then the quantity of water is automatically doubled.

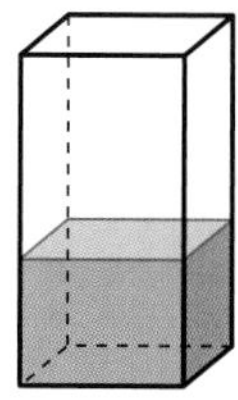
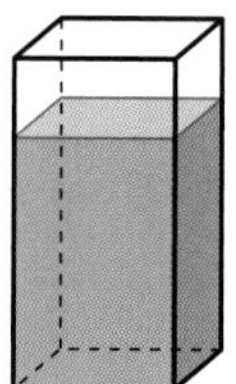

Design a container in which the quantity of liquid it contains is always proportional to the square of the height of the liquid. Indicate the dimensions of your container and demonstrate that this property is respected.

16 The internal clock on Clara's computer can measure time to one ten-thousandth of a second. Clara used the clock's measure of seconds to write a computer program that generates integers from 1 to 10 in what seems to be a random fashion. On a mouse click, the computer reads, from its clock, the number that indicates the seconds, performs a sequence of operations and displays an integer on the screen. The table below shows a few examples:

Numbers generated by the program

Number from the clock indicating seconds	9.6075	18.7850	25.7964	31.9012	35.9639	48.0792
Integer displayed on the screen	6	1	5	3	10	3

Write an equation involving the greatest-integer function that would generate the same values as Clara's program. Explain your method clearly.

> In mathematics and in computer science, the term pseudo-random refers to a sequence of numbers that has the characteristics of a random sequence but is generated by a deterministic and reproducible method.

17 Sophie went downhill skiing on a mountain whose summit is at an altitude of 450 m. During her first ascent by chair lift and the descent that followed, Sophie's altitude varied at different times. The situation can be modelled by expressing the rate of change of her altitude (in m/min) as a function of the elapsed time (in min). One of the possible functions has the following characteristics:

- It is a step function with only two critical values.
- Its domain is [0, 10].
- Its maximum is 60 and its minimum is -35.
- The function is positive in the interval [0, 4[and negative in the interval [3.5, 10].

According to this model, at what altitude is Sophie 6 min after the chair lift starts?

The altitude of a mountain is its height relative to sea level. Altitude is not to be confused with the difference between the altitude at its summit and the altitude at its base.

18 The cost of a trip by taxi is generally based on the number of kilometres travelled. However, when the taxi is stopped or is moving more slowly than a predetermined speed, the rate is a function of the elapsed time. The meter will always choose the rate which is most desirable for the driver. The following is a description of charges (in $) for 2008:

The base fare
$2.75

As determined from elapsed time
$0.05[599t]$,
where t is the time in hours.

As determined by distance travelled
$0.05[26x]$,
where x is the distance in kilometres.

During one trip, a taxi travelled 10 minutes at 40 km/h, 8 minutes at 30 km/h, 7 minutes at 20 km/h, and it was stopped for a total of 5 minutes at red lights. Disregarding the acceleration and deceleration phases, determine the total cost of this trip.

19 While visiting Brussels, Leonard saw the *Manneken-Pis*. He was intrigued by the distance travelled by the water-jet. Upon returning home, he decided to experiment. He filled a milk carton with 2 L of water and placed it so that it was facing a measuring tape. He punctured a hole 3 cm from the bottom of the container and observed the distance to which the water-jet was propelled as a function of the elapsed time.

What is the relation between this distance and time?

To answer this question duplicate Leonard's experiment. Use your data to determine the type of function that could model this situation. Provide all the information needed to justify your answer.

The Manneken-Pis is a famous tourist attraction dating back to the 17th century.

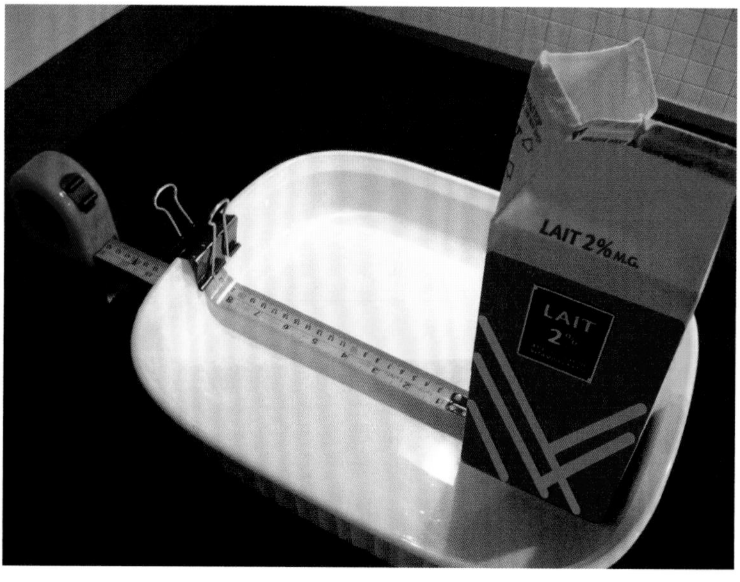

20 First, complete the equalities below by adding the missing expressions. In each case you must obtain a valid equality for all real values of x.

1. $[x] + \left[x + \frac{1}{2}\right] = \ldots$
2. $[x] + \ \ldots \ + \ \ldots \ = [3x]$

Prove that these equalities are now true, for all values of x.

VISION 3

Equivalence in geometry and algebra

Since the Stone Age and the invention of the first tool, to the latest developments in modern technology, peoples' inventive spirit has led to improved living conditions for all. And today, more than ever, science and mathematics are central to this development. In "Vision 3," you will discover how geometry and algebra play key roles in your scientific understanding of the world around you. As a first step, the study of equivalence in geometry shows you that certain forms found in nature are not a matter of chance. Then, equivalence in algebra will provide you with the tools necessary to analyze complex situations represented by algebraic expressions beyond the first-degree. Throughout this study, you will find important connections between geometry and algebra, and this will give you a better understanding of the concepts being explored.

Arithmetic and algebra	Geometry	Statistics
• Manipulating algebraic expressions • Division by a binomial • Rational expressions • Algebraic identities • Factoring polynomials • Solving second-degree equations in one variable	• Equivalent figures • Using the concept of equivalence to find missing measurements	

REVISION 3

PRIOR LEARNING 1 The prestidigitator

During a performance, a prestidigitator asks his assistant to enter a cube-shaped box with edges measuring 1 m. Not exactly a comforting idea with all those sharp swords waiting to be used.

After piercing the box with his swords, the prestidigitator opens the doors so that the audience can see that the box is empty!

Intrigued by this performance, Ben does some research on magic tricks. He discovers that the inside of the box has two identical removable mirrors attached to opposite sides of the box. The assistant can hide behind the mirrors once the doors are closed.

a. What should be the width of the two mirrors in order to form a 90° angle when the door is open?

Once the assistant is hidden behind the mirrors, the swords can only go through the front or the back sections of the box.

b. What is the volume of the back section of the box and of the front section of the box?

c. What fraction of the box's volume can the assistant occupy when the mirrors are pulled back as the door is opened?

Top view of the inside of the box

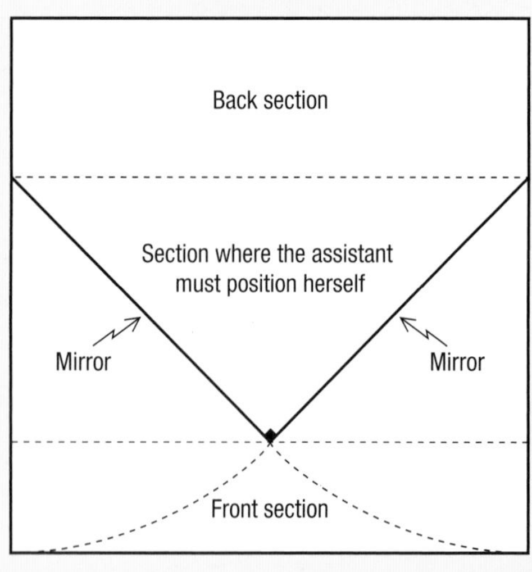

PRIOR LEARNING 2 The magician

A magician walks onto a stage. She announces that she has telepathic powers. The following are two of her acts which leave people speechless.

The magician places nine tokens numbered from 1 to 9 into a bag.

- In front of the blindfolded magician, a spectator is asked to draw three tokens from the bag in order to form a three-digit number. The spectator draws 2, 6 and 5, forming the three-digit number 265.
- She asks the spectator to reverse the order of the digits resulting in a different three-digit number. This means that the spectator's original number 265 becomes 562.
- She then asks the spectator to determine the difference between the number chosen at the beginning of the act and the one obtained by reversing the order of the digits. The spectator substracts 265 from 562 which results in 297.
- At the magician's request, the spectator gives her the last digit of the result obtained from the subtraction. The last digit is 7.

After a few drum rolls, the magician exclaims, "297!"

a. If a, b and c represent the digits on the tokens in the order in which they were drawn from the bag, what algebraic expression represents the number formed?

b. What algebraic expression represents the number obtained by reversing the order of the digits in the first number?

c. Show how the final result obtained by the spectator is a multiple of 99 regardless of which tokens were drawn at the beginning of the act.

The magician places 100 tokens numbered from 1 to 100 in a bag.

- In front of the blindfolded magician, a spectator draws a token from the bag, "Shh! It's 13!"
- She asks the spectator to calculate the square of the whole number that follows this number.
- She then asks the spectator to calculate the square of the whole number that precedes this number.
- At the magician's request, the spectator then states the difference between the two results. "I get 52," says the spectator confidently.

After a second, the magician exclaims, "13! You drew the number 13, didn't you?"

d. Find a way to represent this magic trick in algebraic terms.

MEASUREMENT IN GEOMETRY

The area of solids

The **surface area of a solid** is determined by the sum of the areas of all its faces.

E.g. 1) Right prism

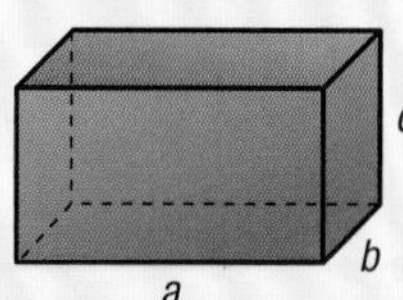

$A = 2ac + 2ab + 2bc$

2) Right cylinder

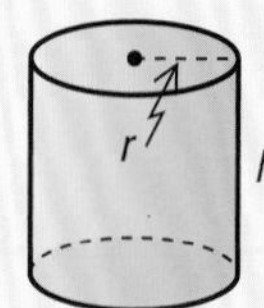

$A = 2\pi r^2 + 2\pi rh$

3) Sphere

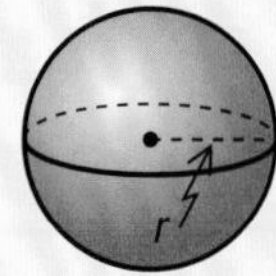

$A = 4\pi r^2$

The volume of solids

The **volume of a solid** is determined by measuring the space occupied by this solid.

E.g. V and A_b respectively represent the volume of the solid and the area of its base.

1) Right prisms and right cylinder

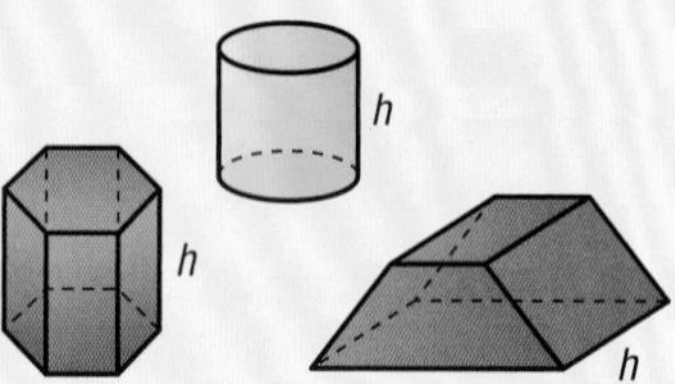

$V = A_b \cdot h$

2) Right pyramid and right circular cone

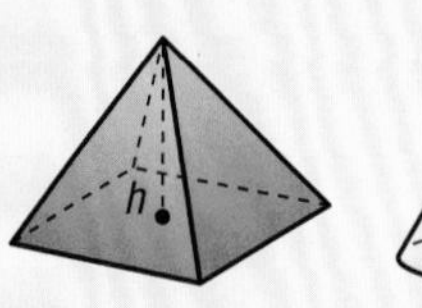

$V = \frac{A_b \cdot h}{3}$

3) Sphere

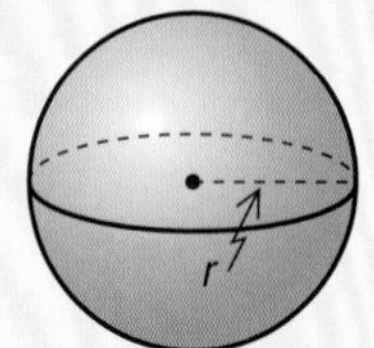

$V = \frac{4\pi r^3}{3}$

The Pythagorean theorem

In a right triangle, the square of the length of the hypotenuse is equal to the sum of the squares of the lengths of the two legs.

If a triangle is such that the square of the length of one side is equal to the sum of the squares of the lengths of the other sides, it is a right triangle.

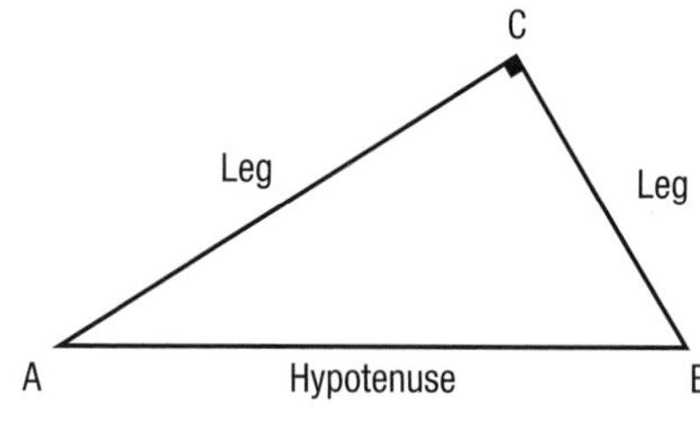

$(m\ \overline{AB})^2 = (m\ \overline{AC})^2 + (m\ \overline{CB})^2$

MANIPULATING ALGEBRAIC EXPRESSIONS

Laws of exponents

The laws of exponents make it possible to perform operations involving written expressions in exponential form. The adjacent table represents these laws for a and $b \neq 0$ given m and n are natural numbers.

Law	Example
$a^m \cdot a^n = a^{m+n}$	$x^3 \cdot x^2 = x^{3+2} = x^5$
$\frac{a^m}{a^n} = a^{m-n}$	$\frac{x^5}{x^2} = x^{5-2} = x^3$
$(ab)^n = a^n b^n$	$(3xy)^3 = 3^3x^3y^3 = 27x^3y^3$
$(a^m)^n = a^{mn}$	$(x^2)^3 = x^{2 \cdot 3} = x^6$
$\left(\frac{a}{b}\right)^m = \frac{a^m}{b^m}$	$\left(\frac{x}{4}\right)^2 = \frac{x^2}{4^2} = \frac{x^2}{16}$

Operations on algebraic expressions

- You can simplify algebraic expressions by adding or subtracting like terms.

E.g.

1) $6x^2 + 3 + 4x^2 + 1 = 6x^2 + 4x^2 + 3 + 1$
$= 10x^2 + 4$

2) $(5a^3 + 6) - (3a^3 - 1) = 5a^3 + 6 - 3a^3 + 1$
$= 5a^3 - 3a^3 + 6 + 1$
$= 2a^3 + 7$

- When multiplying two binomials, each term of the first binomial is multiplied by each term of the second binomial.

E.g. $(4n^2 - 30)(2n + 7) = 4n^2 \cdot 2n + 4n^2 \cdot 7 - 30 \cdot 2n - 30 \cdot 7$
$= 8n^3 + 28n^2 - 60n - 210$

- When dividing a polynomial by a monomial, each term of the polynomial is divided by the monomial.

E.g. $(20b^3 - 10b^2 + 15b) \div 5b = 20b^3 \div 5b - 10b^2 \div 5b + 15b \div 5b$
$= 4b^2 - 2b + 3$

Factoring: Removing a common factor

It is possible to factor certain algebraic expressions by removing the greatest common factor, proceed as follows.

1. Determine the greatest common factor out of all the terms in the algebraic expression.	E.g. In the expression $6a^2 + 15a$, the greatest common factor is $3a$.
2. Divide each term of the algebraic expression by the greatest common factor.	$\frac{6a^2 + 15a}{3a} = \frac{6a^2}{3a} + \frac{15a}{3a} = 2a + 5$
3. Write the greatest common factor obtained in **1)** followed by the quotient obtained in **2)**.	$6a^2 + 15a = 3a(2a + 5)$

knowledge in action

1 Determine the missing measurements in the figures below:

a) Area of the square = ?

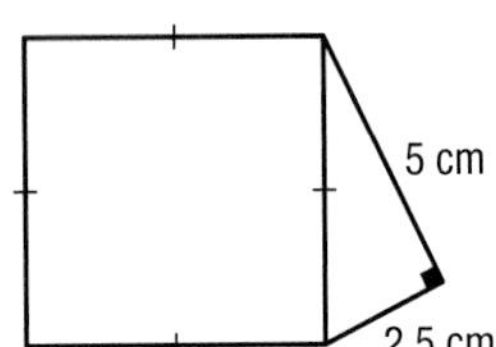

b)

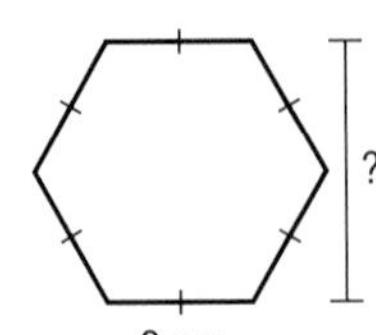

c) m $\overline{AB}$ = ?

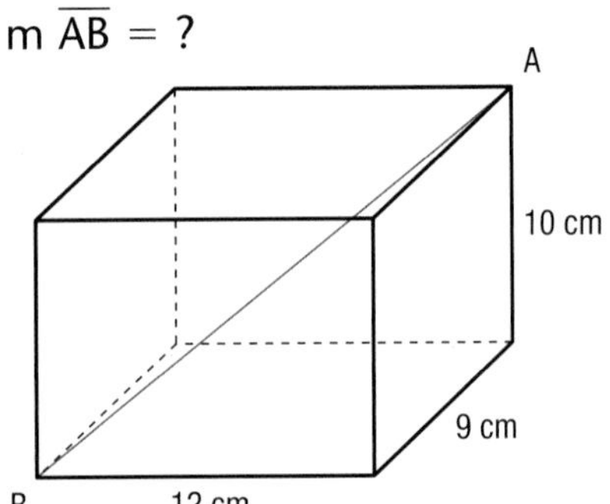

2 Considering that the square-based prism, the cylinder and the sphere shown below each have a volume of 2000 cm^3, determine their surface areas.

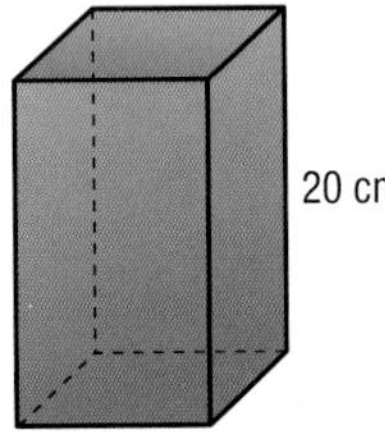

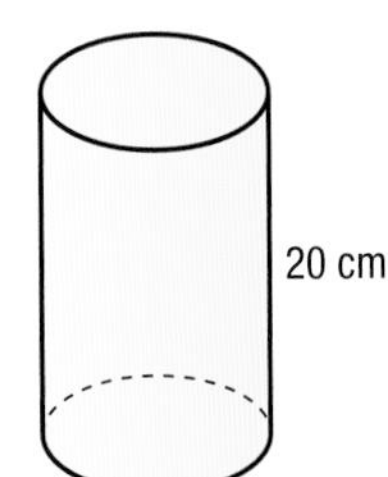

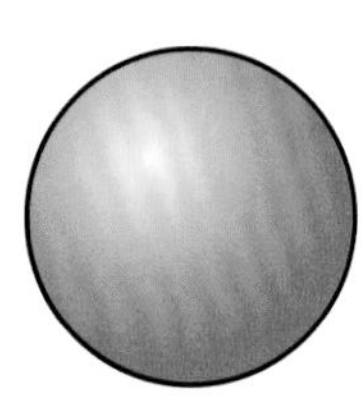

3 Simplify the following expressions.

a) $(3n + 4) + (5n - 2)$

b) $8n^2 - 4 - 2n^2 - 4$

c) $(6a^3 + 4a^2 + a) - (2a^3 + a^2 - 5)$

d) $(2a)^3 + (2a + 4)(3a^2 - 3)$

e) $10(5a^2 + 3a - 8) - 2(25a^2 + 15a)$

f) $(15x^3 + 4x^2 - 12) \div 5x$

g) $\dfrac{8b^3 - 14b^2 + 10b - 4}{2b}$

h) $(2x + 5)(3x - 7)$

4 Maude and Justin decide to rebuild their patio. They choose a square-shaped design with brown tiles in the central area surrounded by a border of white tiles. The border is made up of two tiles on two sides and one tile on the other sides. Regardless of the dimensions of the square formed, they plan to arrange the white tiles and the brown tiles according to this pattern.

a) Let n be the measure of the side of the patio, in number of tiles. Determine three different algebraic expressions that would allow you to calculate the number of brown tiles. In your own words, explain how each of these expressions was obtained.

b) Using algebraic manipulations, show that the algebraic expressions found in **a)** are equivalent.

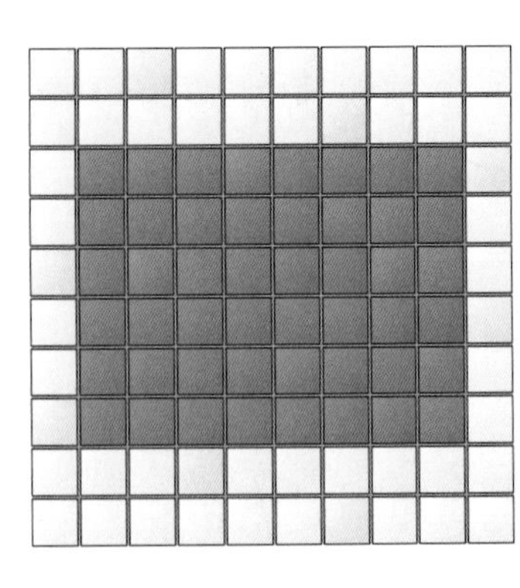

5 A certain quantity of liquid was poured into a cube with 10 cm edges in order to form different prisms. In the pictures below, x, a, b, c and y represent lengths in centimetres.

①
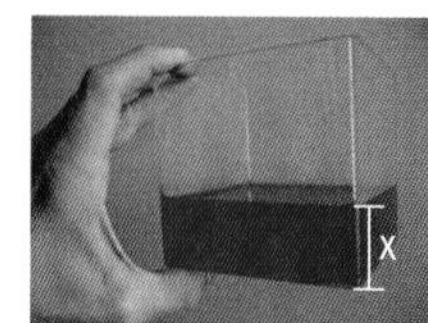

②
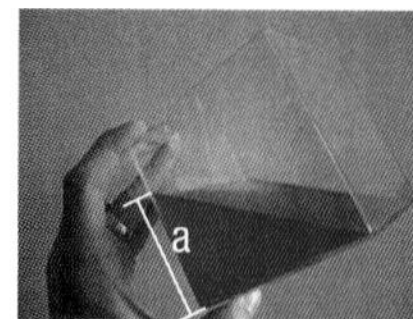

③

④

a) For each of these pictures, write an algebraic expression that represents the volume of liquid in each container. Simplify this expression if possible.

b) Determine the quantity of liquid used in the 3rd cube, considering that b and c measure 2.4 cm and 5.6 cm, respectively.

c) Determine the quantity of liquid used in the 4th cube, considering that y measures:

1) 2.5 cm 2) 4 cm 3) 6.5 cm

6 Solve the following equations.

a) $2(3x + 12) = 36$ b) $\frac{3x}{5} + 8 = 14$ c) $10x^2 + 48 = (2.5x + 1)(4x + 6.4)$

7 Factor the following polynomials by removing the common factor.

a) $4x^2 + 12$ b) $8x^2 - 6x$ c) $3x^3 + 6x + 9$ d) $^-12a^3 + 8a^2 - 4a$

8 A magician tells his audience that he can make a surface of 1 cm² in area magically appear. He first takes a square whose sides measure 8 cm, which he then decomposes as shown below.

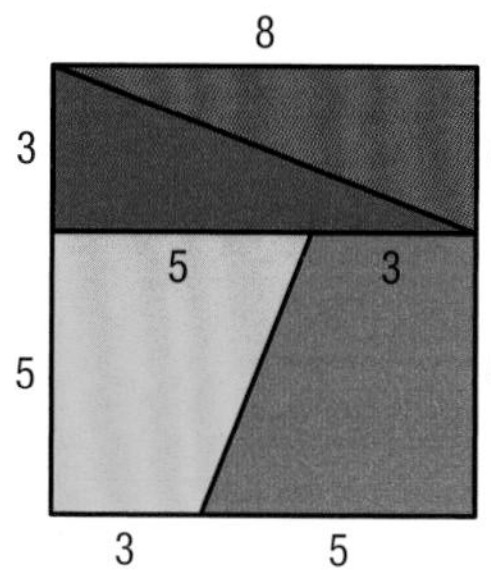

By using different juxtapositions of the four pieces, he forms a rectangle and invites the audience to applaud.

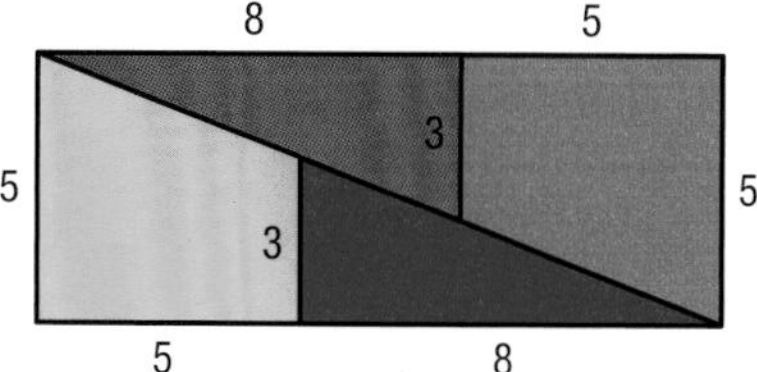

a) Why does he invite the audience to applaud?

b) Find a way to explain this magic trick.

This paradox was used by magician Alain Choquette and was featured in an article on magic. This type of cut-out, attributed to a German mathematician named Oscar Schlömilch (1868), was also found in documents by Lewis Carrol the creator of *Alice in Wonderland.*

SECTION 3.1 Equivalent figures

This section is related to LES 7.

PROBLEM Dido's problem

Though disputed by historians, there is a beautiful legend of how the City of Carthage was founded.

According to this legend, it was Queen Dido who founded the city in 814 BCE. Following a stop in Cyprus, Dido settled on the northern African coasts. Upon her arrival, she was granted a territory by the sea that was "as large as an ox's hide."

Ruins of Carthage (Tunisia)

Not a great welcome for a queen! However, as the legend goes, Dido knew how to make the most out of what she had. She decided to cut the ox hide that had been presented to her into thin strips, resulting in a very long string estimated at a length of 4 km.

Dido's legend has inspired many artists including painter William Turner (1775 - 1851) who depicted her in his own way in his famous 1815 painting entitled *Dido building Carthage.*

Yet, one dilemna remained for Dido:

« How do I border a territory with this string to maximize its area? »

Propose a solution to Dido's problem, and justify your reasoning. Convince your peers that your solution to Dido's problem is better than theirs.

ACTIVITY 1 Figures with the same area

On the preceding page, you saw that it is possible to maximize the area of a plane figure that has a specified perimeter. One can now ask the following question: How can the perimeter of a plane figure that has a specified area be minimized? Consider the following four cases:

A Case 1: The case of a triangle

Consider triangle ABC. Side AB can represent the base of the triangle.

a. Construct at least five different triangles with side AB as a base and having the same area as triangle ABC.

b. Among all the equivalent triangles that can be constructed, which one has the smallest perimeter? Justify your answer.

Plane figures are said to be "equivalent" if they have the same area.

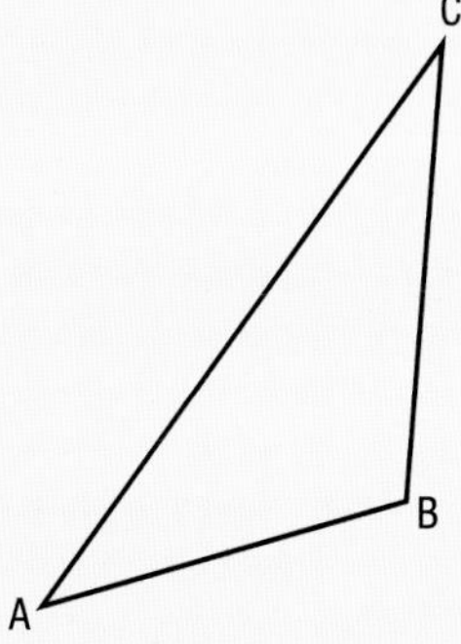

B Case 2: The case of a quadrilateral

Consider quadrilateral ABCD. Using a geometric construction, the perimeter has been minimized while maintaining the same area, as a result of moving point D in a direction that is parallel to segment AC.

c. Explain why quadrilaterals ABCD and ABCD′ have the same area.

d. Explain why the perimeter of ABCD′ is less than that of ABCD.

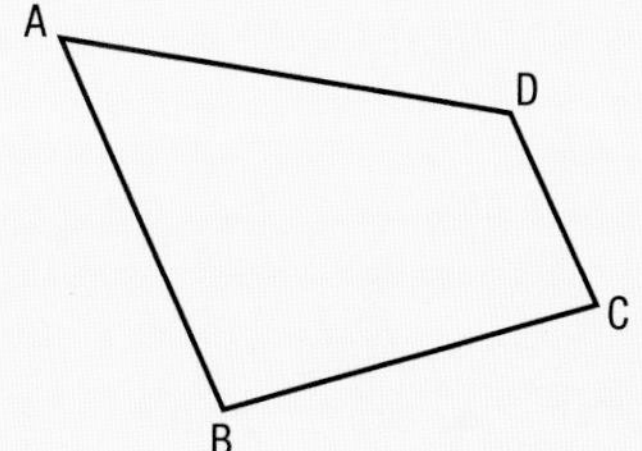

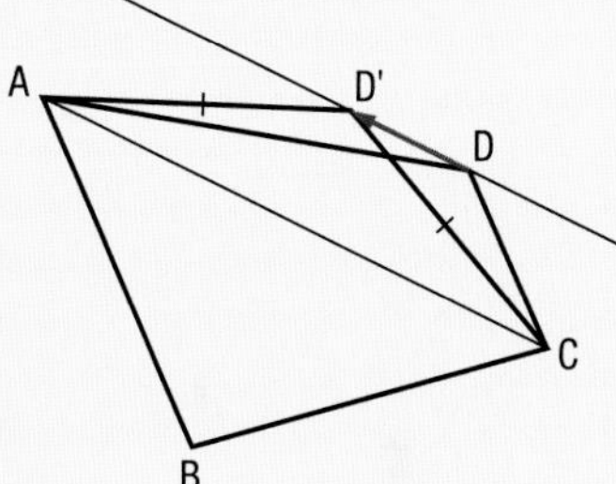

e. From this construction, you may deduce that the quadrilateral with the smallest perimeter for a given area is necessarily a rhombus. Explain why.

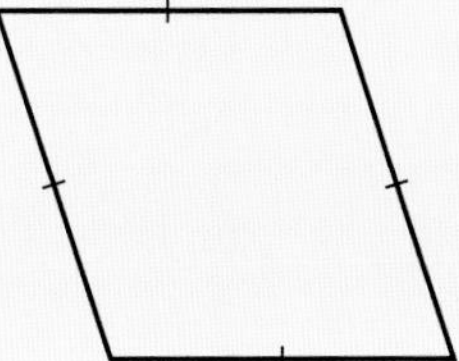

f. The rhombus shown above is equivalent to quadrilateral ABCD. Is it possible to construct a rectangle that would be equivalent to the rhombus but with an even smaller perimeter? Explain how to construct such a rectangle.

g. Which quadrilateral with the same area as quadrilateral ABCD has the smallest possible perimeter? Justify your answer.

C Case 3: The case of a pentagon

Anis, Charlotte and William have each received an illustration of the same pentagon. They were asked to minimize, as much as possible, the perimeter of this pentagon while maintaining its area. Below are the pentagons obtained by each of them:

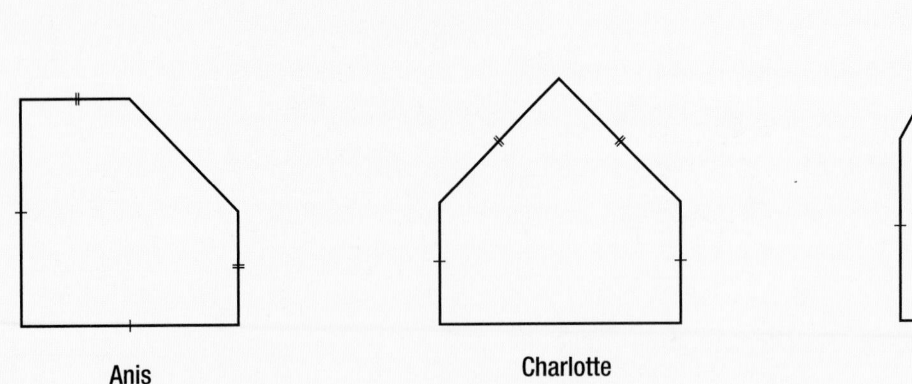

h. If possible, minimize the perimeter of each pentagon while maintaining its area. Provide evidence of your construction.

i. In the above family of equivalent pentagons, which one allows the smallest possible perimeter?

D Case 4: The case of a regular polygon

William thinks that for all equivalent polygons, the one that is regular has the smallest perimeter. He now wonders which, among all equivalent regular polygons, has the shortest perimeter. The following is his reasoning:

Consider the regular pentagon ABCDE.

By placing a vertex F on side AE, you get a hexagon.

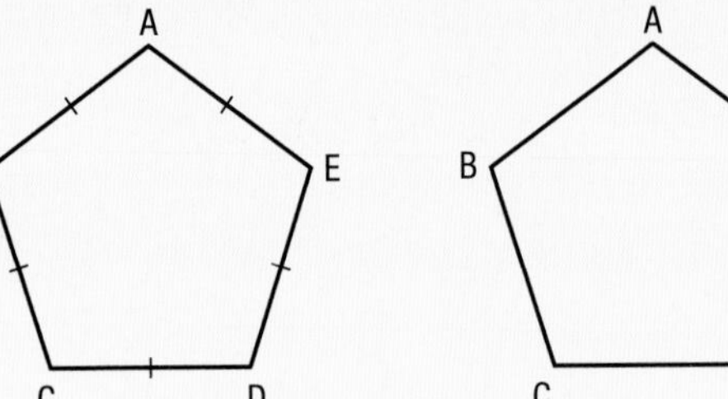

Since hexagon ABCDEF is not regular, one can minimize its perimeter while maintaining its area.

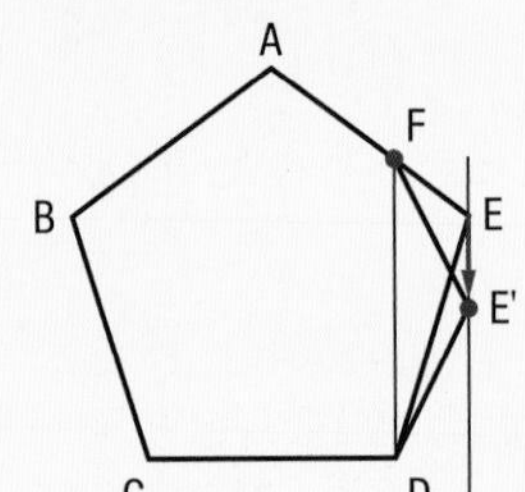

The regular hexagon that is equivalent to pentagon ABCDE will thus have a smaller perimeter.

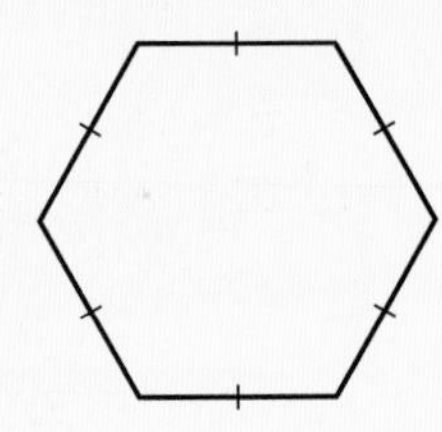

j. Among the following equivalent regular polygons, which one has the smallest perimeter?

1) a square or a regular pentagon
2) a regular hexagon or a regular decagon

k. You want to use a rope to border a plane surface of 100 m^2 in area. What will be the shape of this surface if you want to use the smallest possible length of rope? Explain your reasoning.

ACTIVITY 2 A sweet problem

A sugar refinery asks an industrial designer to improve the packaging of its product. Production costs for the current package, shown below, are too high.

The designer's mandate: design a box shaped as a rectangular-based prism that will contain as much sugar as the current box but will require less material to make.

a. What quantity of sugar can the original box contain?

b. What quantity of cardboard is required to make the original box?

c. What would be the shape of the box that could contain as much sugar as the original box and that would minimize the amount of cardboard used? Justify your answer.

d. Is there an equivalent prism to the one determined in **c.** that has an even smaller surface area? Justify your answer.

Solids are said to be "equivalent" if they have the same volume.

e. Find a solid that is equivalent to all of the previous prisms, but with a smaller surface area. Justify your answer.

A sugar refinery processes the reddish brown sugars produced by cane or beet sugar plantations in order to rid them of impurities. A refinery also takes care of the shaping and conditioning (granulated sugar, icing sugar, sugar cubes, sugar loaves, etc.) as well as the packaging and distribution of sugar products.

Techno math

Dynamic geometry software allows you to draw and manipulate figures in a Cartesian plane. By using the tools: STRAIGHT LINE, PARALLEL LINE, TRIANGLE, LENGTH and AREA, you can explore and observe the effect of displacing a vertex of a triangle along a straight line that is parallel to its base.

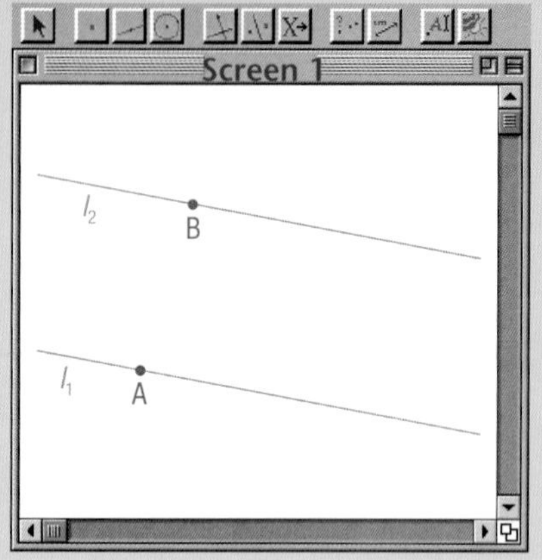

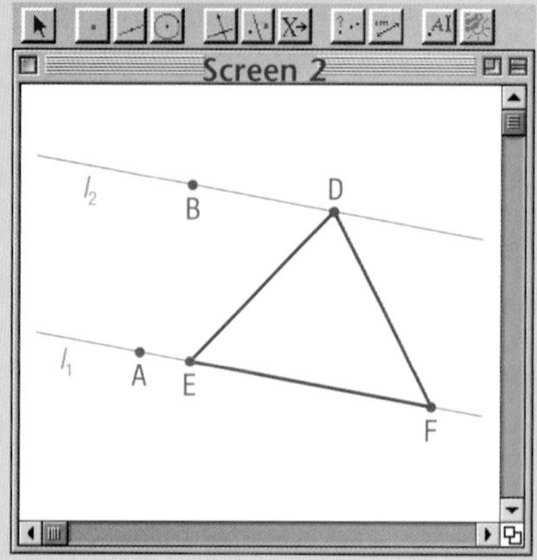

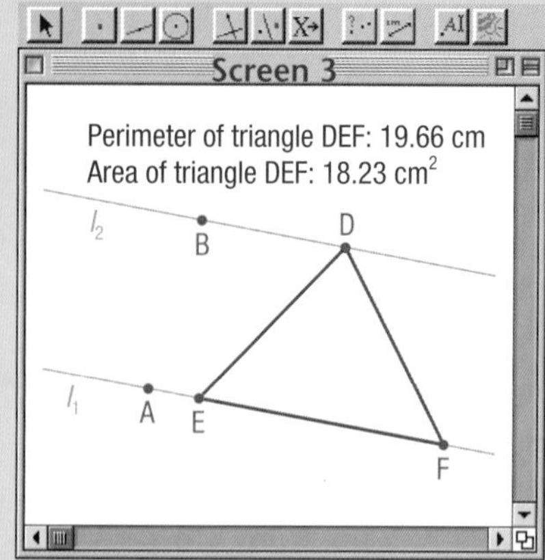

By changing the position of point D, you can see the effects of the displacement on the perimeter and area of triangle DEF.

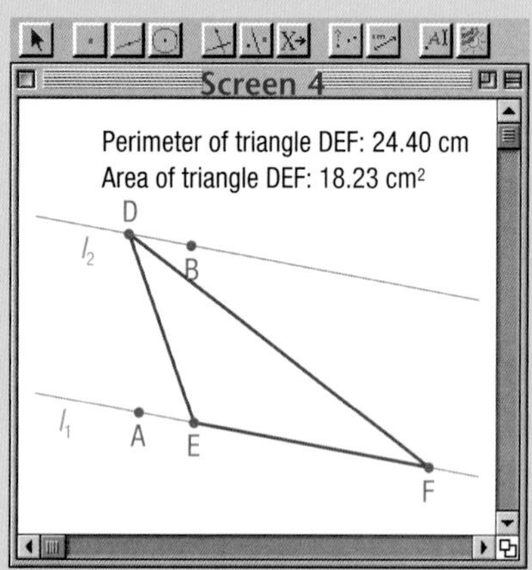

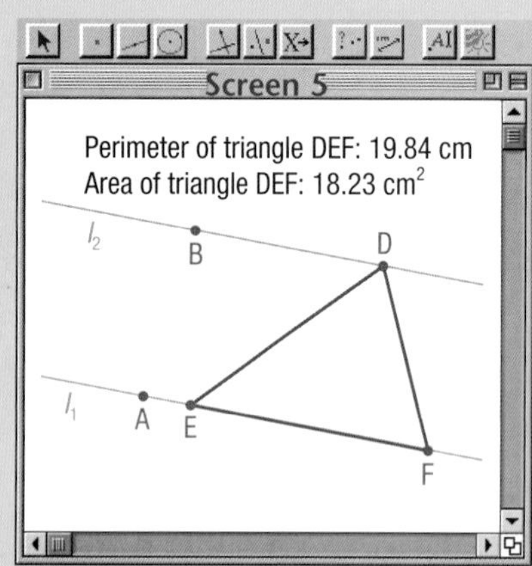

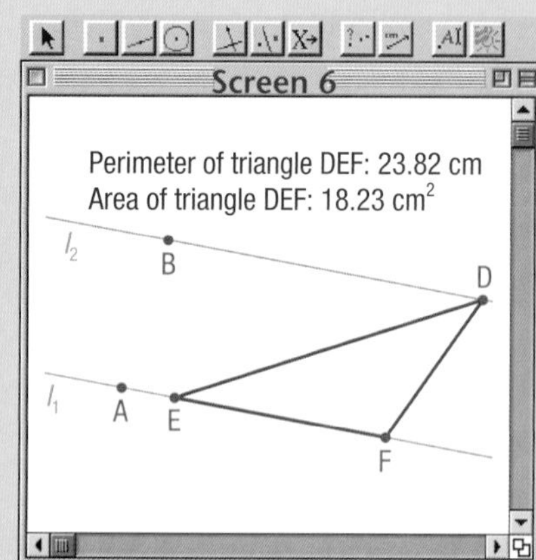

a. What can you say about lines l_1 and l_2?

b. What conjecture can you formulate as you observe the changing areas of the triangles in Screens **4**, **5** and **6**?

c. Where must point D be located so that the perimeter of triangle DEF is minimal?

d. Using dynamic geometry software, construct the three figures below and verify whether it is possible to formulate a conjecture regarding the effect that the displacement of point A has on the area and the perimeter of the figure.

1)

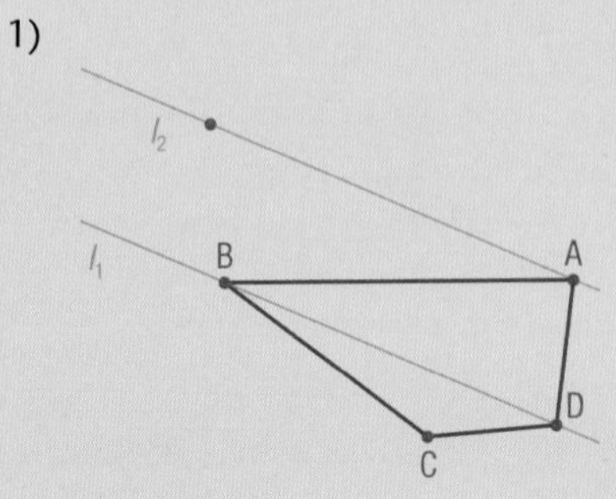

2)

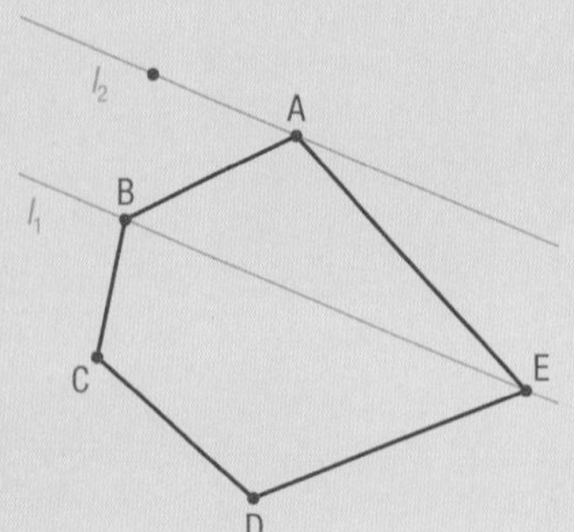

3)

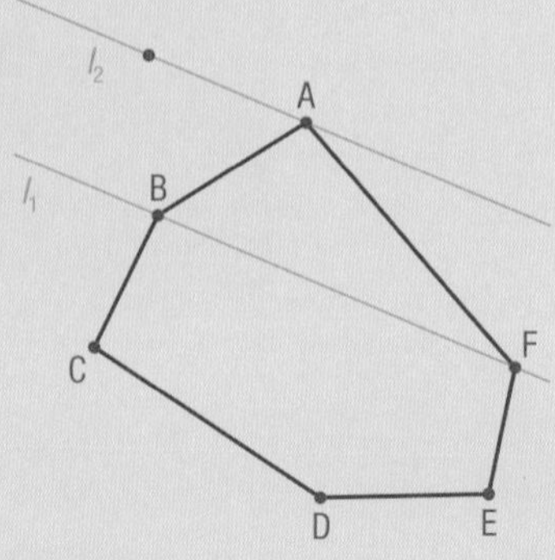

knowledge 3.1

EQUIVALENT FIGURES

Intuitively, you can say that two geometric figures (lines, plane figures or solids) are equivalent if you can decompose one of them to form the other.

More formally you can say:

- Two lines are equivalent if they have the same length.
- Two plane figures are equivalent if they have the same area.
- Two solids are equivalent if they have the same volume.

E.g.

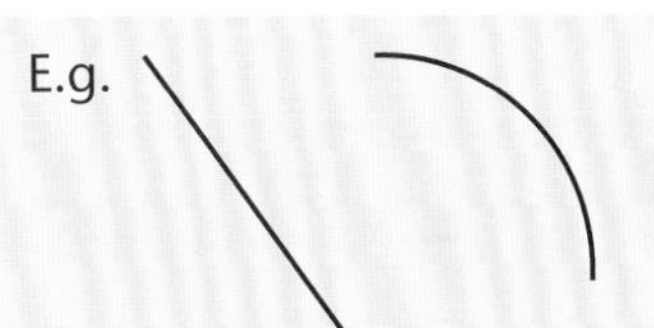

E.g.

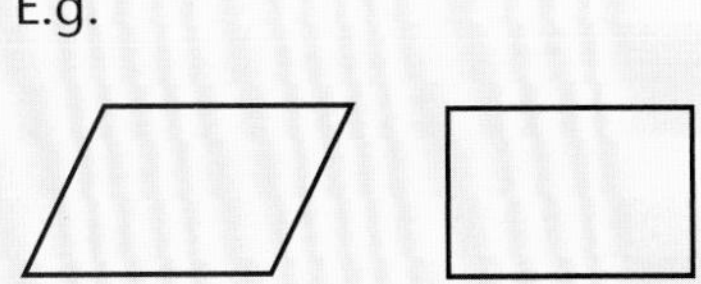

E.g.

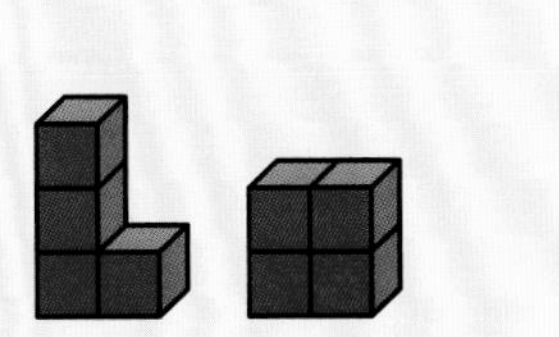

There are different ways of determining whether figures are equivalent.

By decomposing

E.g. 1)

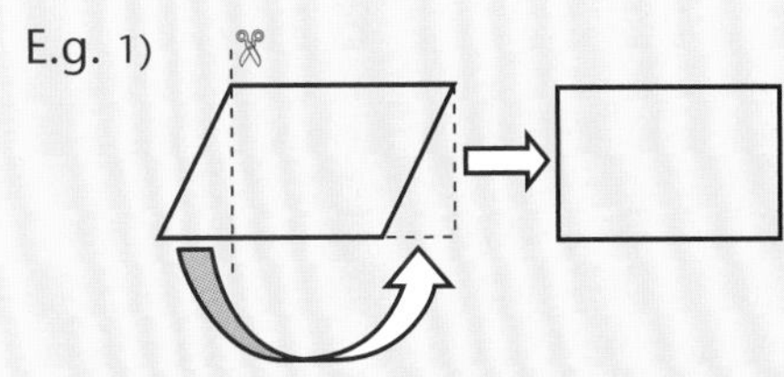

The parallelogram is equivalent to the rectangle.

2)

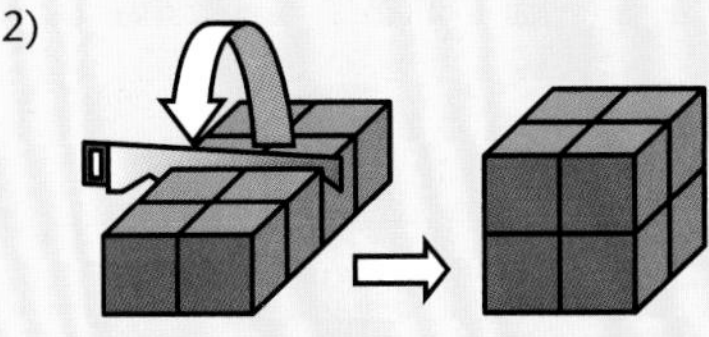

The prism is equivalent to the cube.

Using calculations

E.g. Consider a square with sides measuring 6 cm. What is the length of the sides of an equilateral triangle that is equivalent to the square?

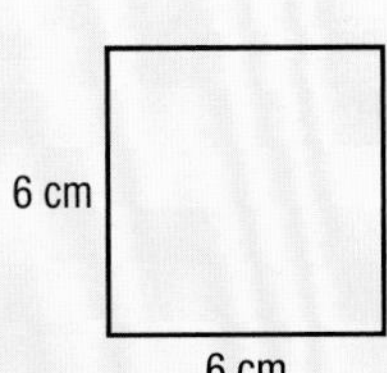

The area of the square is: 6 x 6 = 36 cm^2.

Consider the adjacent equilateral triangle.

Based on the Pythagorean theorem: $h^2 = b^2 - \left(\frac{b}{2}\right)^2$

$$h = \frac{\sqrt{3}}{2}b.$$

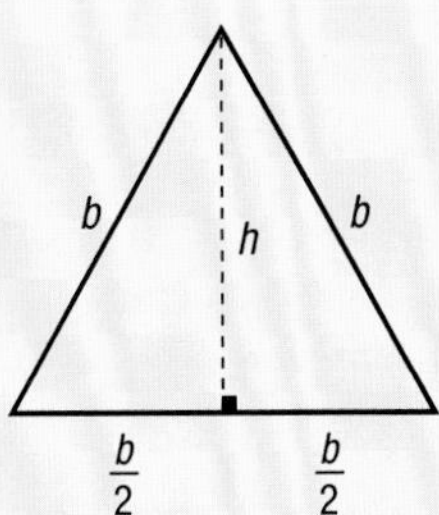

The area of the triangle is 36 cm^2.

Therefore $36 = \dfrac{b \cdot \frac{\sqrt{3}}{2}b}{2}$

$$72 = \frac{\sqrt{3}}{2}b^2$$

and $b = \sqrt{\dfrac{144}{\sqrt{3}}} \approx 9.1.$

The sides of the equilateral triangle equivalent to the square measure approximately 9.1 cm.

Using dynamic geometry

E.g. 1)

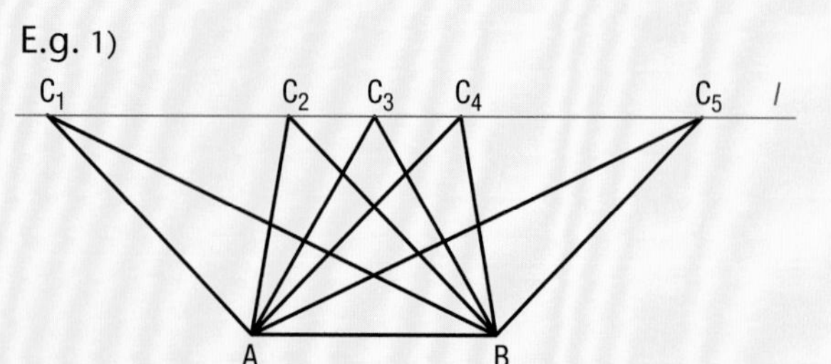

Given line l is parallel to segment AB, all of the above triangles with base AB are equivalent. This is true since they all have the same base and the same height.

2)

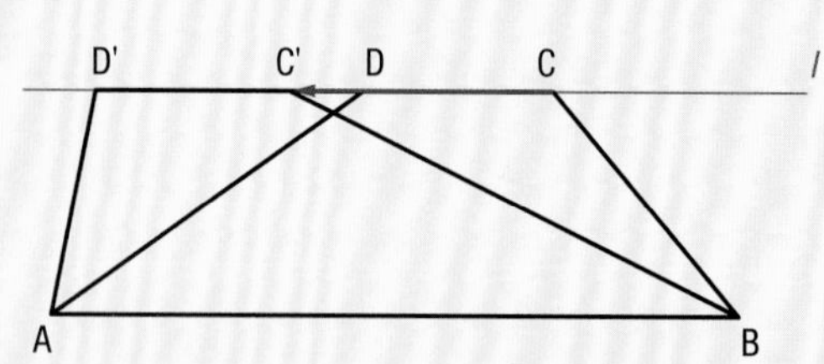

Given line l is parallel to segment AB, trapezoids ABCD and ABC'D' are equivalent. This is true since they have congruent bases and the same height.

3) **Prism A** **Prism B**

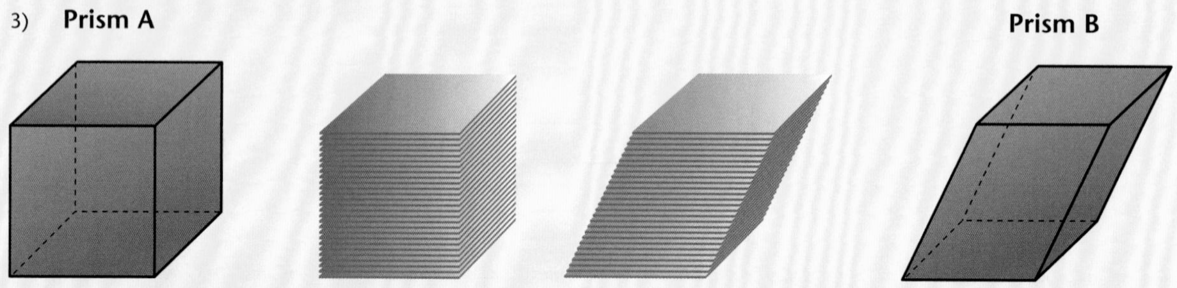

The different "layers" of Prism **A** have been displaced in a direction that is parallel to its base. The volume of the prism is maintained. Prisms **A** and **B** are therefore equivalent.

PROPERTIES OF EQUIVALENT FIGURES

- Of all equivalent polygons with n sides, the regular polygon is the one with the smallest perimeter.
- Of two equivalent regular polygons, the polygon with the greater number of sides is the one that has the smallest perimeter. Ultimately, the equivalent circle is the one with the smallest perimeter (circumference).
- Of all rectangular prisms with the same volume, the cube is the one with the smallest surface area.
- Of all solids with the same volume, the sphere is the one that has the smallest surface area.

practice 3.1

1 On a sheet of graph paper, draw:

a) three polygons of different shapes that have the same area, but different perimeters

b) three polygons of different shapes that have the same perimeter but different areas

c) three polygons of different shapes that have the same area and the same perimeter

2 Consider rectangle ABCD below.

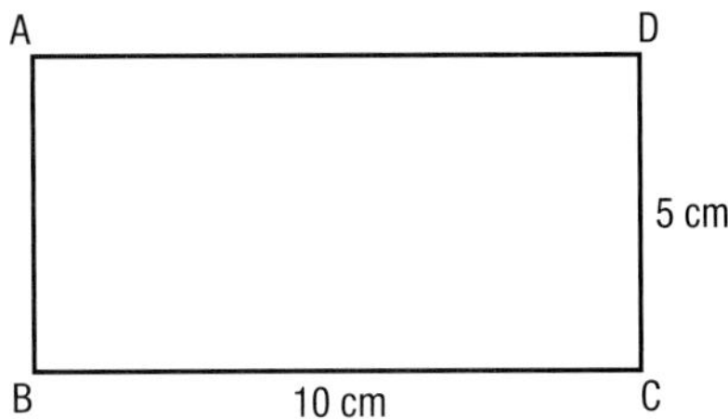

a) Calculate the dimensions of an equilateral triangle, a square and a circle that all have the same perimeter as rectangle ABCD. Are these figures equivalent to rectangle ABCD?

b) Calculate the dimensions of an equilateral triangle, a square and a circle that all have the same area as rectangle ABCD. What can you say about the perimeter of these figures compared to the perimeter of rectangle ABCD?

3 On a sheet of graph paper, following only the horizontal and vertical lines, draw the plane figure that has the smallest possible perimeter for an area of:

a) 20 squared units b) 32 squared units c) 45 squared units d) 121 squared units

4 Minimize the perimeter of each of the figures below while maintaining its area. Show your geometric constructions and your calculations.

a)

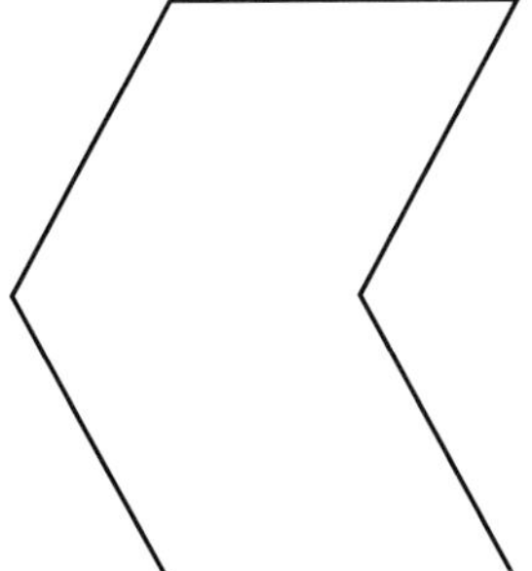

b)

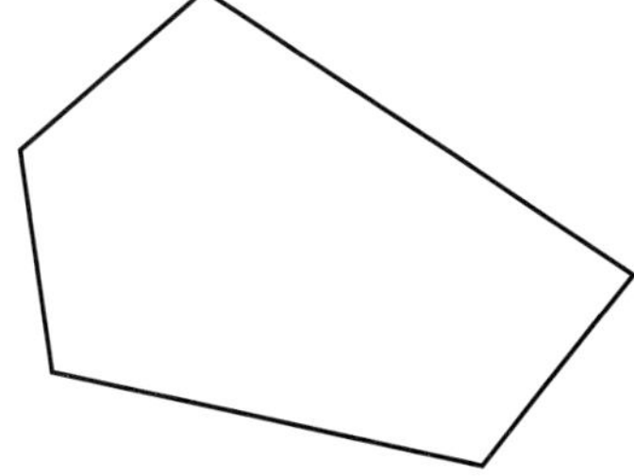

c)

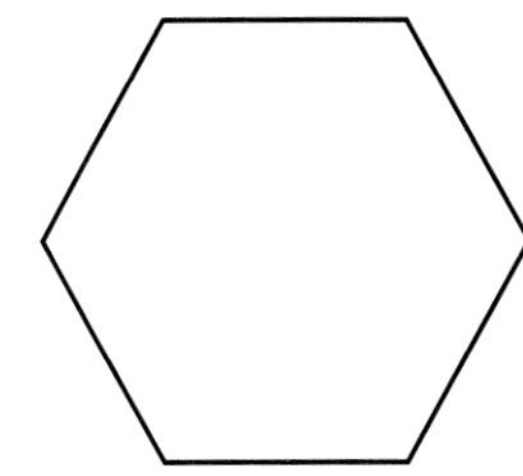

5 The Romans built a monument to honour Archimedes, and on his tomb is a sphere inscribed within a cylinder.

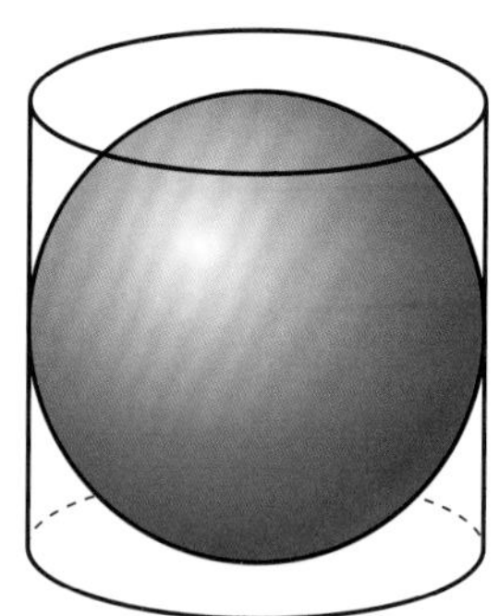

a) Show that the surface area of the sphere is equal to the lateral area of the cylinder.

b) Could this sphere also be inscribed within a cube that is equivalent to the cylinder? Explain your answer.

c) Is the surface area of this sphere equal to the lateral area of the cube that is equivalent to the cylinder? If so, explain your answer. If not, compare the areas.

6 TANGRAM A tangram is a Chinese puzzle made up of seven set shapes with which you can represent different plane figures. The tangram below is composed of the following pieces:

- two large isosceles right triangles
- a medium-sized isosceles right triangle
- two small isosceles right triangles
- a parallelogram
- a square

a) Considering that the smallest perimeter one can obtain on a polygon constructed with these seven pieces is 40 cm, find the area and the perimeter of each piece that is included in this tangram.

b) After removing one of the large isosceles right triangles from the tangram, use the six remaining pieces to construct the polygon that has the smallest possible perimeter. What is the perimeter of this figure?

7 Cement Plus is a company that manufactures custom-made concrete structures. One of its orders is to construct two stacked prisms as shown in the adjacent illustration.

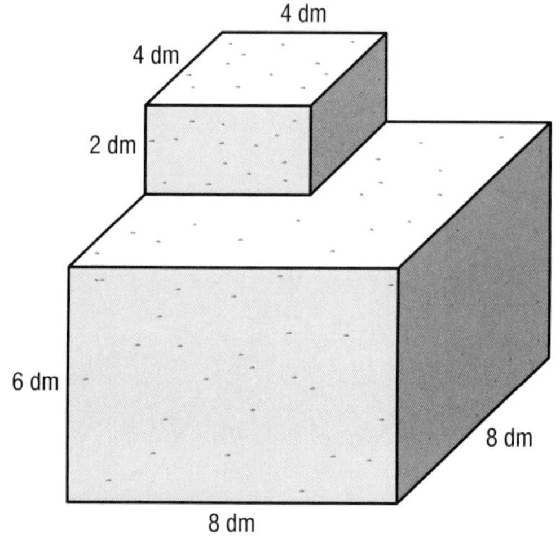

a) Find a simple way to deconstruct a model of this solid so that the resulting pieces can then be assembled to form a single prism with a square base that has an area of 16 dm^2.

b) Compare the area of the newly-created prism with that of the initial solid.

8 Glass blowing is an old technique used to make glass objects. Highly skilled craftsmen can make objects of different shapes (prism, cylinder, sphere, etc...).

a) Determine the possible dimensions of a prism, a cylinder and a sphere, each having a volume of 1200 cm^3. Compare the areas of these solids.

b) Determine the possible dimensions of a prism, a cylinder and a sphere, each having a surface area of 600 cm^2. Compare the volumes of these solids.

9 Copy this figure made of four triangles and three squares onto a sheet of graph paper.

a) Compare the areas of each of the triangles.

b) If the dimensions of the right triangle at the centre of the figure were different, would you come to the same conclusion in **a)**? Formulate a conjecture and find a way to convince your peers of its validity.

c) Does the conjecture formulated in **b)** still hold true if the triangle at the centre of the figure is not a right triangle? Explain your reasoning.

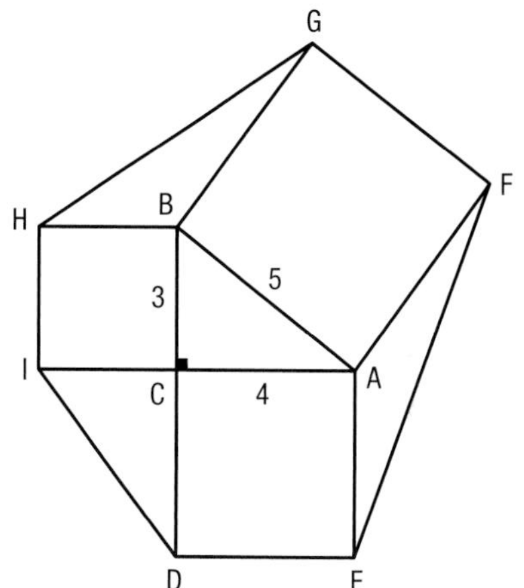

10 Joshua uses the following, five-step geometric reasoning process. In his reasoning the blue rectangle and the red rectangle each have successively transformed into a parallelogram and a square.

1

2
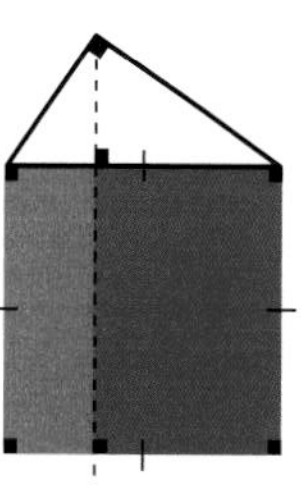

3
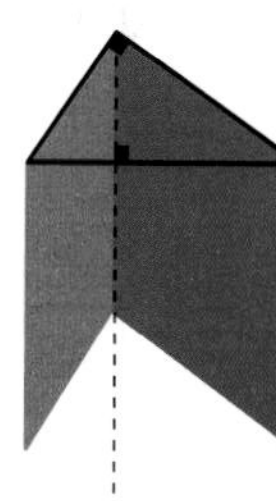

4
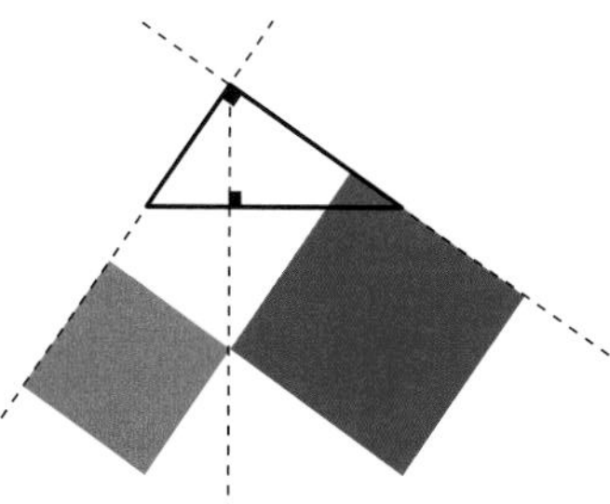

5
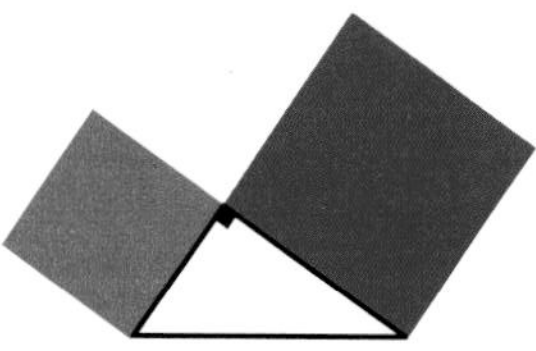

What is he trying to prove? Describe it, explaining each step of his reasoning.

11 Goose feathers and down are used in the making of products such as coats, pillows, comforters, etc. A company specializing in the distribution of feathers and down wants to ship its merchandise in cardboard boxes shaped as rectangular-based prisms. It has a budget of \$0.48 for each box. One square metre of the type of cardboard used in the making of these boxes costs \$0.50.

a) Propose three different models that meet the company's requirements.

b) Among these three models, which one do you consider to be the best? Explain why.

c) Could there be a box shaped as a rectangular-based prism that might be better than the one proposed in **b)**? Explain your answer.

The down that is used in bedding and clothing comes from the underside of waterfowl such as ducks and geese. It grows under a protective layer of feathers. Given how they adapt to extremely cold conditions, Canada's snow geese produce feathers and down of a quality found nowhere else in the world.

12 All the solids shown below have a surface area of 5400 cm^2.

Cube

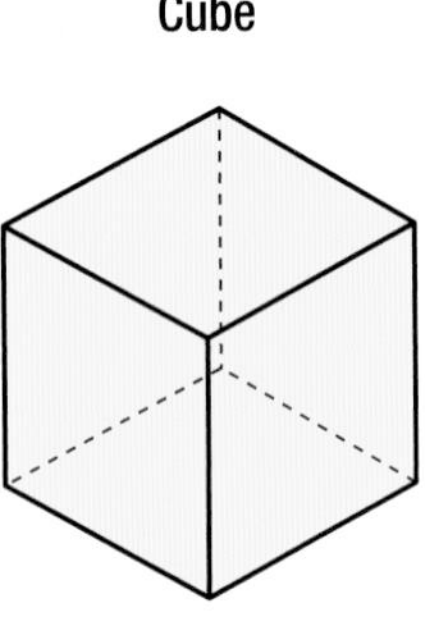

Cone

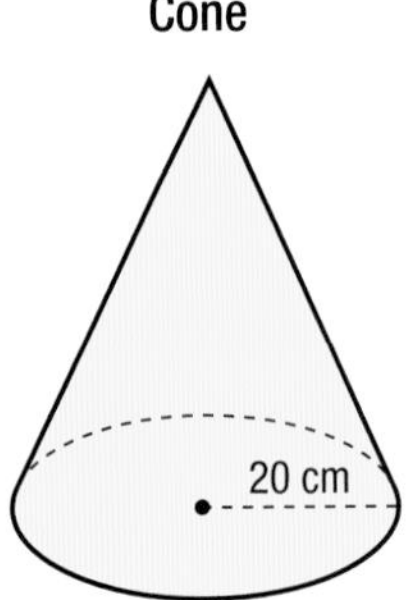

Sphere

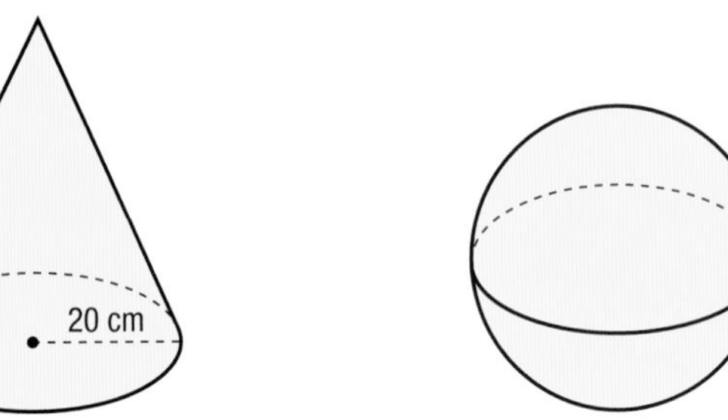

Rectangular-based prism

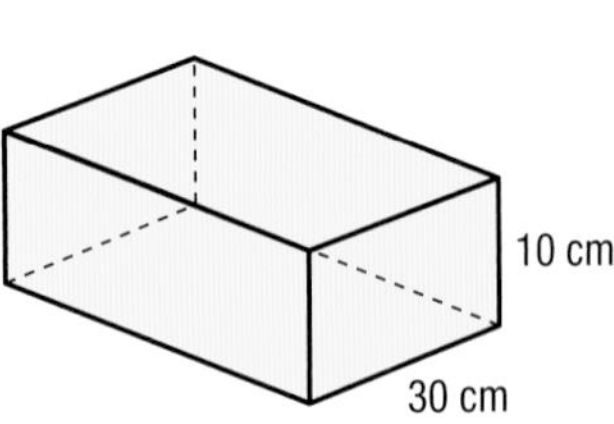

Cylinder

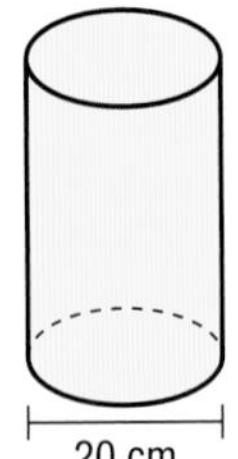

Square-based right pyramid

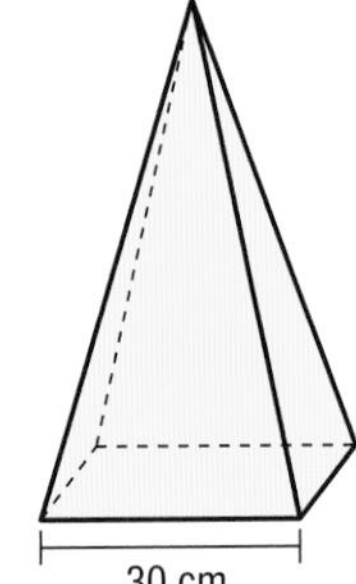

a) Which of these solids has the greatest volume?

b) Could there be another solid with the same surface area that would have a greater volume than the one determined in **a)**? Justify your answer.

13 Your physical education teacher asks you to prepare the soccer field for the next game. One of your tasks is to use lime to draw the boundaries of the rectangular zone of the penalty area at each end of the field.

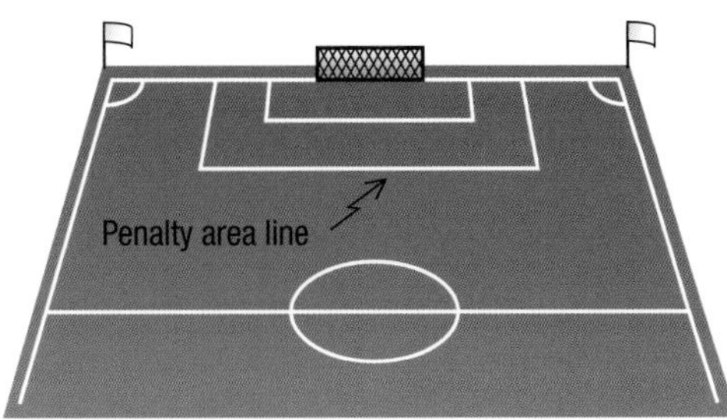

Observing the amount of lime remaining in the field liner's tank, you estimate that you could outline the equivalent of a line that is 120 m long.

a) What should the dimensions be for the penalty area if you want to maximize the area of each?

b) If the penalty areas could be shaped as trapezoids, what should their dimensions be in order to maximize the area of these two penalty areas?

c) What shape should the penalty areas have so that their area would be maximized using the amount of lime available? Explain your answer.

14 In order to reduce the dispersion of canola seeds during a trial cultivation, there is a requirement that no other cultivation take place within a 10 m zone around the perimeter of the trial area. This is called a protective zone and it is prohibited to trespass during the trial cultivation period.

A farmer wants to try the new canola seeds. The farmer allows for a 100 m^2 trial zone. What would be the best shape for the trial zone in order to minimize the area of the prohibited protection zone? Explain your answer.

Canola is a Canadian variety of rapeseed, a plant belonging to the mustard plant family, the seeds of which contain high concentrations of oil. The term *canola* was coined in 1974 from the words *Canada* and *oleaginous* (an adjective used to describe plants containing oil). Though canola was originally produced using traditional methods of hybridization, it is estimated that over half of the canola grown today in Canada is genetically modified.

SECTION 3.2 Equivalent algebraic expressions

This section is related to LES 8.

PROBLEM Retracing the Pythagoreans' footsteps

"All is numbers" was the saying of Pythagoreans. Among these numbers, those that can be represented as regular polygons are particularly favoured by these academics. They extract information from these numbers in order to gain a better understanding of the world around them.

Pythagoras (6th century BCE)

The Pythagoreans were people who shared Pythagoras' beliefs. They lived simply and spent their time studying philosophy, science and mathematics.

The sequence below shows the first six triangular numbers.

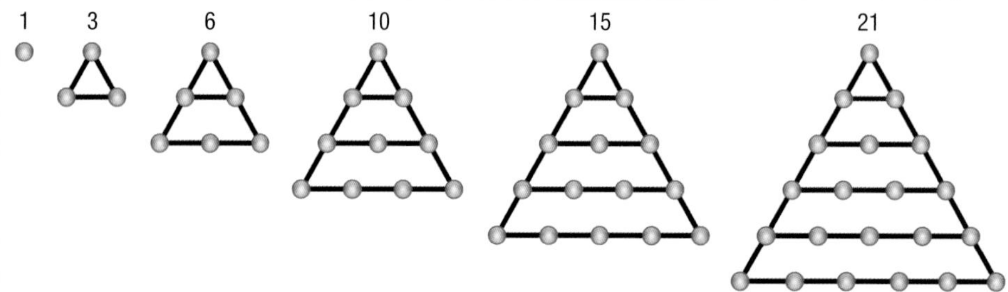

Following are conjectures regarding triangular numbers:

- The sum of two consecutive triangular numbers is a perfect square.
- The octuple of a triangular number increased by 1 is a perfect square.
- The difference of the squares of two consecutive triangular numbers is a cubic number.

In groups, suggest other conjectures to your peers regarding triangular numbers.

Select a conjecture among those presented above or those suggested by the class. Find a way to convince all of the students that this conjecture is undoubtedly true for all triangular numbers, or disprove it with a counter-example.

ACTIVITY 1 Expertise

To become an engineer, it is essential to master algebraic manipulations. What level are you at? Measure your skill by simplifying the following expressions.

Beginner

1. $\dfrac{6x - 2(x + 4)}{4}$

In this first expression, you subtract twice four added to a certain number from 6 times this number, and you divide that result by 4.

2. $(x + y)^2 - y^2 - 3xy$

In this second expression, you square the sum of two numbers, then you subtract the square of the second number and 3 times the product of the two numbers.

Intermediate

3. $(y + 1)^2(y - 1) - (y + 1)(y - 1)^2 - 1$
4. $(x + y - 1)(x - y + 1) + \dfrac{(x - 1)(x + 1)}{1 - x^2}$
5. $\dfrac{(2x + 1)(4x^2 - 2x + 1) - 1}{(4x + 1) - (1 - 4x)}$

Expert

6. $\left(\frac{1}{2}x^2 + x - \frac{3}{2}\right)^2 - \left(\frac{1}{2}x^2 + x - \frac{5}{2}\right)^2$
7. $\dfrac{(x + y)^4 - (x - y)^4}{8xy}$
8. $\dfrac{4x}{\frac{1}{x - 2} - \frac{1}{x + 2}}$

To validate your answers, replace x by 3 and y by 2, and solve the resulting expression. The sum of their values is a perfect square.

ACTIVITY 2 Natural numbers and polynomials

Students at the elementary level answer the following question using division.

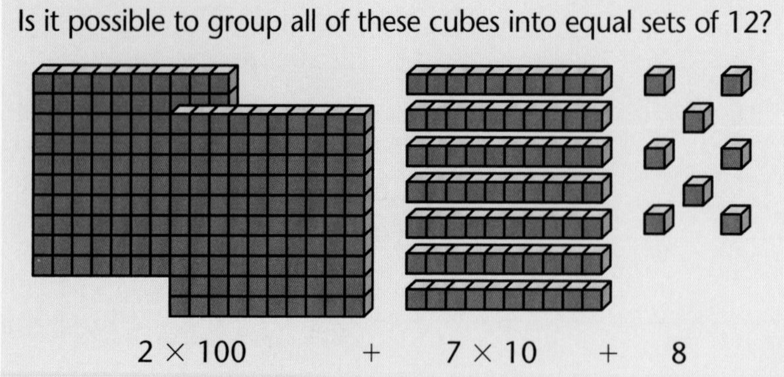

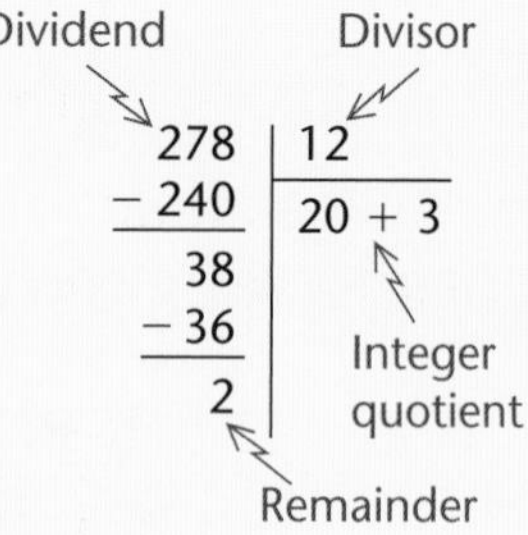

Since the remainder is not 0, the answer is no. The division used is called an "Euclidean division." In this type of division, the result is expressed in the form of an integer quotient and a remainder. This division can also be represented as an equality.

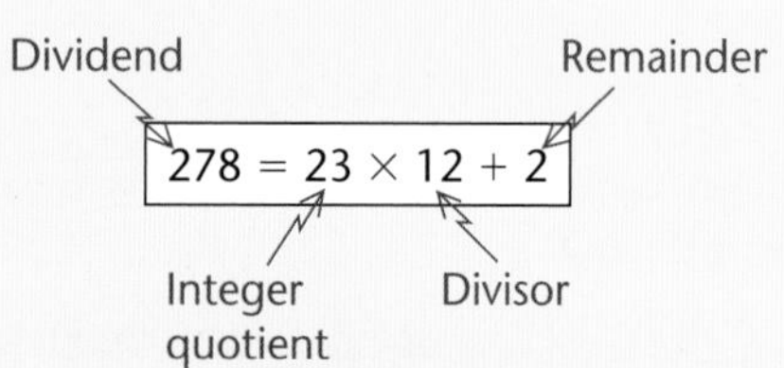

Euclid, a Greek mathematician, showed that the integer quotient and the remainder are unique if one makes sure to obtain a positive remainder that is smaller than the divisor.

Is it possible to establish the same type of equality with polynomials? Consider the following question:

> Could a set containing $(15x^2 + 26x + 10)$ cubes be grouped into sets containing $(3x + 4)$ cubes?

a. Answer this question and explain your reasoning.

b. Using the calculations obtained in **a.**, describe this situation with an equality in the following form:

Dividend — Remainder

$$P(x) = Q(x)D(x) + R(x)$$

Quotient — Divisor

where the degree of $R(x)$ is smaller than the degree of $D(x)$

How could you verify this equality?

c. A polynomial $P(x)$ is said to be divisible by a polynomial $D(x)$ if the remainder $R(x)$ is 0. Which of the following polynomials are divisible by $x - 2$? Justify your answer.

1) $2x^2 - 9x + 8$ 2) $5x^2 + 6x - 8$ 3) $x^3 - 5x^2 + 12$ 4) $x^3 - 2$

ACTIVITY 3 Fractions and rational expressions

Elementary and Cycle One Secondary students learn to manipulate fractions.

Elementary

What irreducible fraction does this diagram represent?

$$\frac{15}{18} = \frac{\cancel{3} \times 5}{\cancel{3} \times 6} = \frac{5}{6}$$

Secondary

Yesterday, Stephanie read one third of a book, and today she read five eighteenths of the same book. What fraction of this book has she read?

$$\frac{1}{3} + \frac{5}{18} = \frac{6}{18} + \frac{5}{18} = \frac{11}{18}$$

a. Answer the two questions below, which reflect the preceding situations. How could you verify your answers?

1) In a set containing $2n^2$ coloured tokens, there are exactly $(n^2 + 2n)$ green tokens. What simplified expression represents the fraction of tokens that are green.

2) On the first day, I read $\frac{1}{n}$ of a book. On the second day, I read $\frac{5}{2n^2}$ of the same book. What rational expression represents the fraction of the book I have read over the two days?

b. The following are two other situations involving rational expressions. In each case, answer the question with a simplified expression, drawing from your knowledge about operations on fractions. Justify the steps in your calculations.

1) In a class, $\frac{n + 2}{2n}$ of the students are boys and $\frac{n}{2n + 4}$ of these boys play football. What fraction of the class represents the amount of boys who play football?

2) A bottle is filled with water to $\frac{n - 2}{n}$ of its capacity; another bottle, at $\frac{2n - 4}{n^2 + 4n}$ of its capacity. What is the simplified ratio of the quantity of water in the first bottle in relation to that of the second bottle?

c. Regardless of the context, are the operations performed in **a.** and **b.** valid no matter what value is assigned to n? Explain your answer.

ACTIVITY 4 Visualizing identities

Four algebraic expressions have been represented through the use of geometry.

A The square of a sum: $(a + b)^2$

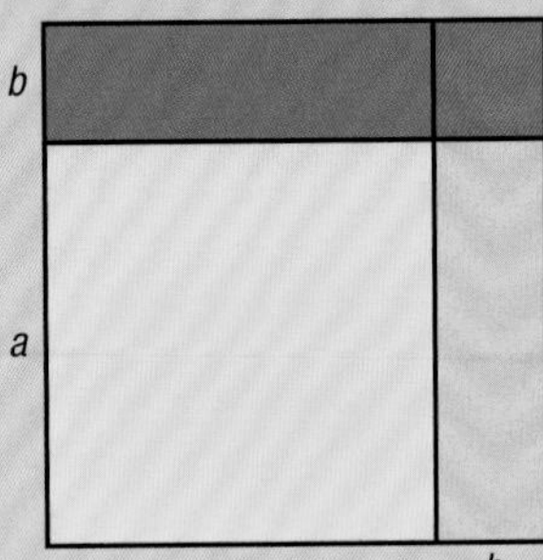

B The cube of a sum: $(a + b)^3$

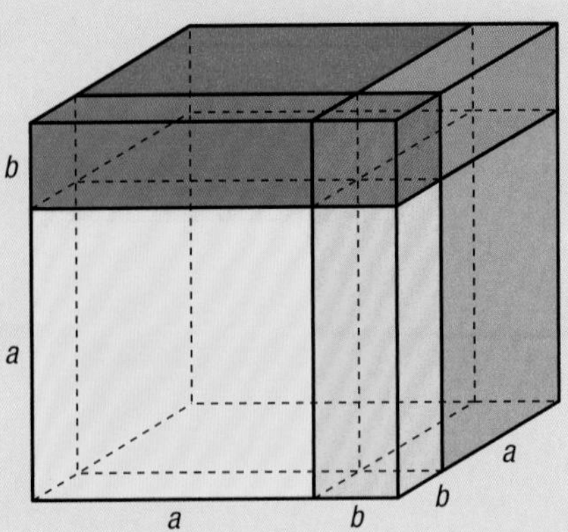

C The difference of two squares: $a^2 - b^2$

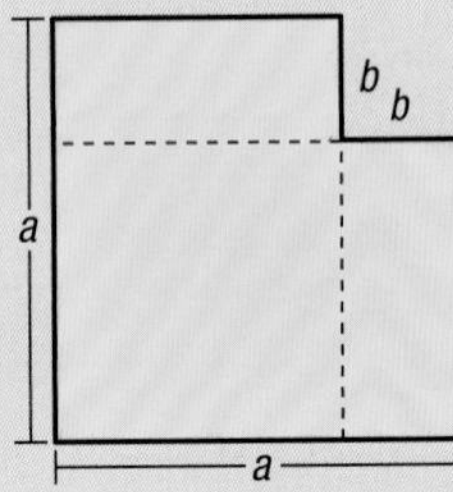

D The difference of two cubes: $a^3 - b^3$

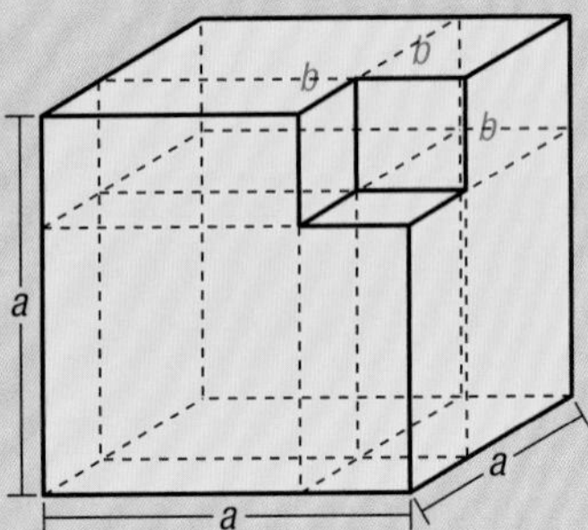

a. In Figures A and B, what expression represent the area of the pieces of the square and the volume of the pieces of the cube?

b. Reorganize the pieces of Figure C to form a rectangle, and the pieces of Figure D to form a prism. What products could represent the area of this rectangle and the volume of this prism?

c. Associate an identity to each of the four figures.

d. Prove these identities algebraically.

An *identity* is an equality that relates two equivalent expressions.

knowledge 3.2

EQUIVALENT ALGEBRAIC EXPRESSIONS

Two algebraic expressions are equivalent if their value is identical for any values assigned to the variables they contain.

Manipulating algebraic expressions

A complex algebraic expression made up of several operations on polynomials can be simplified into an equivalent expression if you respect the order and properties of operations.

E.g. Simplify: $4x(2x) - (x - 3)(3x - 1)$.

This expression contains a subtraction and multiplications of binomials and monomials. You must complete the multiplications before the subtraction.

$4x(2x) - (x - 3)(3x - 1) = 8x^2 - (3x^2 - x - 9x + 3)$ — Apply the distributive principle of multiplication over addition.

$= 8x^2 - (3x^2 - 10x + 3)$ — Subtract $3x^2 - 10x + 3$ from the monomial $8x^2$.

$= 8x^2 - 3x^2 + 10x - 3$

$= 5x^2 + 10x - 3$

Dividing a polynomial by a binomial

To divide a polynomial by a binomial, ensure that the terms of the polynomial and those of the binomial are ordered from the highest to the lowest degree.

E.g. $(5x^2 - 18x + 10) \div (x - 3)$

The division is done in several steps.

In each step, carefully choose the term of the quotient so as to cancel out the highest-degree term in the polynomial to be divided.

It is possible that there is a remainder.

$$\begin{array}{r|l} 5x^2 - 18x + 10 & x - 3 \\ \hline -(5x^2 - 15x) & 5x - 3 \\ -3x + 10 & \\ -(-3x + 9) & \\ \hline 1 & \end{array}$$

Dividend: $5x^2 - 18x + 10$; Divisor: $x - 3$; Quotient: $5x - 3$; Remainder: 1

You can express the solution with an equality relation in the form of $P(x) = Q(x)D(x) + R(x)$.

E.g. $\underbrace{5x^2 - 18x + 10}_{\text{Dividend}} = \underbrace{(5x - 3)}_{\text{Quotient}}\underbrace{(x - 3)}_{\text{Divisor}} + \underbrace{1}_{\text{Remainder}}$

Dividing by $x - 3$ on each side of the equality, you can also write:

$$\frac{5x^2 - 18x + 10}{x - 3} = 5x - 3 + \frac{1}{x - 3}$$

Equivalent rational expressions

A **rational expression** is an expression that can be written as the quotient of two polynomials. A rational expression is well-defined when the divisor is not equal to 0.

E.g. $\frac{1}{x}$, $\frac{3x + 1}{x - 1}$ and $\frac{x + y}{2}$ are rational expressions.

The expression $\frac{1}{x}$ only makes sense if $x \neq 0$. In the same way, $\frac{3x + 1}{x - 1}$ only makes sense if $x \neq 1$.

You can generate equivalent rational expressions by multiplying the numerator and the denominator of an expression by the same quantity other than zero.

E.g. $\frac{1}{x} = \frac{2x}{2x^2} = \frac{2ax}{2ax^2} = \frac{2ax(x + 2)}{2ax^2(x + 2)}$. These equalities are true if $x \neq 0$, $x \neq -2$ and $a \neq 0$.

It is possible to simplify a rational expression if the numerator and the denominator have a common factor. You only need to divide the numerator and the denominator by this common factor, presuming it does not equal 0.

E.g. $\frac{2x + 4}{x^2 + 2x} = \frac{2\cancel{(x + 2)}}{x\cancel{(x + 2)}} = \frac{2}{x}$ These expressions are equivalent as long as they are well-defined, that is, for all the real values of x, except $x = 0$ and $x = -2$.

Operations on rational expressions

To perform operations on rational expressions, apply the same rules as those used for operations on numbers represented in fraction form.

1. Addition or subtraction
   - Using equivalent rational expressions, make sure that all the terms have the same denominator.
   - Add or subtract the numerators while leaving the denominator as is.

E.g. $\frac{2}{x} + \frac{1}{xy} = \frac{2y}{xy} + \frac{1}{xy}$
$= \frac{2y + 1}{xy}$

2. Multiplication
   - Multiply the numerators by each other and the denominators by each other; reduce if possible.

E.g. $\left(\frac{x}{x + 1}\right)\left(\frac{x^2 + x}{2}\right) = \frac{x(x^2 + x)}{2(x + 1)} = \frac{x^2\cancel{(x + 1)}}{2\cancel{(x + 1)}} = \frac{x^2}{2}$

3. Division
   - Dividing by a rational expression results in multiplying by the reciprocal of this expression.

E.g. $\left(\frac{2}{x}\right) \div \left(\frac{x + 1}{2x}\right) = \left(\frac{2}{x}\right)\left(\frac{2x}{x + 1}\right) = \frac{4\cancel{x}}{\cancel{x}(x + 1)} = \frac{4}{x + 1}$

Remarkable algebraic identities

An identity is an equality that relates two equivalent expressions. Some identities have remarkable features that are worth noting.

The square of a binomial

$$(a + b)^2 = a^2 + 2ab + b^2$$
$$(a - b)^2 = a^2 - 2ab + b^2$$

The difference of squares

$$a^2 - b^2 = (a + b)(a - b)$$

Identities can serve different purposes:

- to speed up calculations

E.g. $(3x - 5)^2 = 9x^2 - 30x + 25$

This term is the square of $3x$.

This term is double the product of $3x$ and $^-5$.

This term is the square of $^-5$.

- to factor a polynomial

E.g. Factor $25x^2 - 16$

Recognize the difference of squares:

- $25x^2$ is the square of $5x$.
- 16 is the square of 4.

Therefore $25x^2 - 16 = (5x + 4)(5x - 4)$.

There are also identities for expressions having degrees greater than 2.

E.g. $(a + b)^3 = a^3 + 3a^2b + 3ab^2 + b^3$

ALGEBRAIC DEMONSTRATION

Some properties of natural numbers can be demonstrated through the use of algebra.

E.g. Demonstrate that the difference between the squares of two consecutive odd numbers is always a multiple of 8.

An odd number can be represented as $2n + 1$, where $n \in \mathbb{N}$.
The odd number that follows is $2n + 3$, that is $(2n + 1) + 2$.

The difference of squares of these numbers is $(2n + 3)^2 - (2n + 1)^2$.

You can simplify the expression as follows:

$$\begin{aligned}&(2n + 3)^2 - (2n + 1)^2\\ &(4n^2 + 12n + 9) - (4n^2 + 4n + 1)\\ &= 4n^2 + 12n + 9 - 4n^2 - 4n - 1\\ &= 8n + 8\\ &= 8(n + 1)\end{aligned}$$

Since $n + 1$ is a natural number, then $8(n + 1)$ is indeed a multiple of 8.

For example:
$11^2 = 121$ and $13^2 = 169$.
$169 - 121$ equals 48 which is a multiple of 8.

practice 3.2

1 Perform the following operations mentally.

a) $(x + 5)(3x - 2)$ b) $(2x + 3)(3x + 1)$ c) $(5x + 4)(5x - 4)$

d) $(3x - 4)(4x - 3)$ e) $(3x + 5)^2$ f) $(5x - 2)^2$

2 Perform the multiplications below. Check your answers considering that all the expressions obtained must have the same values when $x = 5$ and $y = 2$.

a) $(2x - y)(x + 2y)$ b) $(2x - 3y)(4x - y)$ c) $(x - 7y)(y - 2x)$

d) $(10x - 13y)(x - y)$ e) $(5x - 12y)(10x + 11y)$ f) $2\left(x + \frac{1}{2}y\right)^2$

3 Perform the following multiplications.

a) $(x + 3)(x^2 - 5x + 2)$ b) $(3x - 4)(4x^2 - 3x + 1)$ c) $(x^2 - 2x - 1)(x + 1)$

d) $(2x^2 + 5x + 1)(2 - 3x)$ e) $(x + y)(x + 2y + 3)$ f) $(x - 2y)(4x + 3y - 5)$

4 Determine the simplified algebraic expression that represents the area of each of the figures below.

a) 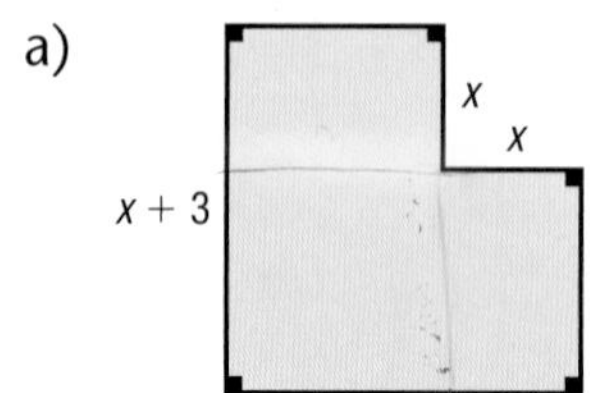

b) 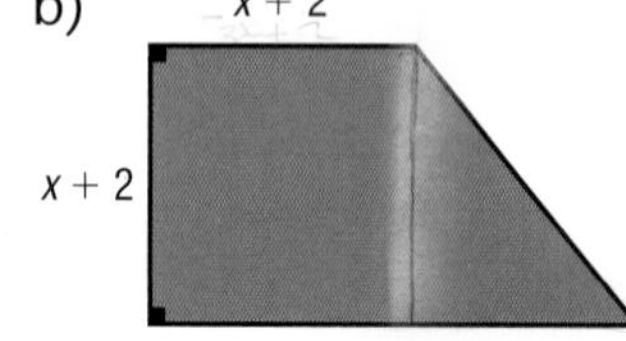

c) 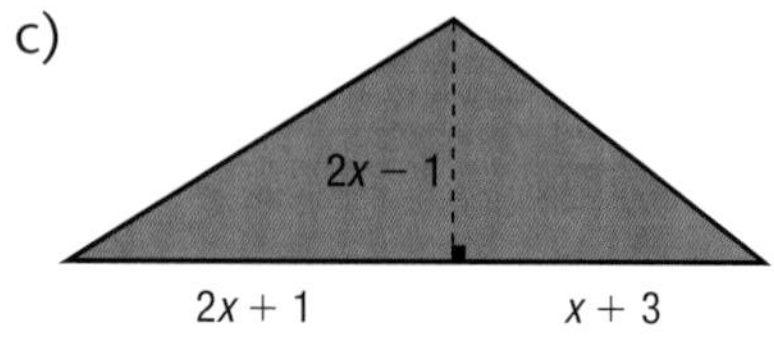

5 The associative property for multiplication allows you to use different ways of regrouping factors in a chain of multiplications without changing the result.

a) Verify this property by simplifying the expression $(2x + 3)(3x + 1)(x - 4)$ in two different ways:

1) Calculate the product of the first two binomials and multiply the result by $(x - 4)$.

2) Calculate the product of the last two binomials and multiply the result by $(2x + 3)$.

b) Simplify the expression $(x + 3)^2(x - 3)$. Check your answer by performing this calculation in a different way.

6 As Claudia was looking at a calendar, she noticed that no matter which four day square she chose, the product of the smaller and the larger numbers was always 7 less than the product of the two other numbers. For example, 2 x 10 equals 7 less than 3 x 9. In the same way, 21 x 29 equals 609, which is 7 less than 22 x 28, that is, 616.

Demonstrate that this is true, no matter which page of the calendar is chosen.

Sunday	Monday	Tuesday	Wednesday	Thursday	Friday	Saturday
		1	2	3	4	5
6	7	8	9	10	11	12
13	14	15	16	17	18	19
20	21	22	23	24	25	26
27	28	29	30	31		

7 Perform the following divisions.

a) $(16x^2 - 8x - 3) \div (4x + 1)$
b) $(10x^2 - 23x + 12) \div (2x - 3)$
c) $(x^3 + x^2 + x + 1) \div (x + 1)$
d) $(2x^3 - 3x^2 + 5x - 14) \div (x - 2)$
e) $(x^3 - 4x + 15) \div (x + 3)$
f) $(8x^3 + 1) \div (2x + 1)$

8 Remarkable algebraic identities can be useful when performing certain calculations. Mentally calculate the results of the operations below. Explain your process.

a) 19×21
b) 76×84
c) 49^2
d) 31^2
e) $20^2 - 18^2$
f) $35^2 - 5^2$
g) $\left(3\frac{1}{3}\right)^2$
h) $\left(5\frac{1}{4}\right)^2 - \left(4\frac{3}{4}\right)^2$

9 Which of the following expressions results in a rational number?

a) $(3 + \sqrt{2})(3 - \sqrt{2})$
b) $(3 + \sqrt{2})^2$
c) $(2 - \sqrt{3})(2 + \sqrt{3})$
d) $(2 - \sqrt{3})^2$
e) $(\sqrt{5} + 3)(5 - \sqrt{3})$
f) $(\sqrt{5} - \sqrt{2})(\sqrt{2} + \sqrt{5})$

10 Of the following polynomials, which are equivalent to the square of a binomial? Justify your answer.

$x^2 - x + 1$ $4y^2 + 20y + 25$ $4a^2 - 4ab + b^2$ $16x^2 + 25x + 9$

11 Factor the algebraic expressions below.

a) $4x^2 - 9$
b) $4x^2 - 8x$
c) $4x^2 - 4x + 1$
d) $x^2 - 6x + 9$
e) $x^2 - 6$
f) $x^2 - x + \frac{1}{4}$
g) $2x^2 + 16xy + 16y^2$
h) $9x^2 - (2x - 1)^2$
i) $(2x + 3)^2 - (x + 1)^2$

12 Simplify the following expressions.

a) $2x(x - 3)(x + 3)$

b) $(x + 3)^2 - (x + 1)^2$

c) $4x(5x - 1) + (2x + 1)^2$

d) $(x - 1)(x - 3) - (x - 2)^2$

e) $(x + 4)(x^2 - 2x + 2)$

f) $(3x + 2)^3$

g) $4x^2(1 - 2x) - 2x(1 - 4x)^2$

h) $(x + 1)(x + 2)(x + 3)$

13 Simplify the following expressions.

a) $\dfrac{(x + 1)^2 - (x + 1)(x - 1)}{2}$

b) $\dfrac{(x + 4)^2 - (x - 4)^2}{4x}$

c) $\dfrac{1 + (2x + 1)(2x - 1)}{(x + 2) - (x - 2)}$

d) $\dfrac{2(3x - 2) + 6(1 - x)}{(x - 1)^2 - (x^2 + 1)}$

e) $\dfrac{(2x + 3)(2x - 3) - 3(4x - 3)}{(2x + 3)^2 - 3(4x + 3)}$

f) $\dfrac{x^2 - 2x(x + 2) + (x + 2)^2}{(x + 1)^2 - 2(x + 1)(x + 2) + (x + 2)^2}$

14 All of the steps of the concrete stairs represented in the adjacent drawing are identical. The variable x represents the depth of each step in centimetres. The width and height are expressed in relation to this depth.

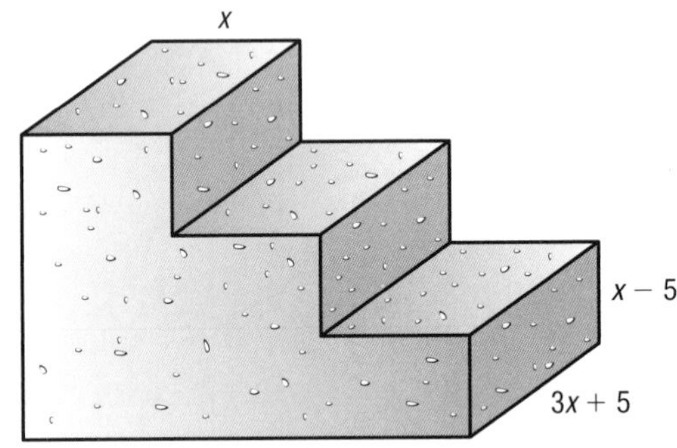

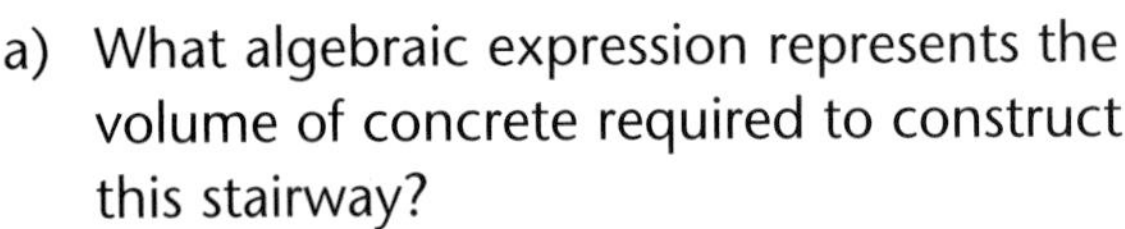

a) What algebraic expression represents the volume of concrete required to construct this stairway?

b) By how many times would the volume increase if the stairway had six steps instead of three?

15 Metal nuts are coated with a thin layer of zinc to protect them from rust. What algebraic expression represents the surface to be protected if the nut is constructed in the shape of a regular hexagon?

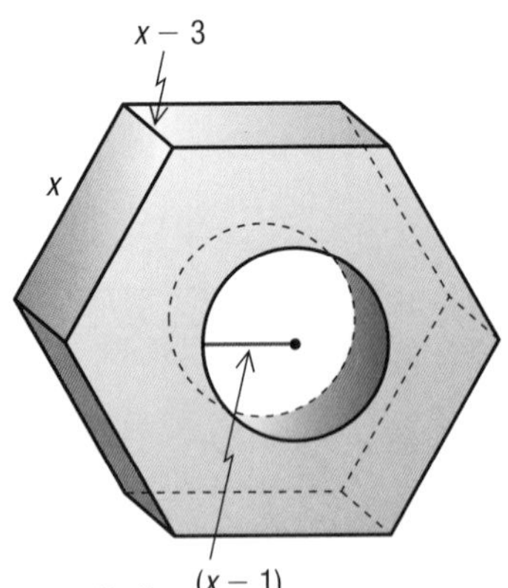

Zinc coating refers to the process of forming a zinc coating on a given surface. Galvinization is a metallurgical process that consists of coating ferrous metals (iron, steel or cast iron) in zinc by immersing them in molten zinc.

16 Below are four rational expressions:

① $\dfrac{x^2 - 1}{x^2 - x}$ ② $\dfrac{x^2 - 4x + 4}{x^2 - 4}$ ③ $\dfrac{4x^2 - 1}{4x^2 + 2x}$ ④ $\dfrac{x^2 - y^2}{x^2 + 2xy + y^2}$

a) What is the value of each of these expressions if $x = 10$ and $y = 5$?

b) What values of x and y would make these expressions undefined?

c) Simplify these expressions.

17 **THE AKHMIM PAPYRUS** The following principle was found on a papyrus discovered in the Nile valley in Akhmim, Egypt. Translated in modern terms, this property reads as follows:

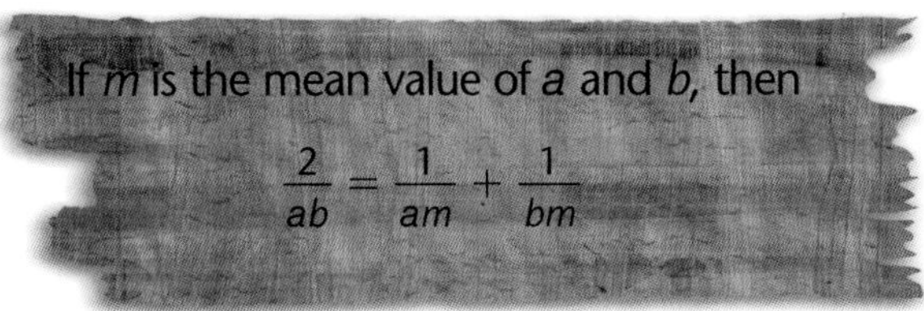

a) Verify this property by substituting values for a and b.

b) Prove this property.

Excerpt from the mathematics papyrus discovered in Akhmim. This papyrus, written in Greek, is said to date back to a period before the 5th century BCE.

18 Perform the operations below and simplify.

a) $\left(\dfrac{x^2 + x}{x^2 - x}\right)\left(\dfrac{x - 1}{x + 1}\right)$

b) $\left(\dfrac{x^2 - 1}{x}\right) \div \left(\dfrac{x + 1}{x^2}\right)$

c) $\dfrac{1}{x} + \dfrac{1}{x^2 - x}$

d) $\dfrac{1}{x^2 + x} + \dfrac{x - 1}{x}$

e) $\dfrac{1}{x} - \dfrac{1}{x + 1}$

f) $\dfrac{x}{x + 1} - \dfrac{x - 1}{x}$

19 Is the triangle shown below a right triangle? Justify your answer.

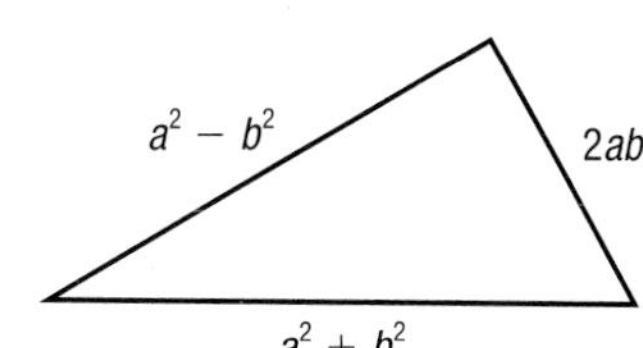

20 The box-shaped device shown in the adjacent illustration is used to measure the electrical insulating capacity of different liquids. After you fill the device with liquid, you connect a power source to the ends of each of the plates, and you gradually increase the difference in potential until there is a flow of current.

Represent the total volume of this device with a simple algebraic expression.

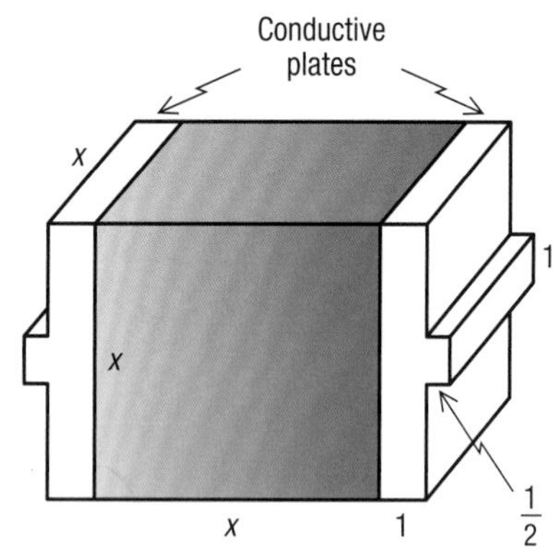

21 Perform the following operations.

a) $(2x - 3)(4x^2 + 6x + 9)$ b) $(x + 4)(x^2 - 4x + 16)$ c) $(3x + 2)^3$

d) $(4x - 3)^3$ e) $(2x - 1)(2x + 1)^2$ f) $(2x - 1)^2(2x + 1)$

22 Each of the divisions below has a remainder. Perform these divisions, then write the result in the form of an equality.

a) $(x^2 + 10x + 26) \div (x + 5)$ b) $(^-8x^3 + 3x + 6) \div (x - 1)$

c) $(2x^2 + 8x + 4) \div (2x + 2)$ d) $(4x^2 - 5x + 1) \div (2x + 1)$

e) $(x^3 - x + 1) \div (x + 2)$ f) $(x^2 - 3x^3 + 1) \div (3x - 1)$

23 A sheet of plywood is twice as long as it is wide. A carpenter cuts out a rectangle of which the length is also double that of the width. The carpenter is then left with an L-shaped piece.

Represent the area of this piece as a product of factors.

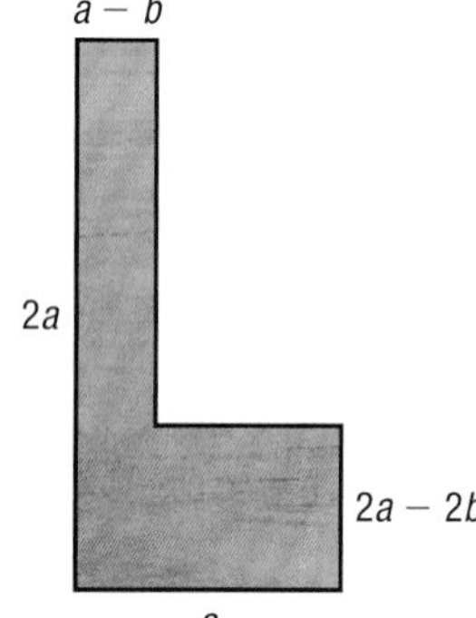

24 In the context of a competition to choose a logo for Car Free Day, Samuel submitted the drawing shown in the adjacent diagram. The vertices of the orange square are the midpoints of the sides of the blue square. The road is represented by a triangle. He used the variable c to represent an extension of the orange square and to create perspective. Express the area of the road with variables a and c.

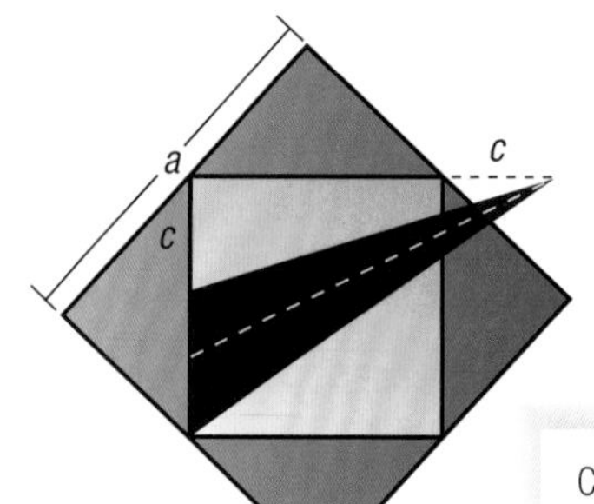

Car Free Day resulted from a 1996 European initiative. This event now takes place every year, usually on September 22, in nearly 1500 cities around the world.

25 **PRESSURE** In 1654, Otton von Guericke used the Magdeburg hemispheres to show the pressure exerted by air.

Using an algebraic expression, express the volume of brass required for the construction of the empty sphere if the measure of its external radius is 60 cm and its thickness is x cm.

Otton von Guericke (1602-1686)

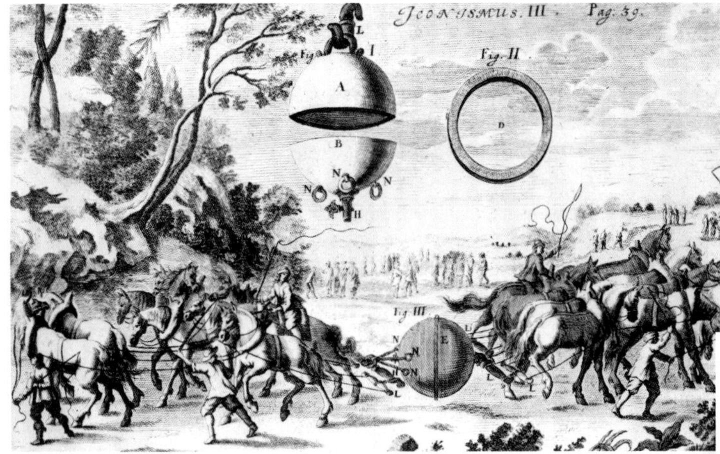

It is said that once a vacuum was created between the two hemispheres, it took two teams of eight horses to successfully separate them.

26 You can determine the distance covered by a moving object by calculating the area under the curve representing the relationship between the speed of an object and time.

The adjacent graph represents a moving object exhibiting constant acceleration. Determine the simplest expression to represent the distance covered between t and nt seconds.

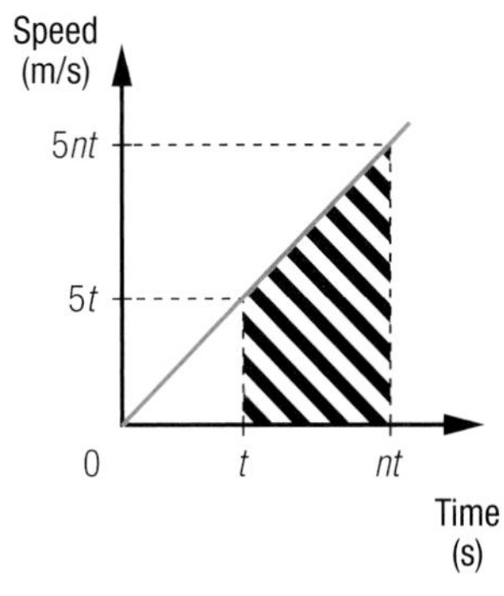

27 Below are some questions based on an admission test for an engineering school. These questions are meant to test the applicants' ability to manipulate algebraic expressions. Would you be able to answer them?

a) Simplify the following expression: $\dfrac{\dfrac{a^4 + ab^3}{ab + b^2}}{\dfrac{a^4 - a^3b + a^2b^2}{a^2 + ab}}$.

b) Consider polynomial $P(x) = 3x^2 + (a - 5)x + (a + 5)$. Determine the value of parameter **a** so that the remainder resulting from the division of $P(x)$ by $(x - 1)$ is 5.

c) Calculate the coefficient of the constant term in the solution of $\left(2x^2 - \frac{4}{x}\right)^3$.

d) For which value of x will the expression $\dfrac{-12x^2 + 192x - 768}{(x - 11)^2 - (x - 5)^2}$ equal 16?

28 In the identity associated with the square of a sum, if b is replaced with $-b$, you get the identity associated with the square of the difference.

> The square of a sum:
>
> $$(a + b)^2 = a^2 + 2ab + b^2$$
>
> Replace b with $-b$:
>
> $$(a + (-b))^2 = a^2 + 2a(-b) + (-b)^2$$
>
> After simplification:
>
> $$(a - b)^2 = a^2 - 2ab + b^2$$

a) Considering that $(a + b)^3 = a^3 + 3a^2b + 3ab^2 + b^3$, determine an identity regarding the cube of a difference, that is $(a - b)^3$.

b) Considering that $a^3 - b^3 = (a - b)(a^2 + 2ab + b^2)$, determine an identity regarding the sum of two cubes, that is $a^3 + b^3$.

c) Considering that $a^2 - b^2 = (a - b)(a + b)$, is it possible to express $a^2 + b^2$ as a product of two binomials? Justify your answer.

29 Consider these conjectures suggested by students concerning odd numbers:

One less than the square of an odd number is always divisible by four.

If you add one to the product of two consecutive odd numbers, you get a perfect square.

A prime number that divides the difference of two odd numbers also divides their sum.

Are these conjectures true or false? In each case, justify your answer with appropriate arguments.

30 Rosalie thinks that the remainder of the division of a polynomial by $(x - 1)$ is always equal to the sum of the coefficients of the polynomial. For example, the remainder of the division of polynomial $x^2 - 3x + 6$ by $(x - 1)$ is 4, and the sum of coefficients 1, -3 and 6 of this polynomial equals 4. But, is this true for all polynomials?

a) Is Rosalie's conjecture true or false? Justify your answer.

b) When you divide a polynomial $P(x)$ by a binomial in the form of $(x - a)$, where parameter **a** is any number, how can you predict the remainder without performing the division? Formulate a conjecture on this subject.

31 Physics uses different relations to account for the motion of objects. The following equations are valid for all objects that are uniformly accelerated.

$$d = s_m \cdot t \qquad s_m = \frac{s_i + s_f}{2} \qquad a = \frac{s_f - s_i}{t}$$

In these equations, d represents the distance covered, s_m, s_i and s_f are respectively the mean, initial, and final speeds, t is the time elapsed, and a is the acceleration.

Deduce a simple formula relating initial speed and final speed to distance and acceleration.

32 The diagram below shows an experiment in which the image of a candle is made to appear on a card through the use of a thin lens. The location where the card must be placed so that the image is perfectly clear depends on the focal length f of the lens and the distance p separating the lens from the candle.

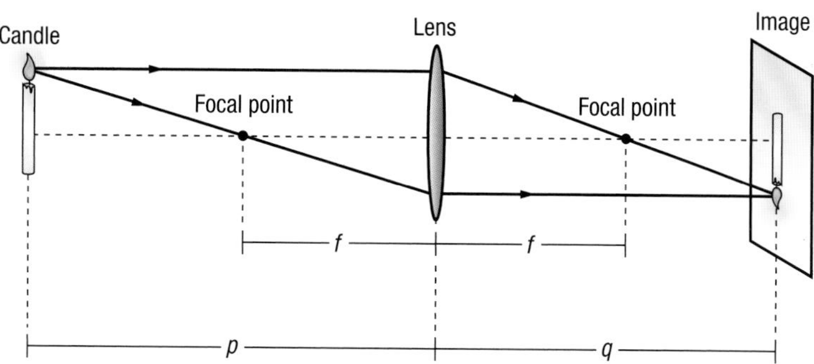

The experiment shows that the image is clear when $\frac{1}{f} = \frac{1}{p} + \frac{1}{q}$.

a) Express the value of q as a function of p, if the focal length is 4 cm. Then determine the expression that represents the distance between the image and the closest focal point, that is $(q - f)$.

b) Show that $f^2 = (p - f)(q - f)$.

33 As she calculated the square of a trinomial, Valerie discovered a new algebraic identity.

a) Complete the equality below to learn about the identity that Valerie discovered.

$(a + b + c)^2 = \square + \square + \square + \square + \square + \square$

b) Prove this identity using an appropriate geometric figure.

c) Use this identity to mentally perform the following calculations.

1) $(2x + 3y + 5)^2$ 2) $(3x - y + 2)^2$ 3) $(x^2 - x - 1)^2$

SECTION 3.3 Factoring and solving equations

This section is related to LES 9.

PROBLEM Beautiful structures!

Triangles are often found in the structures of bridges, pylons and other works designed by civil engineers. This is because triangle-based structures, unlike those formed with other polygons, are shape-retaining.

The following are diagrams of three structures in the form of trapezoids:

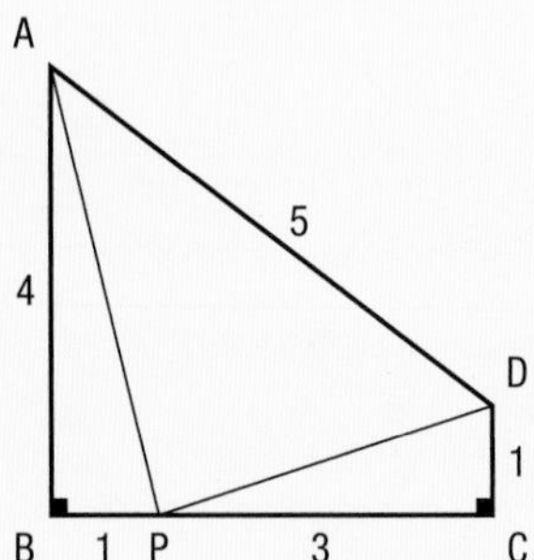

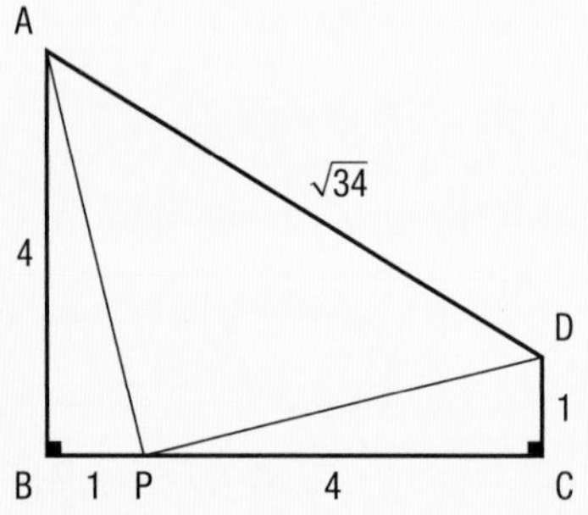

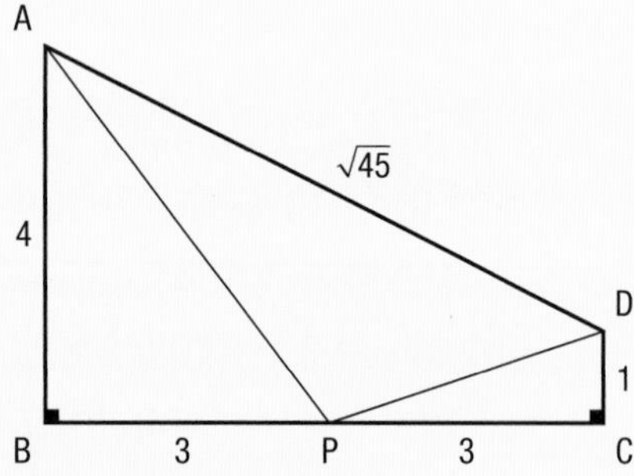

As shown in the diagrams above, vertices A and D are linked to a point P in order to solidify the structures. However, for practical and aesthetic reasons, an engineer decides to displace point P so that the triangle APD is a right triangle with the right angle located at P. In order to solve this problem algebraically, the engineer lets x represent the length of the displacement of point P towards the right.

Look at each structure; for what distance and in what direction can you displace point P so that angle APD is a right angle?

ACTIVITY 1 Two types of intelligence

Alice and Alan have different ways of grasping new mathematical concepts. In algebra, Alice fully understands when she can simplify everything using the properties of operations while Alan prefers to find links to geometry. As an example the following is how they calculate the product $(a + b)(c + d)$.

$$(a + b)(c + d) = a(\square + \square) + \square(\square + \square)$$
$$= \square + \square + \square + \square$$

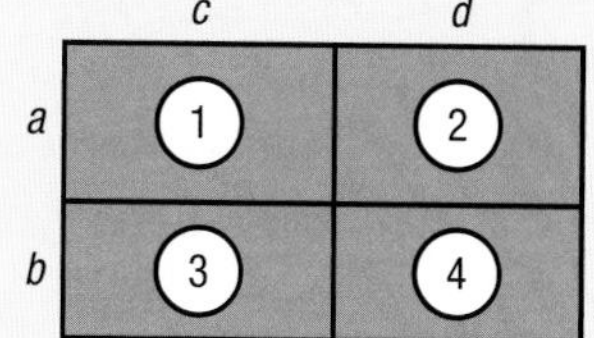

a. Complete the reasoning initiated by each of them.

b. Alan has noticed symmetry in his diagram. What could he have observed?

Intelligence can be defined as the capacity to solve problems and to adapt to new situations. Cognitive science specialists believe that intelligence has multiple forms and that each individual has abilities based on several types of intelligence. For example, to solve the problem described above, Alan prefers an approach that is associated with visual-spatial cognition as much as with logical-mathematical intelligence.

It is possible to factor certain polynomials with four terms.

c. Choose one of the two methods described above and, going backwards, decompose the following polynomial into factors.

$$36a^2x + 48abx + 15ab + 20b^2$$

Alice and Alan have challenged each other to factor a polynomial that each of them has created.

Alice's challenge: $10ab - 15b - 2a + 3$ Alan's challenge: $6x^2 + 12y + 9xy + 8x$

d. Take both of these challenges.

e. Challenge one of your peers by proposing that he or she factors a polynomial with four terms that you have verified to be decomposable into factors.

ACTIVITY 2 The garden in the Abbey

Some problems, like the one below, can be translated into an equation in the form of $ax^2 + bx + c = 0$.

Within the inner courtyard of an abbey, there is a rectangular garden whose length is four times longer than its width. It is bordered by a path that is one metre wide. The garden and the path together cover an area of 130 m². What are the dimensions of the garden?

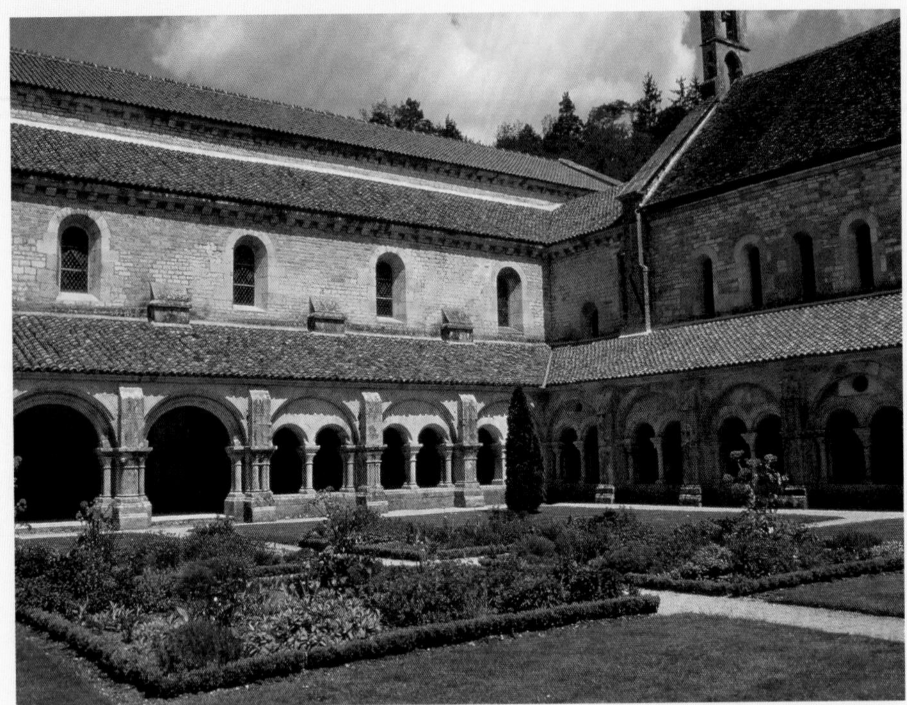

a. If x represents the width of the garden (in m), show that $2x^2 + 5x - 63 = 0$ can represent this situation.

It is possible to solve this equation by decomposing the polynomial $2x^2 + 5x - 63$ into factors.

b. Find a method that can be used to factor the polynomial and determine the dimensions of the garden. Compare your approach to that of your peers.

c. What would the dimensions of the garden be if the surface covered by the garden and the path were 180 m² instead of 130 m²?

d. If the length of the garden were 7 m more than its width, and if the garden covered the same surface as the path, what would be the dimensions of the garden?

ACTIVITY 3 Al-Khawarizmi's algorithm

During the early 9th century, an Arab mathematician named Muhamed Ibn Mussa Al-Khawarizmi wrote a treatise in which he explained the way to solve a second-degree equation. His algorithm can be applied to any equation of this type. Following is how he states the problem:

An algorithm is a sequence of operations that must be systematically performed in order to solve a problem. The word *algorithm* is in fact derived from Al-Khawarizmi's name.

« A square and ten roots equal 39 dirhams. »

The dirham is an ancient Arab, Turk and Persian measure of weight. Today, it is the monetary unit used in Morocco.

Using today's algebraic notation, this translates into the equation $x^2 + 10x = 39$.

To solve this equation, Al-Khawarizmi constructed the adjacent figure. First, he drew the grey square, with sides measuring x. He then separated the term $10x$ into two parts which he represented with the white rectangles. Based on the equation, the total area of this figure equals 39.

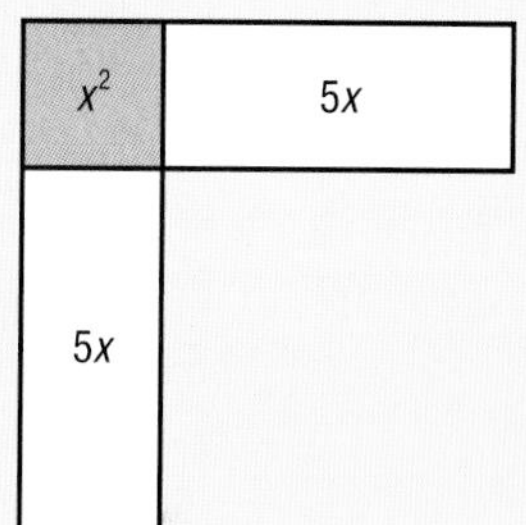

a. Copy this figure and, as suggested by Al-Khawarizmi, complete it to form a square. What is the area of the part you added? What is the total area of the square obtained? Calculate the value of x.

b. Al-Khawarizmi accounted for the positive solutions. What is the negative solution to this equation?

c. It is possible to represent this algorithm with a sequence of equivalent equations as illustrated below. Complete these equations, explaining each step:

$$x^2 + 10x + \_\_\_ = 39 + \_\_\_$$
$$(\_\_\_ + \_\_\_)^2 = \_\_\_$$
$$\_\_\_ = \_\_\_ \text{ or } \_\_\_ = \_\_\_$$
$$x = \_\_\_ \text{ or } x = \_\_\_$$

d. Use the same approach to solve the equation $x^2 + 8x = 4$.

e. Transform the equation $2x^2 - 12x + 10 = 0$ into an equivalent equation by following the steps described in **c.**, and solve the resulting equation.

knowledge 3.3

DECOMPOSING INTO FACTORS

Following are a few strategies that make it possible to decompose polynomials into factors.

Grouping

Certain polynomials with four terms can be decomposed into factors by **grouping**, proceed as follows:

1. Group the terms into groups of two and remove the common factor in each group.
2. Factor the identical binomial appearing in the two new terms.

E.g. $6xy + 3x - 8y - 4$

$3x(2y + 1) - 4(2y + 1)$

$(3x - 4)(2y + 1)$

You can decompose a polynomial using this method if the product of the first and fourth terms equals the product of the second and third terms.

Factoring a trinomial of the form $ax^2 + bx + c$

- A first strategy for factoring a polynomial in the form of $ax^2 + bx + c$ consists of changing it into a polynomial with four terms equivalent to the original expression and decomposable by grouping. In order to do this, you split the term bx into a sum of two terms $mx + nx$ so that the product of these two terms equals the product of ax^2 and c.

Essentially, this amounts to finding two numbers m and n, the product of which is equal to **ac** and the sum of which is equal to **b**.

E.g. $6x^2 + 11x + 4$

The product of coefficients **a** and **c** is 6 x 4 = 24. You must therefore find two numbers m and n whose product is 24 and the sum is 11.

1. Finding m and n through trial and error:

   $1 \times 24 = 24$, but $1 + 24 = 25$.

   $2 \times 12 = 24$, but $2 + 12 = 14$.

   $3 \times 8 = 24$ and $3 + 8 = 11$.

   The two numbers are 3 and 8.

2. Decomposing the polynomial:

   $6x^2 + 11x + 4 = 6x^2 + 3x + 8x + 4$

   $= 3x(2x + 1) + 4(2x + 1)$

   $= (3x + 4)(2x + 1)$

- Another strategy you can use to decompose a polynomial in the form of $ax^2 + bx + c$ is to proceed by trial and error by looking at the different divisors of the product **a** and **c**.

It is preferable to use this method when **a** or **c** equals 1, or when **a** and **c** have few divisors.

E.g. $2x^2 + 7x + 6$

You can write $2x^2 + 7x + 6 = (2x + \square)(x + \square)$, since 2 is a prime number.

The product of the missing numbers must equal 6.
There are 4 possibilities: 1 and 6, 2 and 3, 3 and 2, 6 and 1.
All you need to do next is check each of these possibilities.

$(2x + 1)(x + 6) = 2x^2 + 13x + 6$ No. (outer: $12x$, inner: x)

$(2x + 2)(x + 3) = 2x^2 + 8x + 6$ No. (outer: $6x$, inner: $2x$)

$(2x + 3)(x + 2) = 2x^2 + 7x + 6$ Yes. (outer: $4x$, inner: $3x$)

The answer is therefore $(2x + 3)(x + 2)$.

SOLVING SECOND-DEGREE EQUATIONS IN ONE VARIABLE

Equivalent equations are equations that have the same solutions. To solve an equation, you generally try to determine equivalent equations that are simplified.

Solving by decomposing into factors

This method is based on the following property of real numbers:

$$AB = 0, \text{ if and only if } A = 0 \text{ or } B = 0$$

To solve the equation, proceed as follows.	E.g. $2(x^2 + x) = 20 - x$
1. Write it in the form of $P(x) = 0$.	$2x^2 + 3x - 20 = 0$
2. Decompose the polynomial $P(x)$ into factors.	$(2x - 5)(x + 4) = 0$
3. Apply the above property, and solve the resulting first-degree equations.	$2x - 5 = 0$ or $x + 4 = 0$ $x = 2.5$ or $x = -4$

Solving by completing the square

To solve the equation, proceed as follows.	E.g. $2x^2 - 8x + 1 = 0$
1. Write it in the form of $x^2 + bx = c$.	$x^2 - 4x = -0.5$
2. Add a term on each side of the equality to obtain a trinomial that is a perfect square on the left side.	$x^2 - 4x + \mathbf{4} = -0.5 + \mathbf{4}$ $(x - 2)^2 = 3.5$
3. Determine the solutions by completing the square roots.	$x - 2 = \sqrt{3.5}$ or $x - 2 = -\sqrt{3.5}$ $x = 2 + \sqrt{3.5}$ or $x = 2 - \sqrt{3.5}$

practice 3.3

1 Factor the following polynomials.

a) $6ax + 21x - 8a - 28$

b) $36xy - 9x - 8y + 2$

c) $x^3 + x^2 + x + 1$

d) $24 + 20a + 18ab + 15a^2b$

e) $axy + ay^2 - xy - x^2$

f) $10ab^2 + 4a^2b - 8a - 20b$

2 There are two things in life that Jason loves to do most: watch movies with his girlfriend and do algebra. He has, in fact, rented a few movies for the weekend:

If the price of each movie had been x dollars less, I would have rented y more movies. It would have cost me only \$$(20 - 4x + 5y - xy)$.

How many movies did he rent? What price did he pay?

3 Find two numbers such that their product P and sum S are:

a) P = -30 and S = 1

b) P = 48 and S = -16

c) P = -24 and S = -10

d) P = 32 and S = 12

e) P = -36 and S = 0

f) P = 18 and S = -8.5

4 Factor the following trinomials.

a) $12x^2 + 49x + 4$

b) $20x^2 - 11x + 3$

c) $10x^2 - 13x - 3$

d) $6x^2 + 23x - 4$

e) $40x^2 - 31x + 6$

f) $10x^2 - 9x - 9$

g) $16x^2 - 40x + 25$

h) $25x^2 - 50x + 16$

i) $24x^2 - 2x - 15$

5 The trinomials below differ only in the coefficient of the x term and the sign of the constant term. By exploring the different possible factors, factor each of these trinomials.

a) $3x^2 + 17x + 10$

b) $3x^2 + 13x + 10$

c) $3x^2 + 13x - 10$

d) $3x^2 + 7x - 10$

e) $3x^2 + x - 10$

f) $3x^2 - 11x + 10$

g) $3x^2 - 13x - 10$

h) $3x^2 - 29x - 10$

i) $3x^2 - 31x + 10$

6 Factor the following trinomials using the method of your choice.

a) $x^2 + 4x - 32$ b) $x^2 - 7x + 10$ c) $3x^2 + 16x - 12$

d) $4x^2 + 4x + 1$ e) $4x^2 - 15x - 4$ f) $6x^2 - 7x + 1$

g) $6x^2 + 17x + 12$ h) $10x^2 + x - 3$ i) $12x^2 - 8x - 15$

7 In the adjcent trapezoid, sides AB and BC are congruent. If x is the length of the small base AD, then the expression $6x^2 - 7x + 2$ corresponds to the area of the trapezoid.

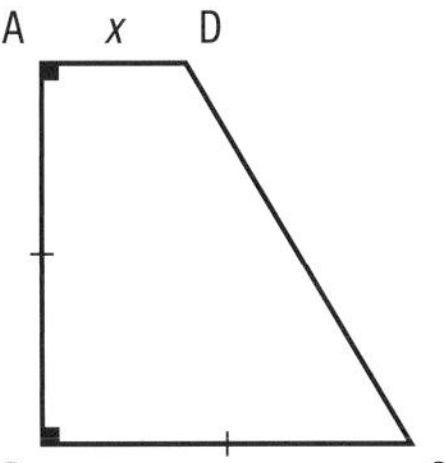

a) Factor the following polynomial $6x^2 - 7x + 2$.

b) What algebraic expression represents the height of this trapezoid?

8 Factor the following polynomials.

a) $4x^2 - 25x + 21$ b) $4x^2 - 25$ c) $4x^2 - 20x + 25$

d) $x^3 - 4x^2 + 5x - 20$ e) $5x^2 - 13x - 6$ f) $12x^2 + 5x - 2$

g) $-15x^2 - 7x + 2$ h) $15x + 6x^2 - 4x - 10$ i) $6x^2 - 10x$

j) $16x^2 + 50x + 25$ k) $16x^2 - 40x + 25$ l) $16x^3 + 40x^2 + 10x + 25$

m) $16x^4 - 25$ n) $3x^2 - 25xy + 8y^2$ o) $49x^2y - 42xy^2$

p) $5x^2y^2 + 16xy + 3$ q) $49x^2y^4 - 42xy^2 + 9$ r) $6x^2y - 9xy^2 - 4x + 6y$

9 It takes at least 17.2 dm^2 of paper to wrap the box shown below. In this representation, the dimensions of the box (in cm) are expressed as a function of its height, x.

a) Show that this situation can be translated as the equation $x^2 + 4x - 285 = 0$.

b) Determine the dimensions of the box.

x

$x + 5$

$x + 1$

10 During a television game show, the following riddle is presented to the competitors who have two minutes to solve it during a commercial break. Would you get the question right if you were a competitor on the show?

> What is the smallest number that would fit the following description? If I double a number, add 10 to the result, square the result, then subtract 10, I'm back to the same number I had at the start.

11 Solve the following equations by factoring.

a) $2x^2 - 16x = 0$ b) $x^2 - 16 = 0$ c) $x^2 - 8x + 16 = 0$

d) $x^2 - 3x + 2 = 0$ e) $x^2 + 5x - 36 = 0$ f) $x^2 + 13x + 36 = 0$

g) $2x^2 - 3x = 2$ h) $9x^2 + 1 = 6x$ i) $2x^2 = x + 15$

j) $8x^2 + 14x = 15$ k) $10x(x + 2) = 10 - x$ l) $4(x - 3) = x(x + 1)$

12 Solve the following equations by completing the square.

a) $x^2 - 10x = 11$ b) $x^2 + 3x = 4$ c) $x^2 + 6x = 1$

d) $x^2 = 3x + 5$ e) $2x^2 + 8 = 8x$ f) $2x^2 + 3x + 1 = 0$

g) $x^2 + 4x - 3 = 0$ h) $4x^2 = 8x + 12$ i) $6x^2 = 2 - x$

13 The cabin in Fabian's backyard is shown below. He intends to build a new one with a floor area that would be twice as large. Determine the dimensions of his new cabin if in relation to his present cabin:

a) He increases the length and width by the same value.

b) He increases the width to measure double the length.

14 Annie cut a length of 85 cm from a strip of wood measuring 2 m long.

85 cm

She now wonders how to cut the remaining length into two pieces so that the three wood strips can form a right triangle of which the hypotenuse will measure 85 cm.

a) Show that this situation can be translated into the equation $x^2 - 115x + 3000 = 0$, where x represents the length (in cm) of one of the strips she must cut.

b) How will Annie cut the remaining strip?

15 The two adjacent rectangles shown are similar. Their sides are therefore proportional.

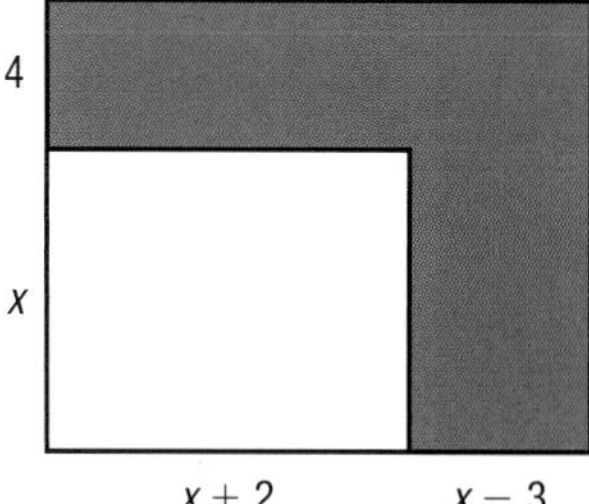

a) Use an equation to describe this proportion.

b) Write a second-degree equation equivalent to the equation found in **a)**.

c) Determine the area of the blue section.

16 The small diagonal in a rhombus measures 2 cm less than its big diagonal. The area of the rhombus is 15 cm^2. Determine the exact perimeter of this rhombus.

17 **HIEROGLYPHICS** In their calculations, ancient Egyptians used only unitary fractions, that is, fractions that today would be represented with a numerator equal to one. Below are two problems involving this type of fraction:

a) Show that there is only one integer n such that

$$\frac{1}{n} + \frac{1}{n+1} + \frac{1}{n(n+1)} = 1.$$

b) Double the fraction $\frac{1}{n}$ equals $\frac{1}{n-2} + \frac{1}{2n+5}$. What is this fraction?

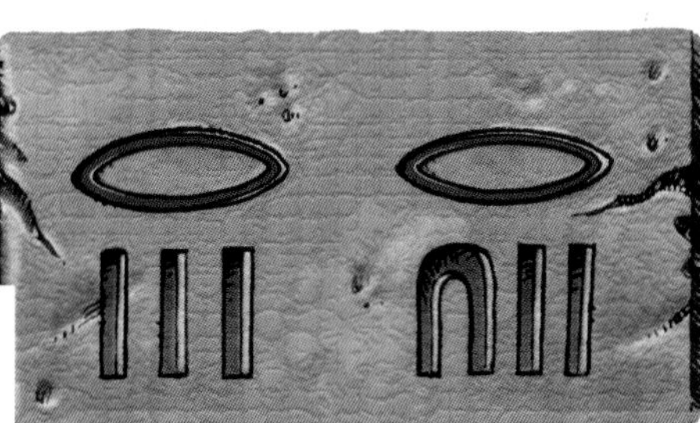

To write unitary fractions, the Egyptians used a symbol in the form of an open mouth placed above the representation of the denominator. The above hieroglyphics represent fractions $\frac{1}{3}$ and $\frac{1}{12}$.

18 Some polynomials with integer coefficients can be decomposed into factors that have irrational terms. For example:

$$x^2 - 2 = (x + \sqrt{2})(x - \sqrt{2}).$$

The steps below show another, more complex example, that decomposes the polynomial $x^2 + 6x + 4$ into factors.

$$\begin{aligned} x^2 + 6x + 4 &= \underbrace{x^2 + 6x + 9}_{(x+3)^2} - \underbrace{9 + 4}_{5} \\ &= (x + 3)^2 - 5 \\ &= ((x + 3) + \sqrt{5})((x + 3) - \sqrt{5}) \\ &= (x + 3 + \sqrt{5})(x + 3 - \sqrt{5}) \end{aligned}$$

a) On the first line, why is 9 added after the term $6x$? Why is 9 then subtracted?

b) Justify how you get from the first to the second line, then from the second to the third line.

c) As you perform the multiplication, check that the product of the two factors obtained is indeed equal to the initial polynomial.

d) Use this method to decompose the following polynomials into factors.

1) $x^2 + 8x + 13$ 2) $x^2 - 4x + 1$ 3) $x^2 + 3x + 2$

19 Tony and Anika are siblings. If you square Anika's age and subtract the product of their ages from this value, the result is the same as if you subtracted the square of Tony 's age from the product of their ages. What can you conclude regarding the ages of Tony and Anika? Justify your answer.

20 To simplify the expression $\frac{x^2 - 6x + 8}{x^2 - 3x + 2}$, a student used the following approach.

She did the following:

- She cancelled the x^2 terms.
- She simplified the x terms.
- She simplified the constant terms.

She got 6 as a final result.

$$\frac{\cancel{x^2} - \cancel{6x}^{\,2} + \cancel{8}^{\,4}}{\cancel{x^2} - \cancel{3x} + \cancel{2}} = 2 + 4 = 6$$

a) Explain what she did wrong.

b) Is there a value for x for which this student would not be entirely wrong?

21 **THE LIGHTHOUSE OF ALEXANDRIA** One of the Seven Wonders of the Ancient World is the Lighthouse of Alexandria, built during the 3rd century BCE. No trace of it remains today because it was destroyed during the 14th century. Based on accounts from that time, it is estimated that the light from the lighthouse could be seen by fishermen within a distance of 40 km.

The diagram below represents the lighthouse and the Earth. The line segment that links the light from the lighthouse to the ship is perpendicular to one of the Earth's radiuses and measures approximately 40 km. Considering that the Earth has a radius of nearly 6380 km, estimate the height of the Lighthouse of Alexandria.

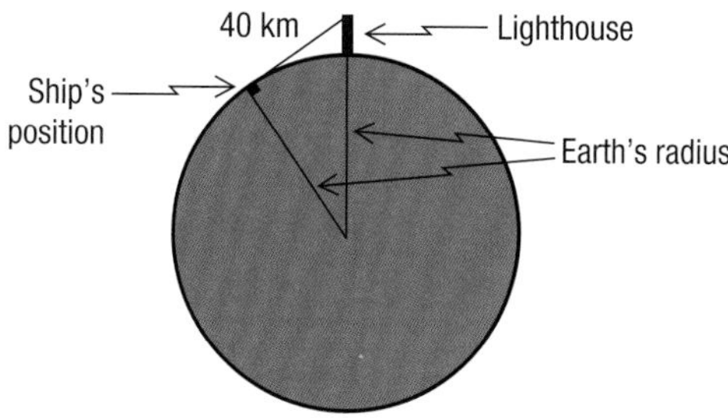

22 The rectangle and the square below are equivalent. Determine their dimensions.

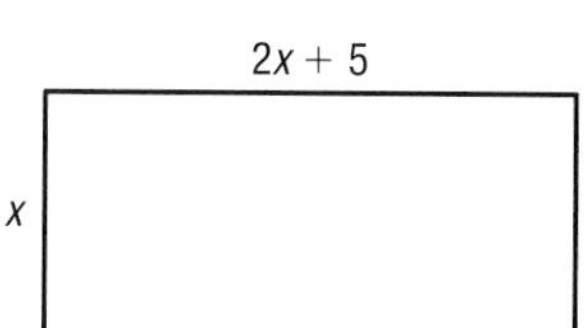

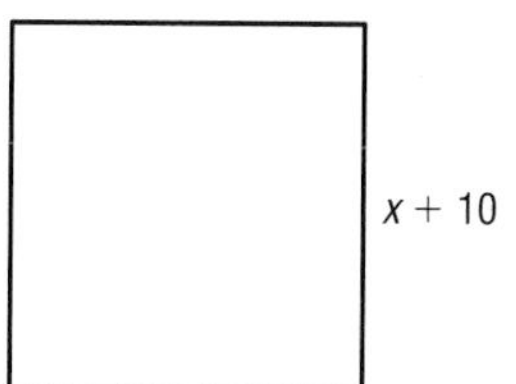

23 The ceiling of an underground parking lot is supported by a set of columns. This set is composed of 3 parallel rows of 5 columns each measuring 1 m in diameter. In each row, the open space separating two adjacent columns is always the same. This distance is also that which separates each row one from the other and that separates each of the parking lot's walls from the closest columns.

Determine the distance that separates each column considering that the rectangular surface of the parking lot's floor measures a total of 1650 m^2.

24 A group of individuals who wants to set up a housing cooperative must invest \$60,000 in equal parts. If there were one less person in the group, each would have to contribute \$1,500 more than if there were one person more.

a) Translate this situation into an equation where x represents the number of individuals in the group. Can your equation be expressed in the form of $ax^2 + bx + c = 0$?

b) How many people are there in the group?

25 Philip raises goats. He wants to build them a rectangular pen with an area of 36 m^2. A wire fence is sold in rolls of 5 m, he figures that the length of his fence should be 20 m, 25 m or 30 m. However, having tried all the factors of 36, he concludes that it is not possible with any of these lengths. Is he right? Justify your answer.

26 Melanie is a carpenter. Sometimes, to make sure two walls form a right angle, she checks whether it is possible to draw a triangle with sides measuring 3, 4 and 5 units, on the floor, along the walls.

Are the numbers 3, 4 and 5 the only consecutive integers that Melanie can use? Justify your answer.

27 **THE DIVINE PROPORTION** In 1509, the Italian monk Luca Pacioli wrote a book entitled *De divina proportione* in which he describes certain properties of a special ratio that is today called "the golden ratio." This ratio is found in several geometric situations and is often associated with beauty and harmony.

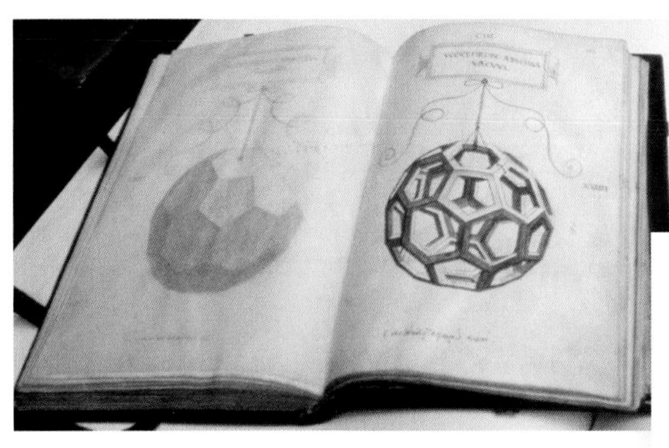

In Pacioli's book, we find this illustration created by Leonardo da Vinci, who was a friend of Pacioli's. In this book, the regular pentagon is very closely linked with the divine proportion, as the ratio between the measure of its sides and that of its diagonals happens to equal the golden ratio.

Greek mathematicians had already taken an interest in this ratio which they called "extreme and mean ratio." In the 3rd century BCE, Euclid wrote the following:

> « A straight line is sectioned in extreme and mean ratio when the entire line is to the greater line segment as the greater line segment is to the lesser. »

A ——————— C ——————— B

$$\frac{m\,\overline{AB}}{m\,\overline{AC}} = \frac{m\,\overline{AC}}{m\,\overline{CB}}$$

Let us suppose that segment AB measures 1 unit. In this case, the golden ratio corresponds to the length of line segment AC.

a) What is this length? Give the exact answer and a value rounded off to the nearest thousandth.

b) What is the value of the ratio $\frac{m\,\overline{AB}}{m\,\overline{AC}}$?
Round off to the nearest thousandth.
Check that you get the same value for the ratio $\frac{m\,\overline{AC}}{m\,\overline{CB}}$.

The value of this ratio is called the golden number. The golden number is symbolized as the Greek letter Φ (Phi). The golden ratio is none other than the reciprocal of the golden number.

Chronicle of the

past

The Arabic mathematicians

Islam's contribution to the field of mathematics

The revelation by Prophet Muhammad, in the 7th century, is the foundation of the Muslim religion. In subsequent years, Islam spread rapidly which then allowed for the unification of different Arab tribes into a single nation. From India to Spain, this new nation spread artistic and scientific notions notably in religion and culture. This formed an empire that spread its religious and cultural influences in artistic and scientific terms from India to Spain; this was a glorious period in the development of mathematics.

An Arab mosaic from the Alhambra, a palace located in Granada, Spain. This provides an example where art and mathematics are joined together as one.

We know little of the personal lives of the mathematicians of that time. Often it is only through the content of their work that we become more familiar with who they were.

Al-Khawarizmi (ca. 790 - ca. 850 BCE)

The first and most famous mathematician of that period was Muhammad Ibn Mussa Al-Khawarizmi. He authored the book whose Arab title is *Kitab al-jabr wa'l muqabala* (*The Science of Transposition and Reduction*). The word *al-jabr* is the origin of the word "algebra" which is used today.

What sets Al-Khawarizmi apart from other mathematicians of that period is the care with which he justifies his algorithms. For example, in his book, when he explains how to solve second-degree equations, he uses geometric figures to demonstrate that his method is valid.

He also does the opposite. To solve certain geometric problems, he uses an algebraic line of reasoning as in exercise **1.** Can you do the same?

1. Inscribe a square into an isosceles triangle whose base measures 12 units and the congruent sides measure 10 units each. What are the dimensions of the square?

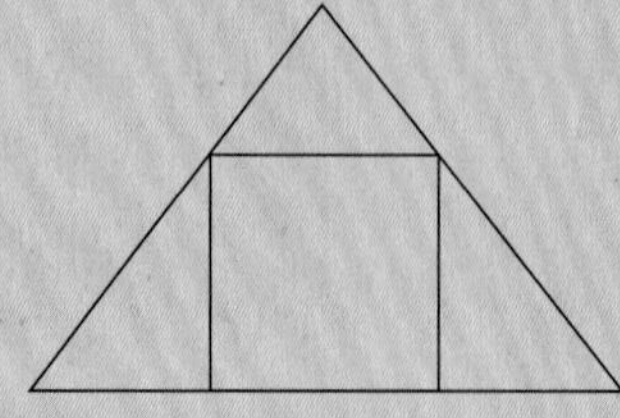

Tabit ibn Korrah (ca. 836 - ca. 901 BCE)

One of this mathematician's legacies is his Arabic translations of several works by ancient Greek mathematicians.

Based on these translations, he suggested a few improvements to known results. For example, he found a generalization of the Pythagorean theorem that is valid for any type of triangle.

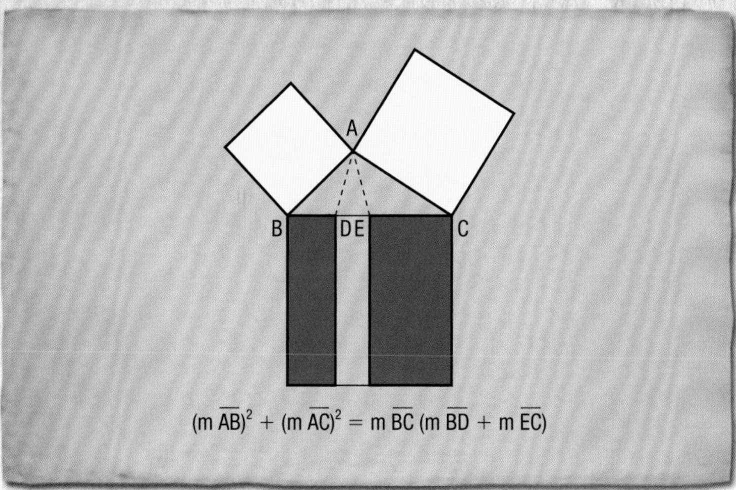

On the sides of triangle ABC, construct three squares. Then draw segments AE and AD so that triangles DBA and EAC are similar to triangle ABC. In this case, the sum of the areas of the yellow squares equals the sum of the areas of the blue rectangles.

2. Consider Tabit ibn Korrah's construction.

a) Can you demonstrate the property stated by him that the sum of the areas of the yellow squares equals the sum of the areas of the blue rectangles?

b) What happens to the two blue rectangles if triangle ABC is a right triangle?

3. Prove the property stated by Al-Karaji.

Al-Karaji (ca. 953 - ca. 1029 BCE)

This mathematician made an important contribution to algebra. He is one of the first to have distanced himself from geometric representations to study, among other things, equations of a degree higher than 2.

Following is an example:
Having noticed that $1^3 + 2^3 = 3^2$, Al-Karaji wondered if there were two other cubic numbers of which the sum is a square number. This amounts to solving the equation $x^3 + y^3 = z^2$.
He found the equivalent of the following:

If $x = \frac{n^2}{1 + m^3}$ and $y = \frac{mn^2}{1 + m^3}$,

then $x^3 + y^3$ is a perfect square.

In the

workplace

Engineers

What do Leonardo da Vinci, Thomas Edison, Soichiro Honda and Joseph-Armand Bombardier have in common? They are all great engineers whose creations transformed their times.

Joseph-Armand Bombardier (1907-1964), inventor of the snowmobile

The job

Engineers are individuals who propose solutions to concrete problems of a technological nature. They hold a wealth of scientific and technical knowledge and exhibit leadership qualities as well as an innovative spirit. Engineers are also excellent project managers. This job involves participating in every phase of completion of a product, from research and development to product recycling, including design, manufacturing, quality control and safety monitoring. Very often, an engineer is called upon to coordinate the activities of a work group.

Among the specialties in engineering, there are various fields of expertise: agro-environmental, civil, biomedical, genetic, industrial, chemical, physical mining, and computer. You will be looking at three of these specialties.

Computer engineering

Computer engineers develop software programs of all types including medical imagery and bank transaction security. No matter what type of software they work on, the objective of these engineers is the same: to design a program that runs reliably and quickly.

A flight simulator

Since these programs often include tens of thousands of programming lines, it is essential that computer engineers exhibit a great deal of thoroughness and strong teamwork skills.

1. When designing a software program, engineers must always make sure the program is prevented from executing divisions by 0 because it would result in a crash.

a) Determine the values that may cause problems during the calculation of the two following expressions by a software program:

1) $\boxed{\dfrac{2a(2a - b) + b(b - 2a)}{b^3 - 2a(b^2 + 2a(b - 2a))}}$ 2) $\boxed{\dfrac{1}{\dfrac{1}{a^2 - 1} + \dfrac{1}{a^2 + 1}}}$

b) Can you write these expressions differently in order to reduce the number of problem cases?

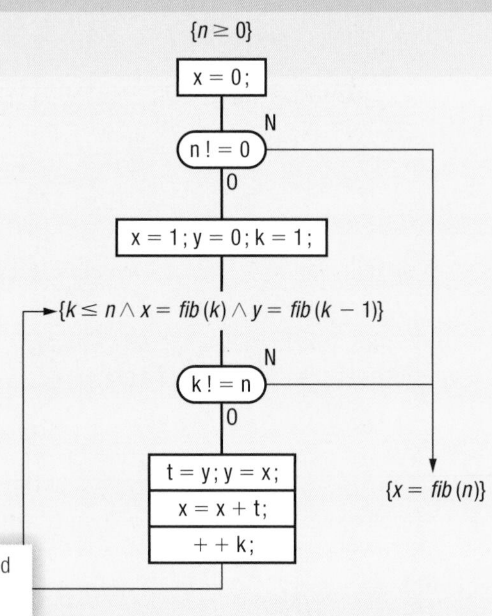

An example of a program developed by students at the Polytechnique.

The Bionic Tower of Shanghai is one of the world's most ambitious civil engineering projects. This tower, for which work is set to begin in 2015, will be the tallest in the world. It will reach a height of over 1 km, and will accommodate 100 000 people.

Mechanical engineering

Mechanical engineers are specialists in energy transfer. They take part in transportation-related projects, and they can be involved with every aspect of power generating plants. These engineers are also the ones who assure building comfort by designing air conditioning and heating systems. In a world where energy demands, and the costs associated with this energy, are constantly on the rise, mechanical engineers are called upon to innovate by creating energy-efficient machines.

Civil engineering

Civil engineers design, build and maintain infrastructures and other installations useful for a variety of human activities. Engineers ensure that these installations are safe, and they assess the environmental impacts related to their construction. In particular, these engineers design roads, bridges and collection lines for waste-water processing. Buildings such as the Notre-Dame de Paris Cathedral, the Eiffel Tower, and the twin Petronas Towers were designed by engineers. The great hydroelectric dams in Québec bear witness to our vast expertise in civil engineering.

2. To determine the resistance of a given type of concrete, an engineer has to design a concrete cylinder that will be subjected to a compression test. This cylinder must meet two requirements.

- The width of its base must measure 10 mm more than half of its height.
- An applied force of 250 000 N must generate a pressure of 32 MPa on the base of the cylinder.

a) Determine the dimensions of the cylinder that meet these two requirements.

b) If the concrete were poured into a square-based prism meeting the same requirements as those for the cylinder, would more or less concrete be used while conducting the tests?

To determine a material's resistance to compression, engineers apply greater and greater force on one of the faces of the sample until the material ruptures. The *force exerted* (in newtons) *per unit of surface* (in square millimetres) equals the *pressure* (in megapascals). Engineers then refer to the material's compression constraints.

overview

1 A compulsory stop sign is shaped as a regular octagon to increase visibility. A reflecting white border highlights the contour of the sign. On a sign 60 cm wide, the white border has a total length of approximately 200 cm.

a) Estimate the area of the visible surface of this traffic sign.

b) If the signs were shaped as a square, a regular hexagon or equivalent circle, estimate the length of the white line in each of these cases.

2 The formulas below relate the area A to the perimeter P of the four figures considered in the above exercise.

Square	Regular hexagon	Regular octagon	Circle
$A = \frac{1}{16}P^2$	$A = \frac{\sqrt{3}}{24}P^2$	$A = \frac{1 + \sqrt{2}}{32}P^2$	$A = \frac{1}{4\pi}P^2$

a) Demonstrate that these equalities are true while explaining each step of your reasoning. For the regular hexagon and the regular octagon, you can refer to the figures shown in the adjacent illustration.

b) With the formulas provided above, show that the proposition stated below is true for the four figures: from two equivalent regular polygons, the one with the greater number of sides has the shortest perimeter. Ultimately, the circle has the shortest perimeter.

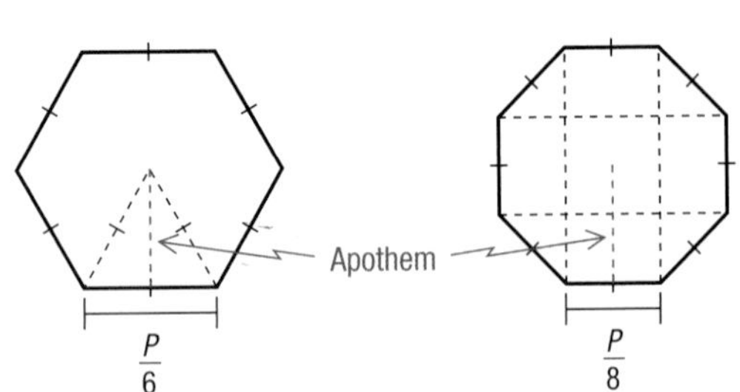

3 The Gagnon family wants to buy a custom-made in-ground pool. Since the Gagnons have many friends, the salesperson suggests that they choose a pool that uses up a surface of 50 m^2. For safety reasons, it is also suggested to border the entire contour of the pool with a fence that would be placed 2 m away from the edge of the pool.

a) What would be the minimum length of this fence? Determine the exact value, then make an approximation to the nearest tenth of a metre.

b) What would be the minimum length of this fence if the pool were shaped as a quadrilateral? Once again, determine the exact value, then make an approximation to the nearest tenth of a metre.

4 A cube has identical square-shaped holes on all sides. The diagonals of these squares are on the faces of the cube. If a represents the length of the edge of the cube, and x the length of the sides of the square holes, what algebraic expression represents the total area of this solid? Express your answer in factored form.

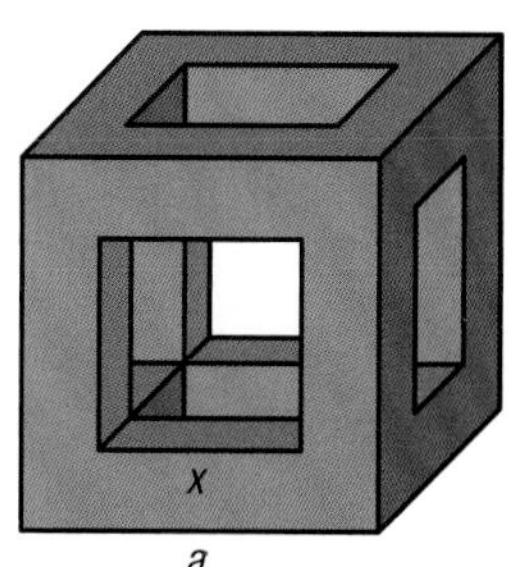

5 At the theatre, Charles buys popcorn which is served in a bag like the one shown in the adjacent illustration. On his return home, he wonders if it is possible to make a bag that would use less paper and have the same capacity. Below is his analysis, using a spreadsheet program:

	A	B	C	D
1	Base length		Heigth	Area of bag
2	10	15	30	1650
3	12	15	25	1530
4	10	12	37.5	1770
5	12	12	31.25	1644
6	10	20	22.5	1550
7	12	20	18.75	1440
8				
9				

In Columns **A** and **B**, he enters different potential lengths (in cm) for the base of the bag. In Column **C**, he calculates the height so that the capacity is always 4.5 L, and in Column **D**, he calculates the area of the bag (in cm^2).

a) If a and b represent the lengths of the base of the bag, what algebraic expression represents:

1) the height of the bag?

2) the external area of the bag?

b) Determine the dimensions of a bag with the same capacity, but with an area that would be even smaller than the one Charles found.

c) What would be the dimensions of the bag having the same capacity but a smaller area?

6 Sandra and Romeo have inherited the family farm. In a corner of a field, Sandra builds a rectangular pen with 35 m of fencing. Thus, she thinks, each of her 20 cows will have a grazing area of 15 m^2.

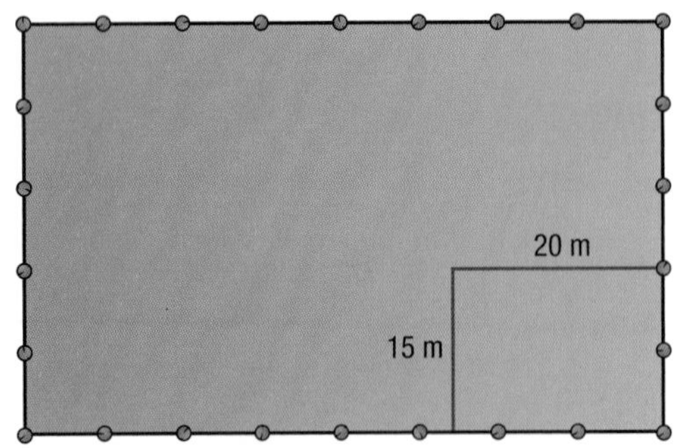

In another corner of the field, Romeo also wants to use 35 m of fencing to build a pen for his 20 cows. However, he wants each of his cows to have a grazing area of 20 m^2. Is it possible to build such a pen? Explain your answer.

7 While taking a carpentry course, Leo and Lea learn to make cuts in wood. Below are the cuts they made in identical wooden prisms.

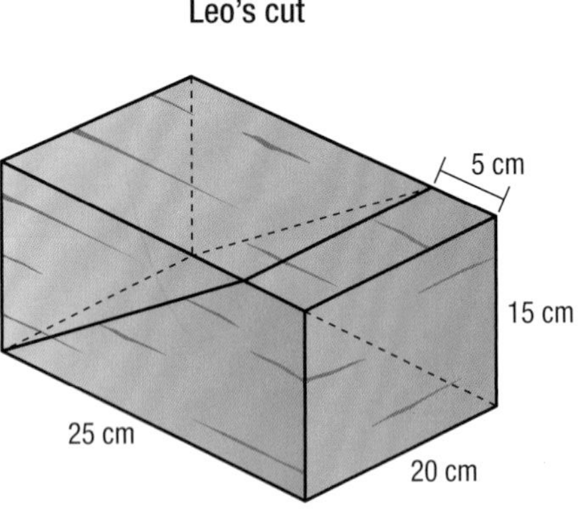

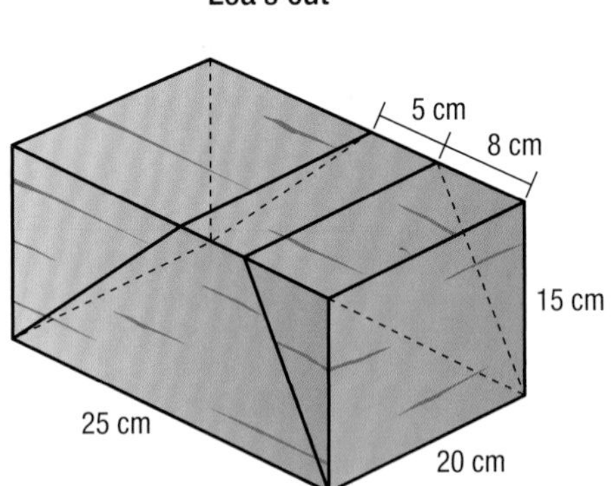

Leo obtained two pieces of wood while Lea got three.

a) Is one of Leo's pieces of wood equivalent to one of Lea's? Justify your answer.

b) Does one of Leo's pieces of wood have the same surface area as one of Lea's? Justify your answer.

8 The dimensions of a rectangular-based prism, equivalent to a cube, are given in the adjacent representation. Variable a represents the length of the edge of the cube:

a) What polynomial represents the volume of this prism?

b) What are the dimensions of the cube?

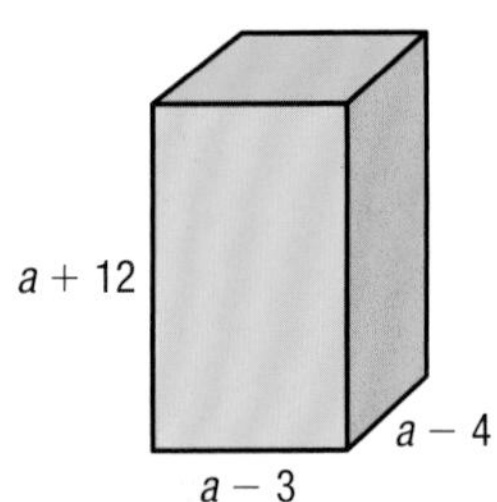

9 A teacher has a group of n students. In the context of a learning activity, she plans to distribute $(2n - 8)$ interlocking cubes to each student, and, in this case, she will have 20 left over. On the day of the activity, two students are absent.

a) Can she distribute all the cubes evenly among the students present? If not, how many will she have left?

b) Determine the value of n if the total number of cubes distributed among the students that day amounts to 968.

10 In order to completely factor certain polynomials, it is sometimes necessary to use more than one method of factoring. Apply this strategy to factor the following polynomials.

a) $6x^2 - 36x + 144$ b) $6x^2 + 63x - 108$ c) $64x^3 - 36x$

d) $2ax^2 - 12ax + 9a$ e) $4x^3 + 5x^2 - 16x - 20$ f) $-2x^2y^2 + 2x^2y + 4xy - 4x$

g) $x^4 - 16$ h) $x^4 - 21x^2 - 100$ i) $9x^2 - y^2 + 3x - y$

11 The product of an integer, the number preceding it and the number following it equals eight times the sum of these 3 numbers. What are these numbers? Find all the possible answers.

12 Using dynamic geometry software, you can observe that the medians of a triangle divide the inner space of this triangle into six triangles of equal area.

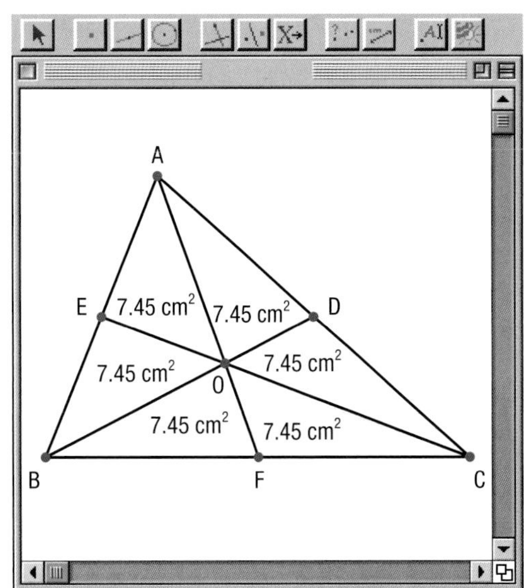

a) Find a way to convince another person that this property is true, no matter what shape triangle ABC may have. To do this, show that:
   1) triangles BFO and CFO are equivalent
   2) triangles AEO and ADO are equivalent
   3) the 6 triangles in the inner space of triangle ABC are equivalent

b) Prove from the above statements that the medians of a triangle intersect at a point that is $\frac{2}{3}$ their length.

13 Calvin discovered proof which demonstrated that $1 = 2$.

To begin with, suppose that $a = 1$ and start with the following equality:	$a^2 = a^2$
Since $a = 1$, you can write:	$a^2 - a = a^2 - 1$
You factor both sides of the equality:	$a(a - 1) = (a + 1)(a - 1)$
You can simplify the common factor on each side:	$a = a + 1$
Since $a = 1$, you get:	$1 = 2$

Where is the flaw in Calvin's reasoning? Explain your answer.

14 Eloise has constructed two cube-shaped structures out of sticks. She needed 12 sticks for the first structure and 54 for the second.

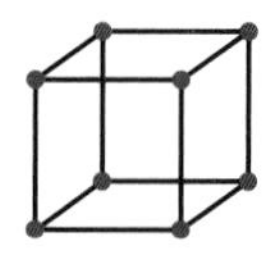

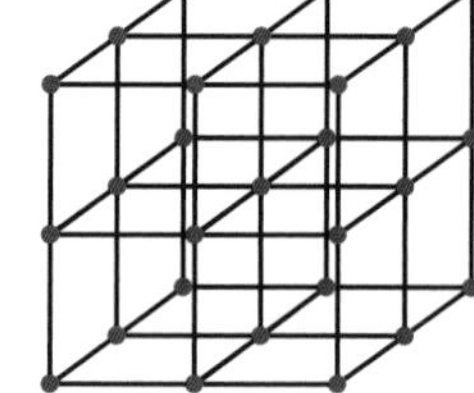

a) How many sticks will she need to build a similar structure measuring three edges in length?

b) What expression represents the number of sticks required for the construction of a structure measuring n edges in length?

c) What would be the length of the edge of the structure composed of 2700 sticks?

15 In the regular hexagon ABCDEF, the interior space between diagonals AE and BD has been shaded in pink. Prove that the area of this pink space equals $\frac{2}{3}$ the area of the hexagon.

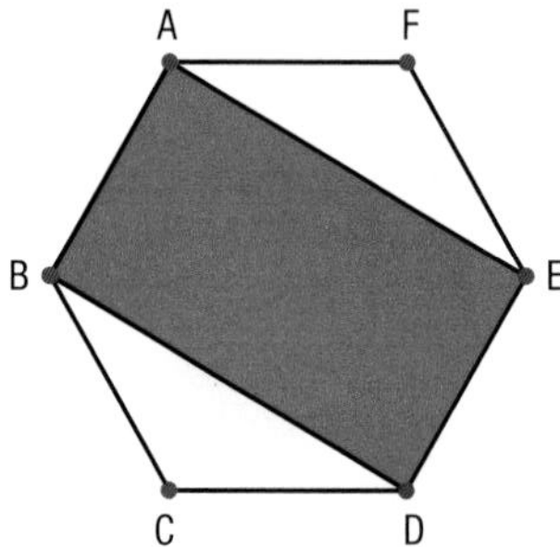

16 Consider any two natural numbers a and b. Do the following expressions represent rational or irrational numbers? Justify your answers.

a) $(\sqrt{a} + \sqrt{b})^2 + (\sqrt{a} - \sqrt{b})^2$

b) $(\sqrt{a} + \sqrt{b})^2 - (\sqrt{a} - \sqrt{b})^2$

c) $(\sqrt{a} + \sqrt{b})^2(\sqrt{a} - \sqrt{b})^2$

d) $\left(\frac{1}{\sqrt{a} + \sqrt{b}}\right)^2 + \left(\frac{1}{\sqrt{a} - \sqrt{b}}\right)^2$

17 Naomi has a business card with rather interesting dimensions. When the card is cut into two pieces, one piece will form a square and the other, a rectangle which is similar to the initial card.

Naomi Doré Engineer Telephone: 123-1618 Fax: 123-0618

Naomi Dor Engineer Telephone: 12 Fax: 1	é 3-1618 23-0618

What is the length of this card if its width is 5 cm?

18 FIBONACCI Consider the Fibonacci sequence:

$$1, 1, 2, 3, 5, 8, 13, 21, \ldots$$

Each term in this sequence is the sum of the two terms preceding it. This sequence is very special, as you can observe it in different places in nature, and it has several interesting mathematical properties.

This pine cone has 8 spirals going in one direction and 13 spirals going in the other direction.

You can observe that if you square two successive terms and then calculate their difference, the result you get is the product of the two terms adjoining them. For example,

$$13^2 - 8^2 = 105 \text{ and } 5 \times 21 = 105.$$

a) If a and b represent two successive terms in the sequence, what algebraic expressions represent the two subsequent terms?

b) Using the expressions found in **a)**, prove the conjecture stated above.

c) Formulate at least one other conjecture concerning this sequence.

Leonardo of Pisa, also know as Fibonacci (1175 - 1250) paved the way for the introduction of Arab mathematicians in Europe. His main work entitled *Liber Aboci*, presents the famous sequence that bears his name.

bank of problems

19 A 30-cm wide safety cushion is installed around a hexagonal trampoline with sides measuring 1.2 m as shown in the illustration below.

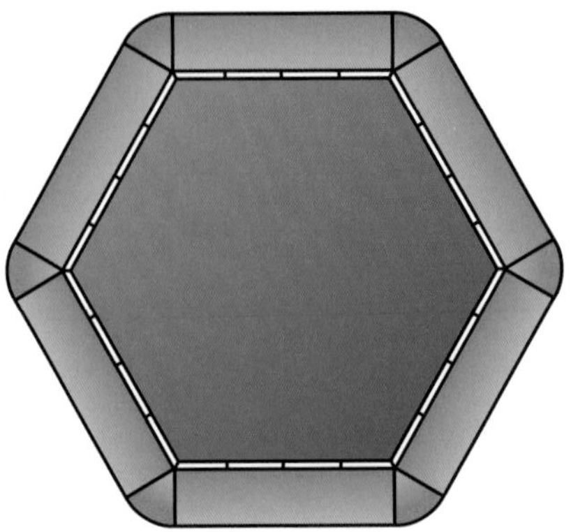

The trampoline could have another shape while still having the same perimeter. For example, it could take the shape of a square, a pentagon, an octagon, or even a circle. What can you state regarding the area of the safety cushion installed around these trampolines?

20 Inside a rectangle, line segments were drawn parallel to each side at a distance (a) from each other, then four sections were coloured, as illustrated in the example below.

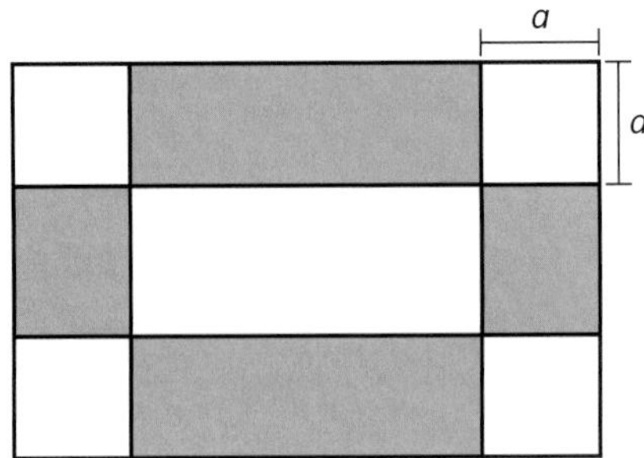

How should you choose the value of a so that the total area of the orange sections is equal to that of the white sections?

21 In parallelogram ABCD, a line parallel to diagonal BD was drawn so that it intersects with the parallelogram at points E and F.

Are triangles ABE and AFD equivalent? Justify your answer.

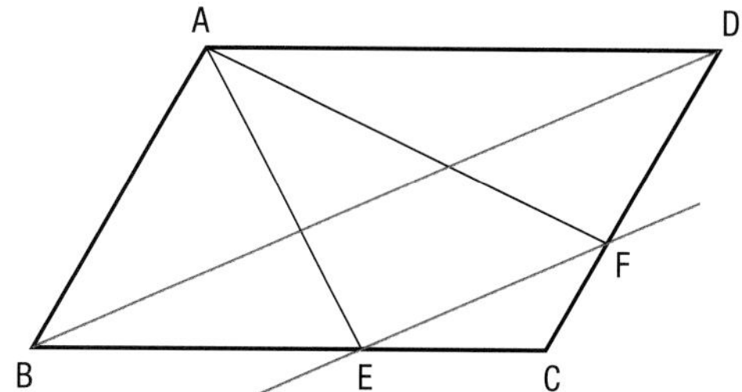

22 **PENTAGONAL NUMBERS** The Pythagoreans did not only focus on square numbers and triangular numbers. They also looked at other sequences of polygonal numbers. For example, consider the sequence of pentagonal numbers. Each of them can be represented with a drawing or a sum showing an obvious regularity.

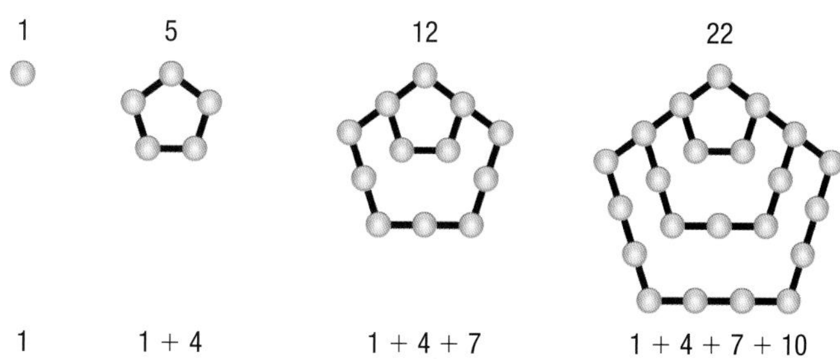

If you compare this sequence with that of triangular numbers, you see that each pentagonal number seems to equal one-third of a triangular number. Triangular numbers include:

1, 3, 6, 10, 15, 21, 28, 36, 45, 55, 66, 78, ...

Prove that this is true.

23 Consider the solid of which you have already calculated the total area. It is a cube pierced on all sides with identical square-shaped holes. The measure of the edge of the cube is a units, and that of the square holes is x units.

Determine the simplest algebraic expression that would represent the ratio between the total area of this solid and the total area of an equivalent right prism of which the square base measures $(a - x)$ units for each side.

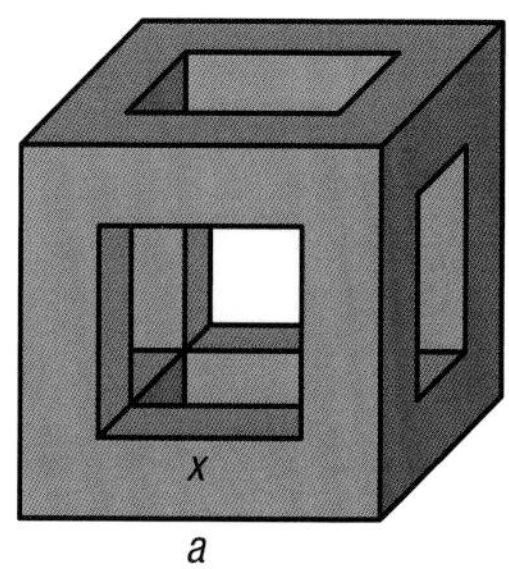

24 Jenny loves mathematical formulas. In geometry, she knows all the formulas for calculating areas and volumes. She understands the underlying reasoning when calculating but finds it more practical not to go through the rationalization each time she has to calculate a missing measurement. "It would be nice," she muses, "if there were a formula, in algebra, to solve second-degree equations."

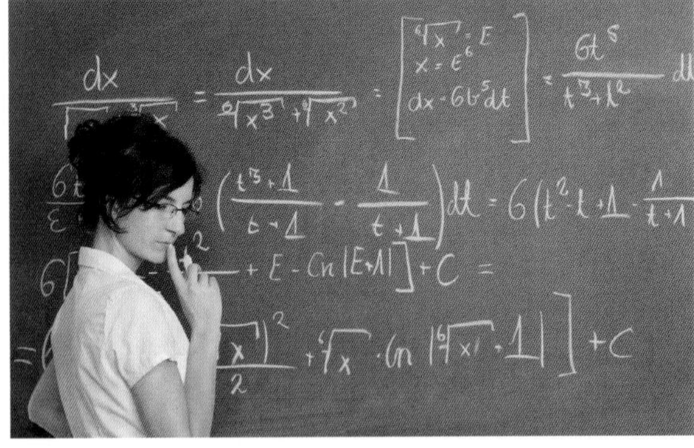

Since Jenny is rather inquisitive, she decides to try to find one. To represent the most general equation, she first writes: $ax^2 + bx + c = 0$. By subtracting **c** and dividing by **a** on each side of the equality, she gets an equation that is similar in form to the one studied by Al-Khawarizmi in the 9th century. Complete her calculation and find the formula that she is looking for and explain each step of your reasoning.

25 An entrepreneur has decided to change the shape of the boxes used for delivering merchandise. From now on, they will be using cubic boxes with a greater capacity. On the other hand, he will only be able to make 19 new boxes with the cardboard formerly used to make 20. In the representation below, the dimensions (in dm) of the bottom of the old box are expressed in relation to the dimensions of the new one. The difference between the capacities of the two boxes (in dm^3) can also be expressed in the form of $ax + b$.

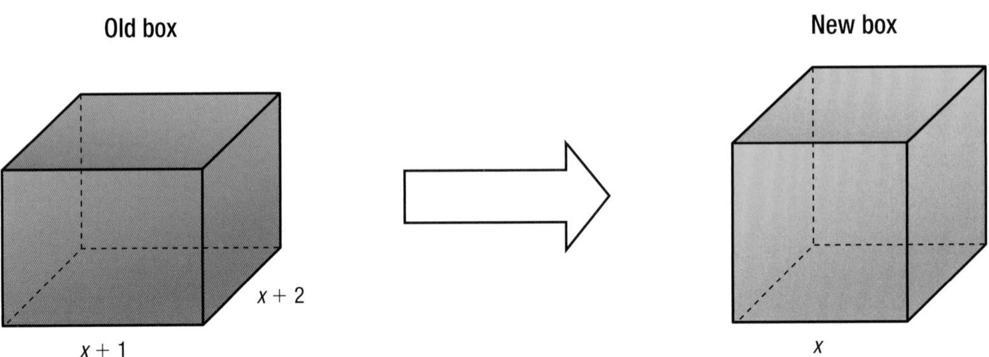

Calculate the difference in capacity between the two boxes. Round off to the nearest cubic decimetre.

26 Felix has unsuccesfully been trying for some time now to decompose an algebraic expression into factors. He has reached the conclusion that there must be an error in the question asked in his textbook. What do you think?

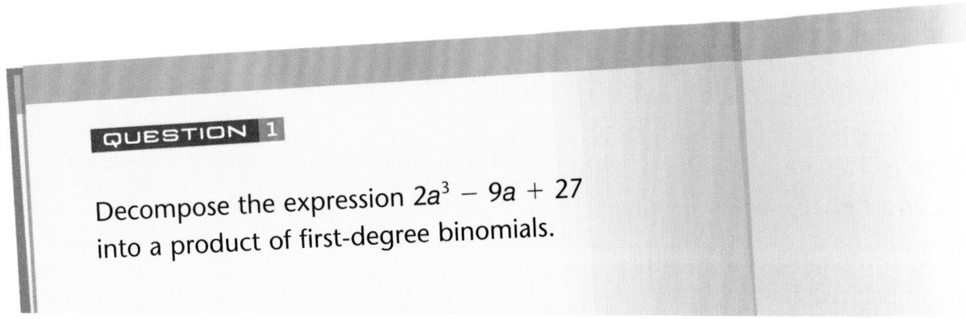

QUESTION 1

Decompose the expression $2a^3 - 9a + 27$ into a product of first-degree binomials.

If you, like Felix, believe that there must be an error in the textbook, suggest a correction and explain your choice. If you feel that Felix is wrong, justify your answer.

27 Consider three cubes constructed of small interlocking cubes. To Martine's surprise as she was taking these three cubes apart, she noticed that she could form a square plate with all of the little cubes. In addition, she noticed that the side of the plate measured 6 units, that is, exactly $1 + 2 + 3$, which corresponds to the 3rd triangular number.

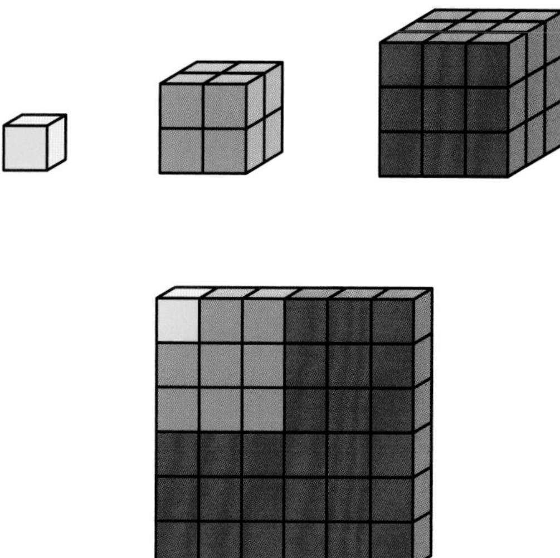

She then formulated the following conjecture: The sum of the first n cubic numbers equals the square of the nth triangular number.

Presuming that the conjecture is true for the first k numbers, show that it is true for the first $(k + 1)$ numbers. Can you conclude that it is true for all natural numbers? Explain your reasoning.

VISION 4

Quadratic functions and trajectories

Mathematical language is an important tool used to explain a number of phenomena. This is especially true in "Vision 4" where you will discover the many aspects of the quadratic function, which were introduced in "Vision 2." You will use the different forms of its rule by drawing links between them. You will see how this function can help you solve second-degree inequalities. You will learn to model various situations using a second-degree equation in two variables that represents a function or a trajectory. Finally, links will be made between the concept of distance and the quadratic function. You will see that this concept can be used to define the parabola that appears in the graphical representation of such functions. All this will allow you to explain various phenomena in every day life, from the way that parabolic mirrors operate to how to calculate the trajectory of a hot air balloon.

Arithmetic and algebra	Geometry	Statistics
• Graphical representations and properties of second-degree polynomial functions • Converting from one written form to another (general, standard and factored) • Finding the rule • Interpolation and extrapolation • Solving inequalities of the second-degree in one variable	• Distance between two points • Finding missing lengths using the concept of distance	

SATELLITE NETWORK

REVISION 4

PRIOR LEARNING 1 Discovering some inequalities

The statements below describe differences in income for different individuals.

Ms. Beausoleil works in the textile industry. Her annual income does not exceed $20,000.

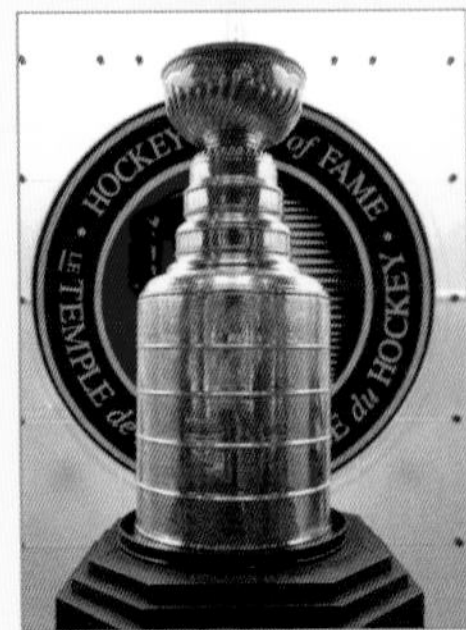

In his second season in the National Hockey League, Victor Karpov earns more than $20,000 per game.

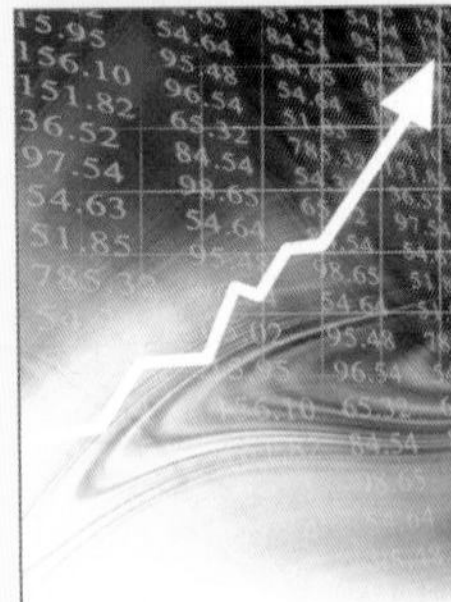

Ms. Parvenue, Marketing Vice President in a major brokerage firm, earns at least $20,000 per month.

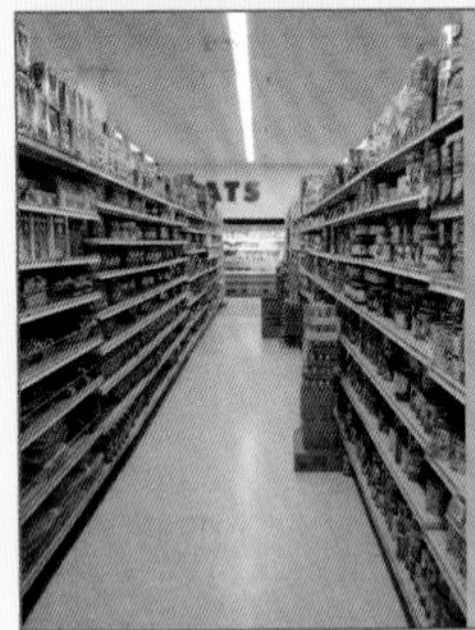

Mr. Leboeuf, President of a chain of grocery stores, receives less than $20,000 per hour for his work.

a. Associate each of the statements above with one of the following inequalities and identify each of the variables *a*, *b*, *c* and *d*.

$a < 20,000$ $\qquad$ $b \leq 20,000$ $\qquad$ $c > 20,000$ $\qquad$ $d \geq 20,000$

b. Following is some additional information regarding these individual's income. In each case, translate the information into an inequality using the variables defined in **a.**

1) Ms. Beausoleil would rather earn $10,000 more than half of her annual salary than get a raise of $1,000 per year.
2) Ms. Parvenue's annual income is less than $300,000.
3) Considering that Victor Karpov plays approximatively 15 minutes per game, it can be said that he earns at least $2,000 a minute on the ice.
4) If he added $10,000 to his hourly salary, Mr. Leboeuf would only double his income at most.

c. Solve the inequalities in **b.**

d. Taking the context into account, represent the income of each of these individuals using interval notation.

PRIOR LEARNING 2 Monopoly versus choice

In the field of economics, a monopolistic situation is said to exist when a company is the only one making and selling any given product. In such instances, the company will generally seek to produce only the quantity of goods that will allow it to maximize its profits.

The quantity of goods produced by a monopoly is not of optimal benefit to society. If several companies were in competition, the quantity produced would be greater and the price of goods would be lower.

Presume, for example, that a pharmaceutical company has a monopoly over the sale of a patent medicine. Taking into account production and distribution costs, as well as the cause/effect relationship between price and demand, an economist estimated that the profit gained by the company on the sale of this medicine over a certain period of time can be translated as the following function:

$$P(x) = {}^{-}0.08\,(x - 65)^2 + 210$$

where x is the quantity produced in thousands of packages and $P(x)$ is the profit in thousands of dollars.

a. Determine the value of $P(10)$, $P(30)$ and $P(100)$. Interpret these values in this context.

b. Draw a graphical representation of function P.

c. What is the y-intercept of this function? What does this value imply?

d. What quantities produced will generate zero profit for the company? Determine the exact amount of these quantities, then make approximations to the nearest hundred packages.

e. To the nearest hundred, what amount of quantities produced by this company will generate:

1) a loss?

2) a profit?

f. Considering that the company is seeking to generate maximum profits, determine the quantity of packages it should produce. What will its profits amount to?

knowledge summary

INEQUALITY

An inequality is a mathematical statement comprised of one or more variables and an inequality symbol (<, >, ≤ or ≥).

The meaning of the symbols

When representing a situation as an inequality, you need to fully understand the meaning of the statements in order to choose the proper symbol of inequality.

E.g. Consider x as representing Marie-France's age. Following are the statements and their representation as an inequality:

Statement	Some possible values	Inequality
Marie-France is less than 20 years old.	She can be 19, 18, 17, ...	$x < 20$
Marie-France's age is greater than 10 years.	She can be 11, 12, 13, ...	$x > 10$
Marie-France's age is no more than 20 years. Marie-France's age is at most 20 years.	She can be 20, 19, 18, ...	$x \leq 20$
Marie-France is at least 10 years old. Marie-France's age is not less than 10 years.	She can be 10, 11, 12, ...	$x \geq 10$

SOLVING AN INEQUALITY OF THE FIRST-DEGREE IN ONE VARIABLE

Inequalities are **equivalent** if they have the same solution set.

To solve a first-degree inequality, you can use the **transformation rules** in order to convert the initial inequality into the simplest possible equivalent inequality.

Transformation rule	Example of equivalent inequalities
• Add or subtract the same number to/from each side of an inequality.	$2x + 5 > 6$ $2x + 5 - 5 > 6 - 5$ $2x > 1$
• Multiply or divide each side of an inequality by the same positive number, other than zero.	$3x \geq -15$ $\frac{3x}{3} \geq \frac{-15}{3}$ $x \geq -5$
• Multiply or divide each side of an inequality by the same negative number, other than zero while changing the direction of the inequality.	$-4x > 12$ $\frac{-4x}{-4} < \frac{12}{-4}$ $x < -3$

PROPERTIES OF A QUADRATIC FUNCTION (STANDARD FORM)

When the rule of a quadratic function is expressed in standard form, that is $f(x) = a(x - h)^2 + k$, parameters **a**, **h**, and **k** can be used to find certain properties of the function.

In particular, you can conclude the following:

- The function's graph is a curve, called a parabola, of which the vertex is (**h**, **k**).
- The vertical axis of symmetry intersects the x-axis at point **h**.
- If **a** > 0, the curve is open upwards and **k** is the minimum of that function.
- If **a** < 0, the curve is open downwards and **k** is the maximum of that function.

E.g. Consider $f(x) = 2(x - 3)^2 - 4$

The graph for f has the following characteristics:

- Its vertex is located at (3, -4).
- The axis of symmetry intersects the x-axis at 3.
- The parabola is open upwards and the minimum of f is -4.

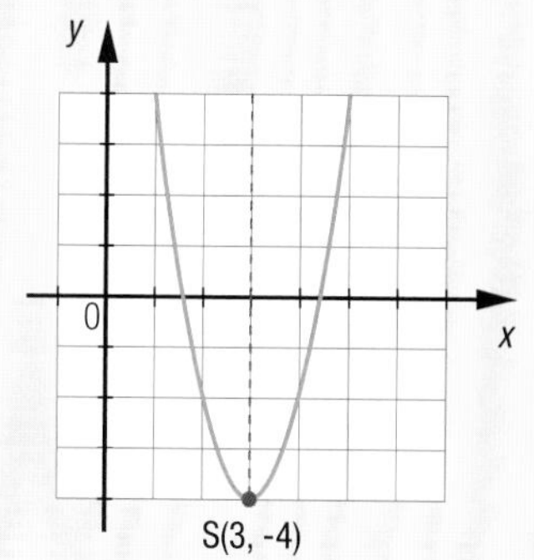

The zeros of a function

To determine the zeros of a function, if any exist, you can solve the equation: $a(x - h)^2 + k = 0$.

E.g. To determine the zeros of the function: $f(x) = 2(x - 3)^2 - 4$.

You solve the equation $2(x - 3)^2 - 4 = 0$.

You can proceed as follows:

$2(x - 3)^2 = 4$	(adding 4 on each side)
$(x - 3)^2 = 2$	(dividing by 2 on each side)
$x - 3 = \pm\sqrt{2}$	(finding the square roots)
$x = 3 \pm \sqrt{2}$	(adding 3 on each side)

The sign of a function

To study the sign of a quadratic function, it is preferable to draw its graph, and specify the value of its zeros.

E.g. The adjacent graph shows that the function $f(x) = 2(x - 3)^2 - 4$ is positive over the intervals $]-\infty, 3 - \sqrt{2}] \cup [3 + \sqrt{2}, +\infty[$.

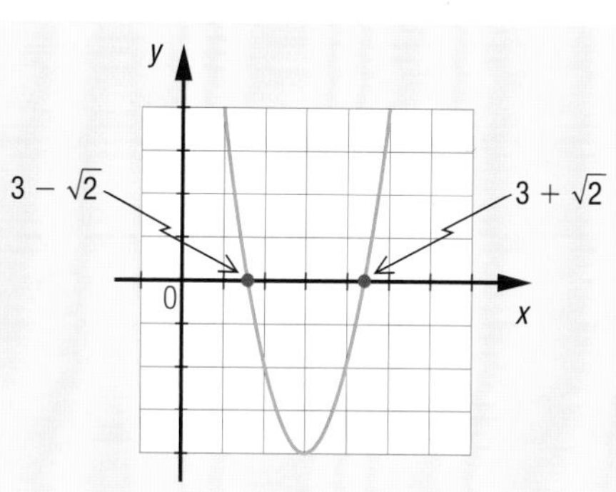

knowledge in action

1 Consider x to be the newsstand price of a scientific journal.

a) Translate each of the statements below into an inequality.

1) The journal costs more than $7.
2) Its price does not exceed $10.
3) When paying for two copies of the journal with a $20 bill, you get less than $4 in change.
4) A subscription for 12 copies of this journal costs 60% of the newsstand price; this represents a saving of more than $40.
5) If the price of the journal amounted to $4.50 more than its current price, it would cost at least three times more than if its price were $4.50 less.

b) Determine the possible price of a magazine that would satisfy all of these inequalities.

It is estimated that around 100 000 scientific articles are produced daily across the world, and that there are 200 000 scientific, technical and medical journals that publish them.

2 Solve the inequalities and express your answers using interval notation.

a) $3x + 6 < 0$ b) $2 - 4x \leq 0$ c) $\frac{-x}{2} + 2 > 0$

d) $3 - x \geq 7$ e) $4x - 5 < 1$ f) $2(x - 4) \leq 3x$

g) $3(x - 2) > 3x$ h) $4x + 1 < x - 5$ i) $x + 4 > x - 6$

3 Today, the temperature is 8°C less than it was yesterday at the same time, but the mean of these two temperatures is still above -5°C.

a) Translate this situation as an inequality and identify the variable used.

b) Considering that the thermometer has not hit 0°C on either days, in what interval does the present temperature fall?

4 Consider A and B, two real numbers such that $AB \leq 0$. What can you say about the value of B:

a) if $A < 0$? b) if $A > 0$? c) if $A = 0$?

5 Pat throws a stone from the top of a cliff. The stone first rises, then descends and falls into the sea. The height of the stone could be expressed in relation to the sea level, but it is also possible to express it in relation to the top of the cliff, that is, from the viewpoint of Pat as he stands there. In this case, the height of the stone (in m) is described by the function h whose rule is:

$h(t) = {}^{-}4.9(t - 1)^2 + 7.1$, where t is the time elapsed (in s).

a) Draw a graph of this function for the time interval from 0 to 3 s.

b) For how long does the stone rise?

c) What height does it reach in relation to the top of the cliff?

d) What is the y-intercept of this function? What does this value represent?

e) What do the negative values in your graph represent?

f) At what time interval is the height of the stone lower than the top of the cliff?

g) Considering that the stone fell into the sea after 3 s, determine the height of the cliff in relation to the sea level.

6 Following are three quadratic functions and their graphical representations. For each, determine the interval over which the function is negative.

a) $f(x) = (x - 2)^2 - 1$ b) $g(x) = {}^{-}0.8(x - 2)^2 + 5$ c) $h(x) = 2(x + 1)^2 - 3$

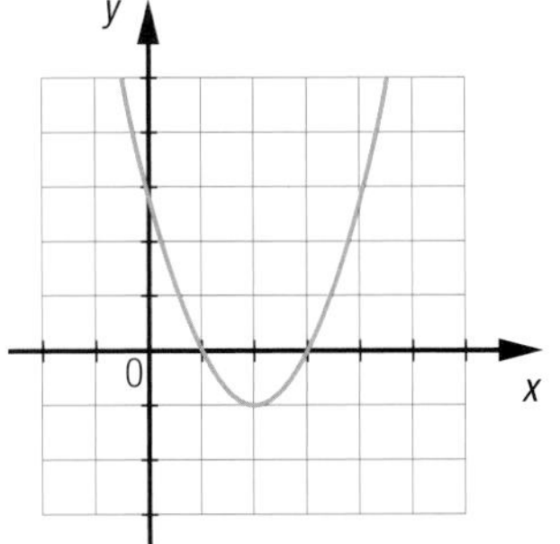

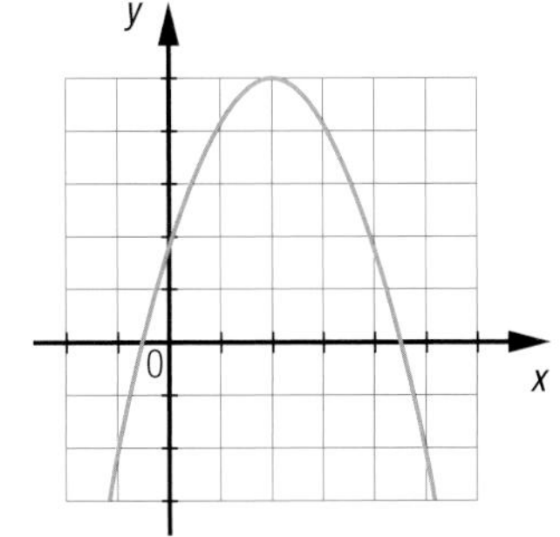

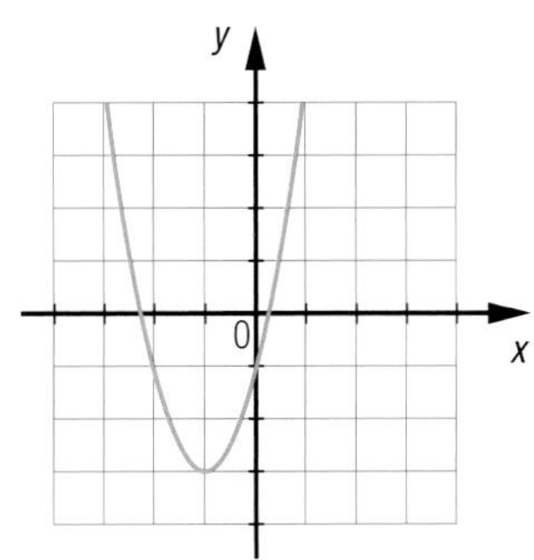

SECTION 4.1 The quadratic function: general form

This section is related to LES 10.

PROBLEM From the Earth to the Moon

The gravitational force on the Moon is around six times weaker than on Earth. This means that a free falling object on the Moon is subjected to six times lower acceleration than it would be if it were free falling on Earth. The laws of physics make it possible to study this phenomenon in greater detail.

The motion of an object in a gravitational field

When an object is thrown upward, the height (in m) of this object at any given moment varies according to the time elapsed (in s). The rule of this function is:

$$h(t) = \mathrm{a}t^2 + \mathrm{b}t + \mathrm{c}$$

Parameter **a** is proportional to the gravitational force. On the Moon, **a** $\approx$ -0.8 and on Earth, **a** $\approx$ -4.9. Parameter **b** refers to the initial velocity of the throw (in m/s), and parameter **c** represents the initial height (in m) of the object.

An astronaut who jumps from the last step of the ladder of the lunar module takes more than one second before landing on the lunar soil. On Earth, this same jump would take less than half a second.

On Earth, a ball is thrown from a height of 1 m at such velocity that it reaches a height of 3.5 m and falls to the ground 1.56 s later.

What would happen if this pitch were thrown on the Moon with the same initial velocity?

ACTIVITY 1 From general form to graphing

Observe the six following graphs; each represents a quadratic function.

Screen 1

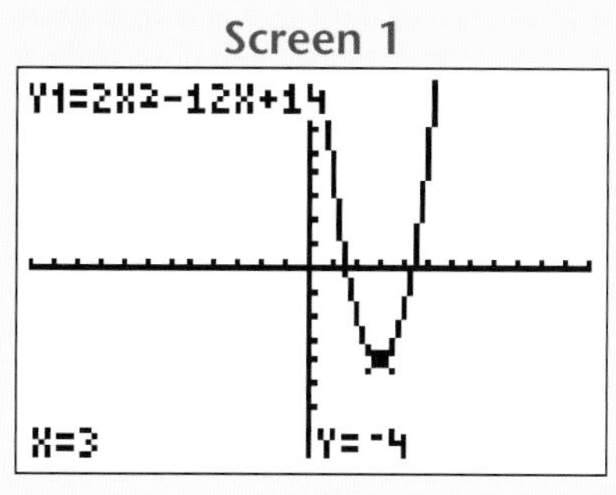

Screen 2

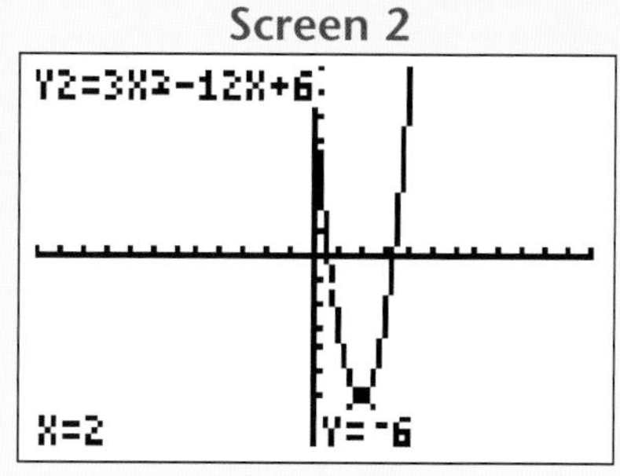

Screen 3

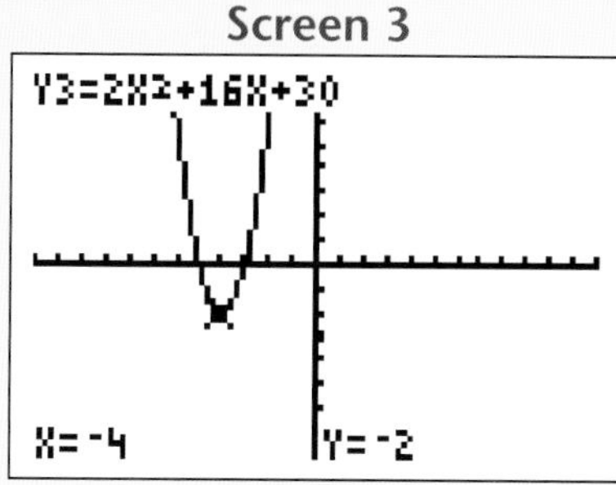

Screen 4

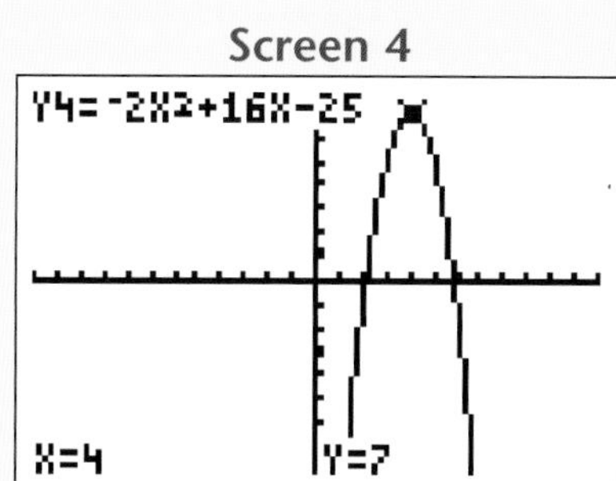

Screen 5

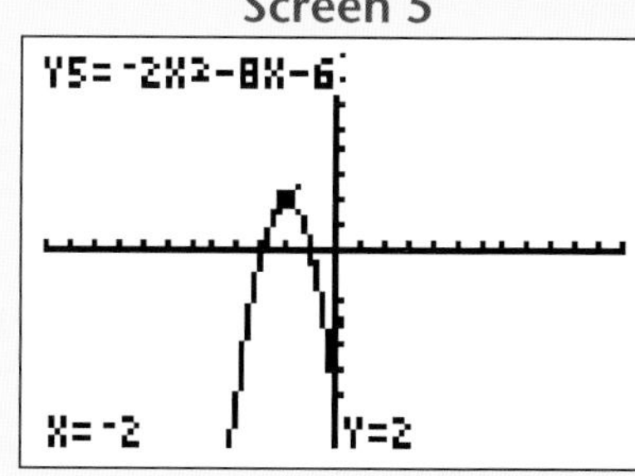

Screen 6

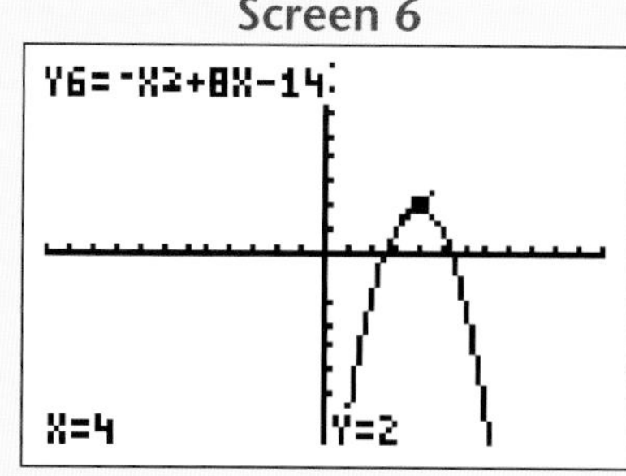

As in each of the above cases, the rule of a quadratic function can be written in general form:

$$f(x) = ax^2 + bx + c, \text{ where } a \neq 0.$$

The position of the vertex depends on parameters **a**, **b** and **c** of the equation.

a. Based on the information given, complete the table below, then formulate a conjecture that describes the relationship between the parameters of the function and the first coordinate of the vertex. If necessary, verify your conjecture by drawing the graphs of the quadratic functions with different values for parameters **a**, **b** and **c**.

Rule of the function	Value of a	Value of b	Value of c	x-coordinate of the vertex
$y_1 = 2x^2 - 12x + 14$				
$y_2 = 3x^2 - 12x + 6$				
$y_3 = 2x^2 + 16x + 30$				
$y_4 = -2x^2 + 16x - 25$				
$y_5 = -2x^2 - 8x - 6$				
$y_6 = -x^2 + 8x - 14$				

b. Prove the conjecture stated in **a.** by transforming the rule of a quadratic function from its standard form $f(x) = a(x - h)^2 + k$ into its general form $f(x) = ax^2 + bx + c$.

c. How can you determine the second coordinate of the vertex based on the general form of the rule? Use the function $f(x) = 2x^2 + 8x + 3$ as an example to illustrate the steps you propose.

ACTIVITY 2 Going from one form to the other

Part 1: Exploring the rule

a. The table below contains the rules for different quadratic functions expressed in the standard form or the general form. Copy and complete the table describing each step in your calculations.

Rule in the standard form	Rule in the general form	Coordinates of vertex	*y*-intercept
$f_1(x) = (x + 2)^2 - 9$		(,)	
$f_2(x) = 3(x - 1)^2 - 3$		(,)	
$f_3(x) = -2(x - 3)^2 + 10$		(,)	
	$f_4(x) = x^2 + 6x + 5$	(,)	
	$f_5(x) = 3x^2 - 6x - 2$	(,)	
	$f_6(x) = -4x^2 + 9x + 5$	(,)	

b. Use your own words to explain the steps one can follow to transform the rule of a quadratic function from the general form into the standard form.

c. Represent the rule of the function $f(x) = ax^2 + bx + c$ in its standard form using only parameters **a**, **b** and **c**.

In other words, you must write the rule in the form of:

$$f(x) = \blacksquare(x - \blacksquare)^2 + \blacksquare,$$

replacing each grey square with an expression using the parameters **a**, **b** and **c**.

Part 2: Look for the zeros

d. Based on the standard form of their rule, determine the zeros of functions f_1 to f_6 in the table above.

e. Find a formula that yields the zeros of a quadratic function written in the standard form $f(x) = a(x - h)^2 + k$.

f. Based on your answers in **c.** and in **e.**, find a formula that yields the zeros of a quadratic function written in the general form $f(x) = ax^2 + bx + c$.

ACTIVITY 3 Run for your life!

At the Science Centre, there is a booth dedicated to predators and their prey found in the African savannah. The lioness is an extremely fearsome predator.

A video shows a hungry lioness closing in on a kudu at a speed of 20 m/s. The kudu sees its predator and at the moment when the lioness is 30 m away, the kudu flees at a constant acceleration of 5 m/s^2.

During its acceleration, the kudu's lead (in m) on the lioness at time t of the pursuit (in s) can be translated as the following function: $f(t) = 2.5t^2 - 20t + 30$.

Will the lioness manage to sink her teeth into some kudu meat?

a. Using one of the methods proposed by these four students, find a solution and share it with a peer who used a different method.

b. Would the lioness have caught up with the kudu if the latter had started to flee when she was 50 m away?

c. If the kudu had started to flee when the lioness was 40 m away from it, would it have been able to save itself from its predator's fangs?

d. Compare the number of solutions obtained from solving the equations used in **a.**, **b.** and **c.** How can one predict the number of zeros of a quadratic function using the rule written in the general form?

Techno math

Dynamic geometry software allows you to simultaneously display the curves of several polynomial functions in the same Cartesian plane. One of the possibilities are the curves of second-degree polynomial functions. The software allows you to use tools such as: DISPLAY AXES, NUMBER, EXPRESSION AND APPLY EXPRESSION. Below are some explorations whereby you can observe the effect of changing parameters **a, b** and **c** on the graphical representation of a function whose rule is written in the form $f(x) = ax^2 + bx + c$.

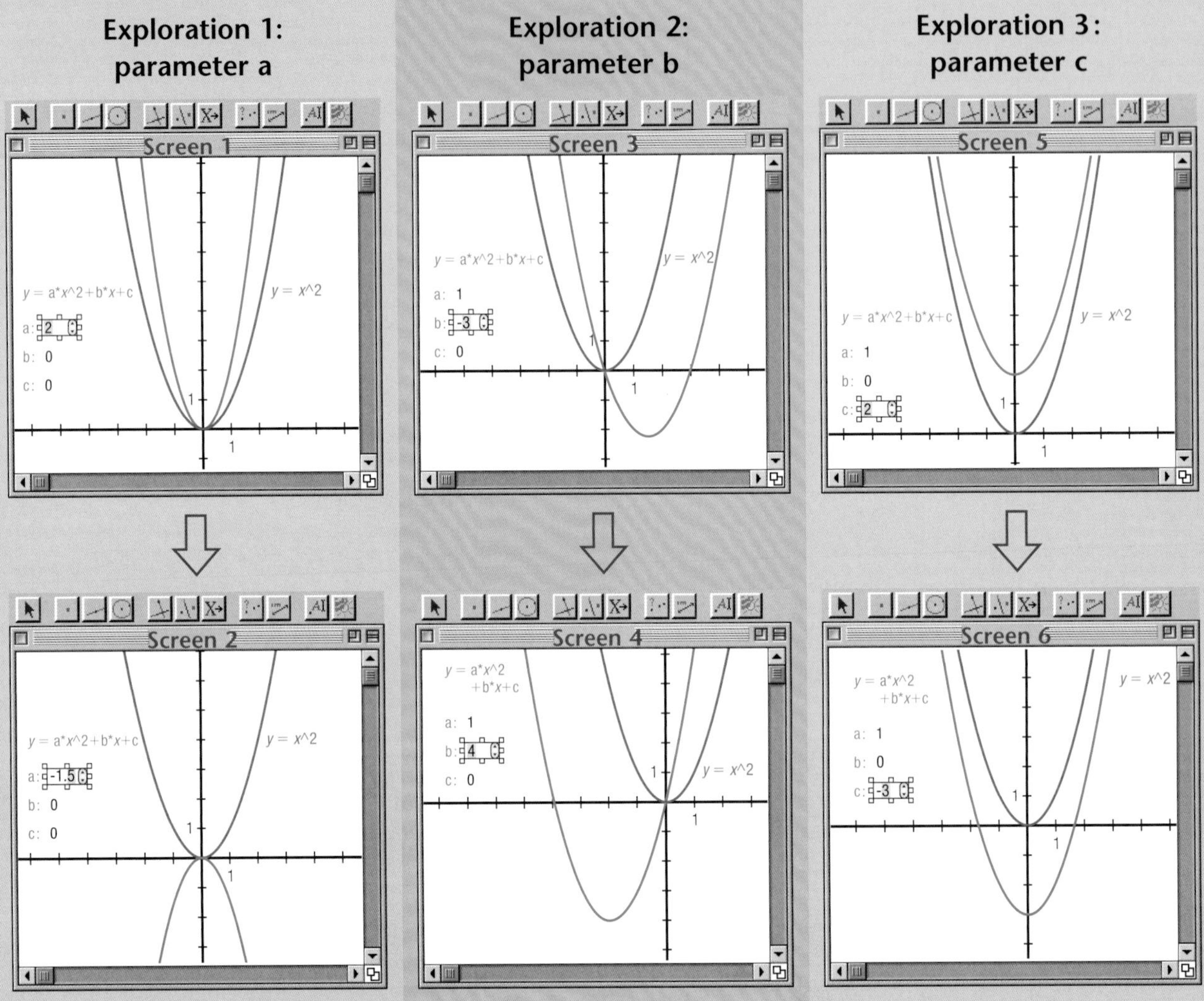

a. What is the effect on the graph of a second-degree polynomial function, written in the general form, when:

1) the value of **a** is increasingly distant from zero?
2) the value of **b** is increasingly distant from zero?
3) the value of **c** is increasingly distant from zero?

b. What parameters must be changed in order to generate a change in the coordinates of the vertex of the parabola?

c. Explore the effect of changing parameter **b** on the position of the vertex. What conjecture can you formulate as a result of this exploration?

knowledge 4.1

QUADRATIC FUNCTIONS EXPRESSED IN GENERAL FORM

The rule of a quadratic function can be represented in different forms as shown below.

1. The standard form $f(x) = a(x - h)^2 + k$, where $a \neq 0$.
2. The general form $f(x) = ax^2 + bx + c$, where $a \neq 0$.

Converting from the standard form to the general form

To convert from the standard form of the rule to its equivalent general form, expand and simplify the algebraic expression that describes the image of x.

E.g. Consider $f(x) = 3(x - 2)^2 - 5$

Expand and simplify: $3(x - 2)^2 - 5 = 3(x^2 - 4x + 4) - 5$

$= 3x^2 - 12x + 7$

The general form of the rule is therefore $f(x) = 3x^2 - 12x + 7$.

Converting from the general form to the standard form

By expanding the standard form $f(x) = a(x - h)^2 + k$ and comparing the result to the general form, observe that **b** = $-2ah$ and **c** = $ah^2 + k$.

From these equalities, you can also deduce that:

$$\mathbf{h} = \frac{-b}{2a} \quad \text{and} \quad \mathbf{k} = \frac{4ac - b^2}{4a}$$

It is therefore possible, based on the general form of the rule, to deduce the coordinates (h, k) of the vertex, then to determine the standard form of this rule, considering that the value of **a** is the same in both forms.

E.g. Consider $f(x) = 2x^2 - 28x + 110$.

The x-coordinate of the vertex is 7 since $\frac{-b}{2a} = \frac{-(-28)}{2(2)} = 7$.

The y-coordinate of the vertex can be calculated as follows:

$f(7) = 2(7)^2 - 28(7) + 110$

$= 12$

The vertex is therefore located at (7, 12).
The standard form of the rule is
$f(x) = 2(x - 7)^2 + 12$.

It is also possible to calculate the y-coordinate of the vertex using this expression:

$$\frac{4ac - b^2}{4a} = \frac{4(2)(110) - (-28)^2}{4(2)} = 12$$

Graphical representation

To draw the graph of a quadratic function, you can first determine the position of the vertex and the axis of symmetry.

E.g. Consider $f(x) = 2x^2 - 28x + 110$.

The vertex is point S(7, 12).

The axis of symmetry is a vertical line of which the equation is $x = 7$.

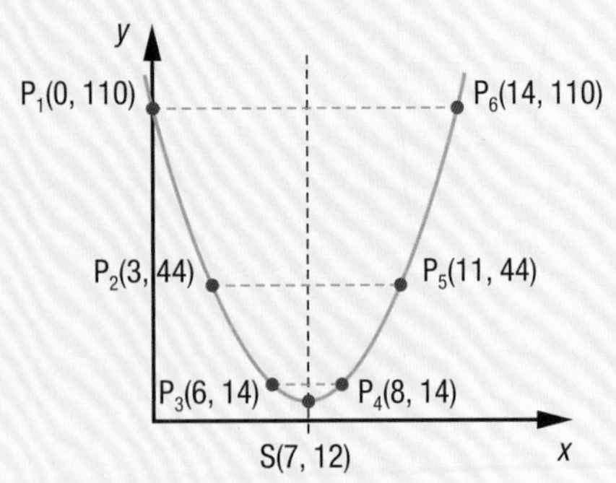

The equation of the axis of symmetry of the curve representing a quadratic function is in the form $x = h$.

Zeros of the function

Different methods are used to determine the zeros of a quadratic function:

- using a technological tool
- by factoring
- by completing the square
- using the quadratic formula

Determining the zeros of a quadratic function expressed in the general form amounts to solving the equation of the form $ax^2 + bx + c = 0$.

The quadratic formula

When the quadratic function is represented as an equation in the general form $f(x) = ax^2 + bx + c$, you can determine the zeros (x_1 and x_2) using the following formula:

$$x_1 = \frac{-b + \sqrt{b^2 - 4ac}}{2a} \quad \text{and} \quad x_2 = \frac{-b - \sqrt{b^2 - 4ac}}{2a}$$

E.g. The zeros of the function $f(x) = -2x^2 + 3x - 1$ are: $x = \frac{-b \pm \sqrt{b^2 - 4ac}}{2a} = \frac{-3 \pm \sqrt{3^2 - 4(-2)(-1)}}{2(-2)} = \frac{-3 \pm 1}{-4}$

$x_1 = 0.5$ and $x_2 = 1$

The number of zeros and the role of the discriminant

In the quadratic formula $x = \frac{-b \pm \sqrt{b^2 - 4ac}}{2a}$, the word "discriminant" is used to refer to the expression $b^2 - 4ac$. The sign of the discriminant allows you to predict the number of zeros in the function.

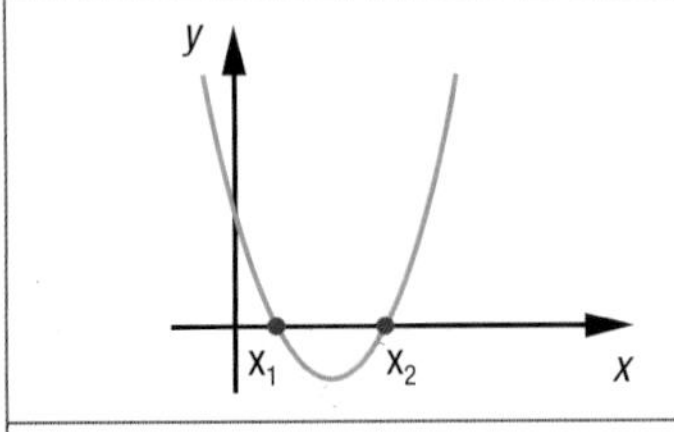	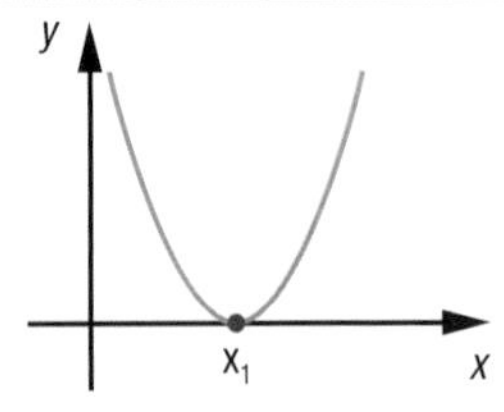	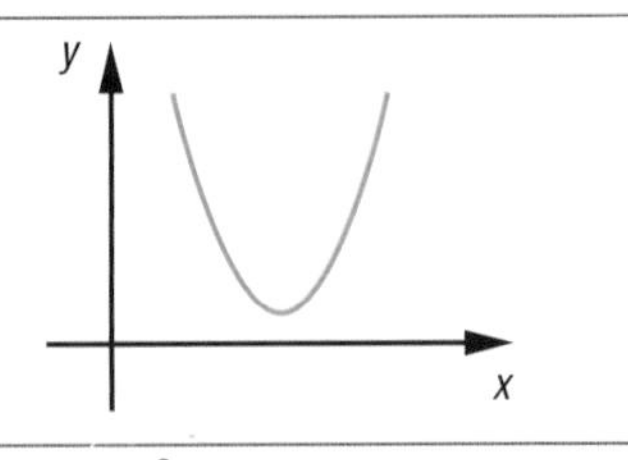
If $b^2 - 4ac > 0$, there are two zeros.	If $b^2 - 4ac = 0$, there is only one zero.	If $b^2 - 4ac < 0$, there is no zero.

practice 4.1

1 The following are six quadratic functions:

① $f(x) = 8x^2$ ② $f(x) = x^2 - 5x + 6$ ③ $f(x) = 3x^2 + 3x - 60$

④ $f(x) = -4x^2 + 16$ ⑤ $f(x) = -2.5x^2 + 5x$ ⑥ $f(x) = 2x^2 + 3.4x - 9.6$

For each of these functions, do the following:

a) State the location of the axis of symmetry.

b) Determine the coordinates of the vertex.

c) Determine at least five other points on the graph.

d) Sketch the graph of the function.

2 The following are the rules, in standard form, of four quadratic functions:

① $f_1(x) = (x - 3)^2 - 1$ ② $f_2(x) = -2(x + 1)^2$

③ $f_3(x) = -3(x + 2)^2 + 12$ ④ $f_4(x) = -2(x - 4)^2 - 6$

For each of these functions, do the following:

a) Determine the coordinates of the vertex.

b) Determine the zeros of the function algebraically, if any.

c) Convert the rule from the standard form to the general form algebraically.

d) Based on the general form, check that the first coordinate of the vertex indeed equals $\frac{-b}{2a}$ and the second coordinate equals $\frac{4ac - b^2}{4a}$.

e) Based on the general form, calculate the zeros of the function by applying the quadratic formula. Check that you get the same answer as in **b)**.

3 The following are the rules in general form, of four quadratic functions:

① $f_1(x) = x^2 - 10x + 10$ ② $f_2(x) = 2x^2 + 4x - 12$

③ $f_3(x) = -3x^2 + 12x + 10$ ④ $f_4(x) = 2x^2 + 3x + 4$

For each of these functions, do the following:

a) Determine the coordinates of the vertex.

b) Convert the equation from the general form to the standard form.

4 Parameter **c** of the rule of a specific quadratic function expressed in the general form equals parameter **k** of the standard form. What can you say regarding the value of parameters **b** and **h**? Justify your answer.

5 Specify the number of zeros in the following quadratic functions and, where they exist, determine their value.

a) $f(x) = x^2 + 5x - 6$
b) $f(x) = x^2 + 4x + 4$
c) $f(x) = -2x^2 - 20x - 48$
d) $f(x) = 5x^2 - 8x + 4$
e) $f(x) = x^2 + 3\sqrt{2}x + 4$
f) $f(x) = -x^2 + 2x - 1$

6 The following are three quadratic functions:

1 $f(x) = x^2 - 6x + 5$
2 $g(x) = -4x^2 - 16x - 16$
3 $h(x) = -3x^2 + x - 4$

For each of these functions, determine the following properties:

a) the equation of the axis of symmetry
b) the range of the function
c) the coordinates of the vertex
d) the *y*-intercept
e) the maximum or the minimum
f) the zeros
g) the increasing interval
h) the decreasing interval
i) the interval(s) where the function is positive
j) the interval(s) where the function is negative

7 From the top of a cliff, 120 m above sea level, a device launches a clay pigeon up into the air. You can represent the pigeon's height $h(t)$ (in m) in relation to the sea according to the amount of time t elapsed (in s) since the launch with the equation $h(t) = 120 + 15t - 5t^2$.

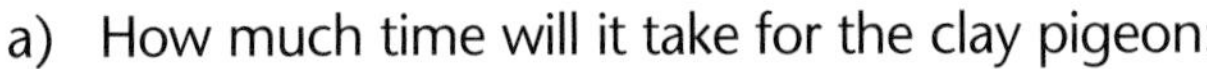

a) How much time will it take for the clay pigeon:
   1) to reach its maximum height?
   2) to reach the sea?

b) A marksman's bullet reaches the clay pigeon at a height of 130 m. How much time after the launch will the pigeon be hit?

Clay pigeons, or targets, are used in moving target practice.

8 It is possible to convert the rule of a quadratic function from the general form to the standard form using algebraic manipulations. Observe the adjacent example.

$$\begin{aligned} f(x) &= x^2 + 8x + 3 \\ &= x^2 + 8x + 16 - 16 + 3 \\ &= (x^2 + 8x + 16) - 13 \\ &= (x + 4)^2 - 13 \end{aligned}$$

a) Using the same approach, convert the following rules into the standard form:
   1) $f_1(x) = x^2 - 4x + 1$
   2) $f_2(x) = x^2 + 3x - 4$
   3) $f_3(x) = x^2 - x - 1$

b) For all of the preceding functions, parameter **a** equals 1. How could you proceed, using algebraic manipulations, in order to obtain the standard form if parameter **a** were different from 1? Apply your method to the function $f_4(x) = 3x^2 - 6x + 5$.

9 **TEMPERATURE** It sometimes happens for a few hours that the outside temperature varies according to a quadratic function. The adjacent graph represents the temperatures recorded in Montréal between 7:00 a.m. and 9:00 p.m. on a February day. The scatter plot was modelled using a function T whose rule is shown below the graph.

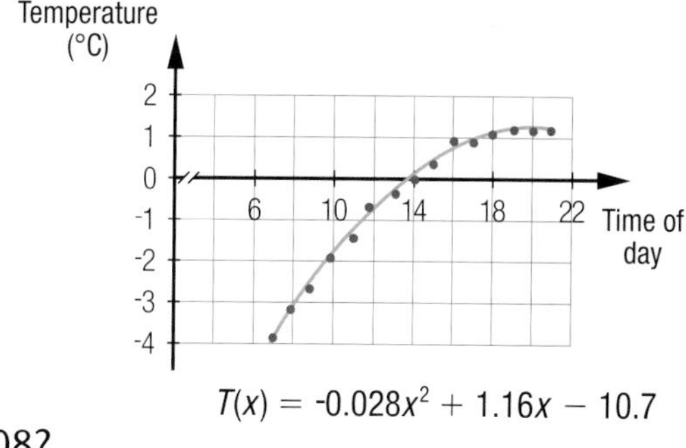

$T(x) = -0.028x^2 + 1.16x - 10.7$

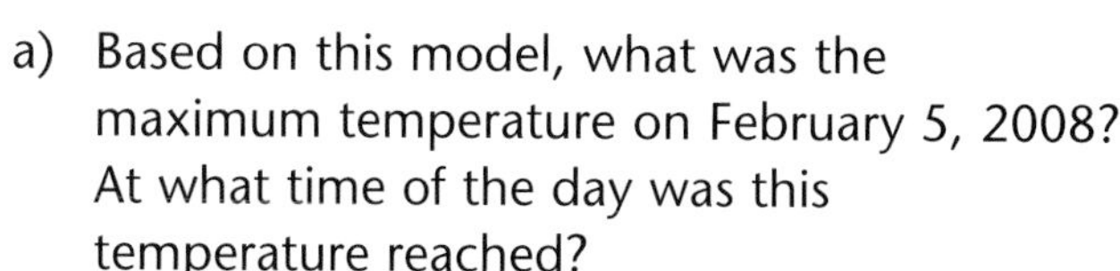

a) Based on this model, what was the maximum temperature on February 5, 2008? At what time of the day was this temperature reached?

b) Around what time was it 0°C?

c) What is the y-intercept of this function? How might you interpret it in this context?

10 Fred is a cartoonist. During the summer, he offers his services to tourists. He has noticed that the price he charges to do a cartoon has a major impact on the number of clients he attracts. In fact, the demand to be met by his small business can be modelled using the function $D(x) = 32 - 0.8x$, where x is the price (in \$) of a cartoon and $D(x)$, is the mean number of daily clients he attracts with this price. Of course, the higher the price, the fewer clients he gets.

a) Determine the rule of the function $R(x)$ which represents his mean daily income in relation to the price charged.

b) Determine the domain and range of function R in this context.

c) What do the zeros of this function represent in this context?

d) What price should Fred charge in order to maximize his income?

e) What price should he charge to get a mean income of \$250 per day:

   1) if his goal is to become well-known?

   2) if his goal is to work as little as possible?

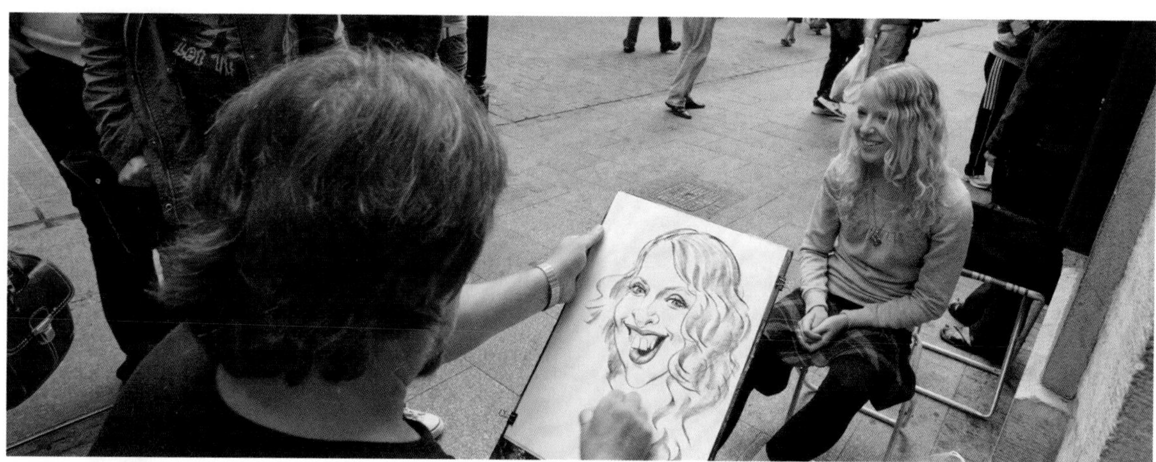

11 Objects have been falling since the beginning of time. It was not until the 16th and 17th centuries that scientists really understood the physical and mathematical principles underscoring the phenomenon. Galileo (1564-1642) and Newton (1642-1727) took a keen interest in falling objects. Their studies opened the door to the following principle:

If an object, initially at rest, free falls from a height of h_0 metres with negligable air resistance, its height, t seconds after the start of its fall, is approximately $(h_0 - 4.9t^2)$ metres.

Thus, if you drop a marble from the top of the Tower of Pisa, you can determine the height of the marble in the course of its fall according to the elapsed fall time with the following function:

$$h(t) = 54.5 - 4.9t^2$$

As soon as it was completed in 1350, the Tower of Pisa was already leaning at an angle of nearly 1.5°. The tower was closed to the public during the 1990s for some reinforcement work. Its inclination at the time had reached 5.5°.

a) What distance will the marble have travelled:

1) during the first second of its fall?

2) during the first two seconds of its fall?

b) How much time will have elapsed before it reaches the ground?

c) How much time will have elapsed by the time it is 10 m from the ground?

d) Answer questions **a)**, **b)** and **c)** again considering that this same marble is thrown from the top of a tower twice as high as the Tower of Pisa.

12 Natasha represented the equation $y = -0.3x^2 + 15x - 125$ on her calculator and obtained the display shown below in Screen **1**. Not satisfied with the result, she checked the dimensions in the window of Screen **2**.

Screen 1

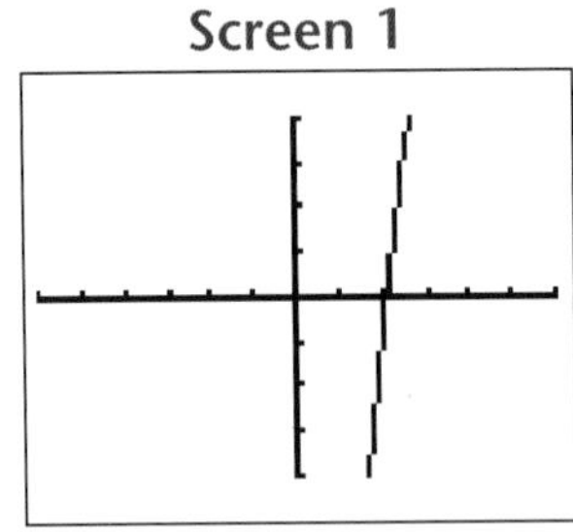

Screen 2

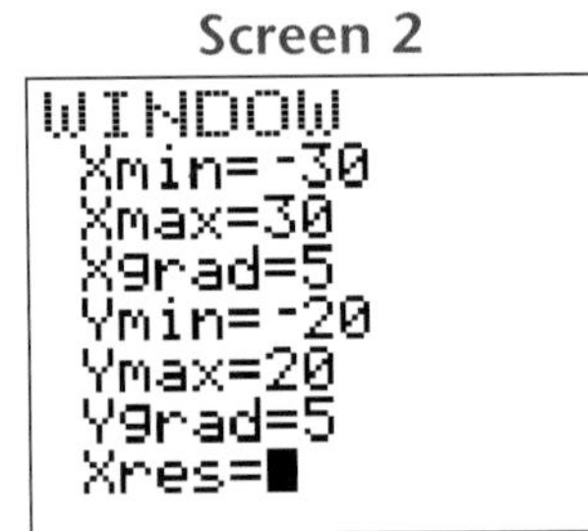

a) How might she change the parameters Xmin, Xmax, Ymin and Ymax in order to make sure that all the characteristics of the parabola (vertex, y-intercept, x-intercepts) appear in the graphical display?

b) Check your answer in **a)** by displaying this graph on a calculator. Then, sketch the representation obtained and show all coordinates that define the properties of this function.

13 An artist wants to make a stained glass square with sides measuring 60 cm. By placing four points at equal distance from the vertices ABCD of the large square, he creates a new square EFGH. Both squares are shown below.

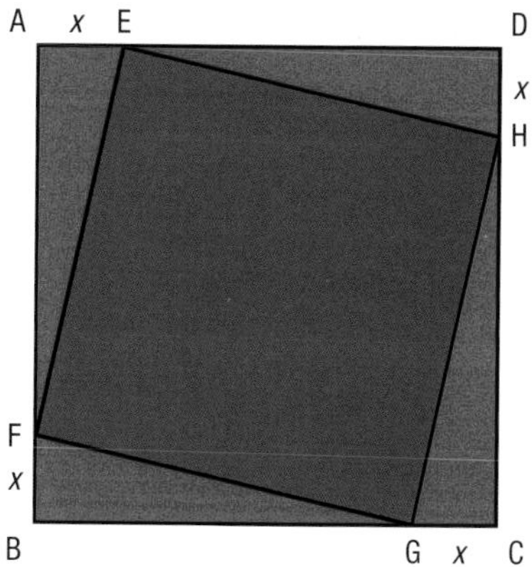

a) Define, in the general form, the rule of function *f* that allows you to determine the area of square EFGH according to the specified distance *x*.

b) Determine the *y*-intercept of this function and specify what this value represents in the present context.

c) Determine the minimum of this function. What does it represent in this context?

d) Determine the increasing and decreasing intervals of function *f*.

14 Along a wall, there is a rectangular garden with a fence that is 10 m long. As illustrated in the adjacent diagram, variable *x* represents the length in metres of the two parallel sides of the fence. The area of the garden can be expressed as a quadratic function of *x*.

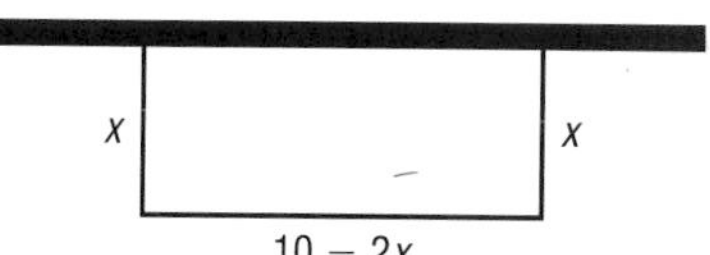

a) Determine the rule of this function in its general form.

b) What is the domain of the function in this context?

c) What is the range of the function?

d) For what value of *x* will the function reach the maximum?

e) What should the dimensions of the garden be so that the area is exactly 10 m^2?

15 Using the properties of the quadratic function, prove the following property for equivalent figures:

> Among all rectangles with a given perimeter, the square has the greatest area.

SECTION 4.2 The quadratic function and inequalities

This section is related to LES 10.

PROBLEM Colonizing space

Is it conceivable that we may some day be able to build an immense habitat in which a colony of human beings would live permanently somewhere between the Earth and the Moon? Is this science fiction? Perhaps not... Many scientists have pondered this very question.

In his book entitled *The High Frontier: Human Colonies in Space*, Gerard K. O'Neill, a physicist and professor at Princeton, explores this potential for human settlement in space orbit. In this book, he proposes a space habitat in the form of a glass cylinder 30 km long!

Why a cylinder?

Amongst the obstacles facing life in space, there is the fact that human beings cannot survive long periods of weightlessness. Therefore, gravity must be stimulated by making our environment rotate. The cylinder is probably the best possible shape to do this.

Inside view of O'Neill's cylinder.

Of course the inner surface of the cylinder would have to be large enough to sustain the entire colony's needs and well-being.

What should the radius of O'Neill's imagined cylinder be in order for its surface area to be at least 500 km²?

ACTIVITY 1 A room with a view

A company is in the business of designing and manufacturing windows. One of these, a rectangular-shaped window, has an opening of 30 dm by 10 dm. A real estate developer is interested in this model for one of his projects, but he would like the window to provide an outside view of at least 350 dm^2.

The company's manager asks the following question: Is it possible to design a window with an opening of at least 350 dm^2 while maintaining this model's perimeter? In this case, one would have to increase the width and decrease the height.

Consider x to be the width (in dm) of the new window.

a. Determine the rule of function f which represents the area of this window.

b. Draw the graph of function f.

c. What values should be applied to variable x so that $f(x) = 350$?

d. What x values could the company choose in order to meet the requirements of the developer?

Now imagine that the original model of the window measured 28 dm by 10 dm.

e. With this window model, is it possible to meet the requirements of the developer? Explain your answer.

ACTIVITY 2 Two strategies

Alice and Alan are struggling with the following problem.

Side AB is the longest side of triangle ABC shown in the adjacent illustration. For what x-values will this be an acute triangle?

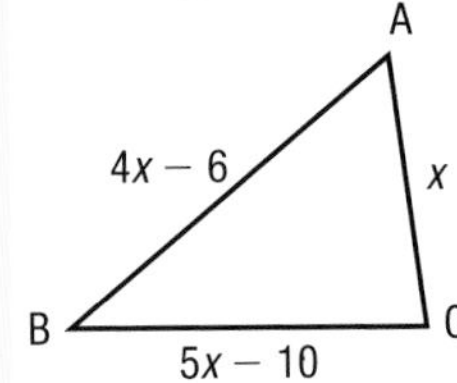

Considering that a triangle is an acute triangle if and only if the square of the longest side is less than the sum of the squares of the two other sides, you can write: $(4x - 6)^2 < x^2 + (5x - 10)^2$.

a. Show that the inequality above is equivalent to $5x^2 - 26x + 32 > 0$.

As usual, Alice and Alan have two very different ways of solving this last inequality.

In my opinion, all you need to do is to factor the trinomial then apply the sign rules in the multiplication of two numbers.

For my approach, I prefer a more visual solution... It seems the problem would be clearer using the graph of a function.

b. Following Alice's suggestion, factor the trinomial.

c. If the product AB of two numbers is positive, what can be said about the sign of A and of B?

d. Complete the sign chart below in order to analyze the sign of the two binomials found in **b.**

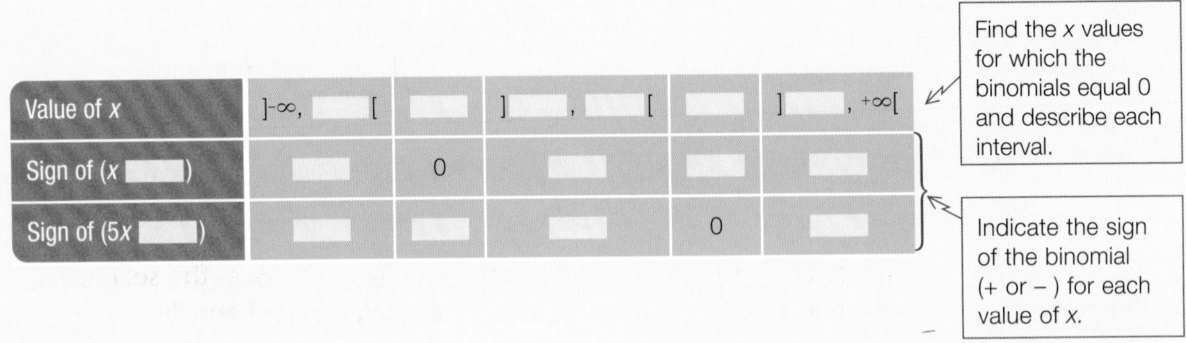

Value of x	]-∞, ___ [	___	] ___ , ___ [	___	] ___ , +∞[
Sign of (x ___)	___	0	___	___	___
Sign of ($5x$ ___)	___	___	___	0	___

e. For what x values will the product of the two binomials be greater than 0?

f. Alan's way of tackling the problem is quite different. He says, "Let's imagine a function of which the rule will be $f(x) = 5x^2 - 26x + 32$. Then let's conduct a graphical analysis of the sign of this function." Show that with this approach Alan will get the same answer as Alice.

g. For what x values will triangle ABC be an acute triangle?

knowledge 4.2

INEQUALITIES INVOLVING A QUADRATIC FUNCTION

In certain situations represented by a quadratic function, sometimes it is necessary to try to determine what the values of the independent variable should be in order for the dependent variable to be part of a given interval. For a function f, this type of problem generally translates into one of the following inequalities:

$f(x) <$ given value $f(x) \leq$ given value $f(x) >$ given value $f(x) \geq$ given value

To solve such an inequality, you can draw the graph of the function in the Cartesian plane as well as a horizontal line passing through the given value. The intersection point of the curve of the function and the horizontal line will result in the values that you are looking for.

Determining the sign of a function is a special case in this type of problem. Under such circumstances, the given value is 0 and the horizontal line is the x-axis.

E.g. The height of the centre of gravity of an acrobat during one of her trampoline jumps is represented by the function $h(t) = -5t^2 + 12t + 1$. At what moment is her centre of gravity at a height of more than 5 m?

- In the graph of function h, draw the horizontal line passing through the given value 5.
- This horizontal line intersects the curve at two points, resulting in 0.4 and 2 as values for t.
- The t values for which $h(t) > 5$ is between $t = 0.4$ and $t = 2$.
- Therefore, the acrobat's centre of gravity at a height of more than 5 m is between 0.4 s and 2 s.

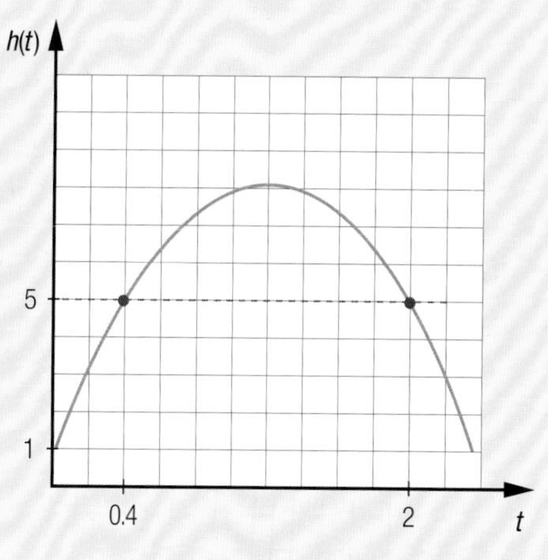

It is possible that the horizontal line does not intersect the curve. In this case, the solution will be the empty set or the whole domain of the function depending on the inequality of the function being considered.

E.g. In the above situation, at what moment is the acrobat's centre of gravity at a height of more than 9 m? And at less than 9 m?

The maximum height reached is 8.2 m; therefore, the centre of gravity is never higher than 9 m. The acrobat's centre of gravity is always lower than 9 m.

Second-degree inequalities in one variable

Other situations not explicitly linked to a quadratic function can be translated as a second-degree inequality in one variable.

E.g. A rectangular whiteboard has a perimeter of 14 m. What dimensions can it have so that its area is less than 10 m²?

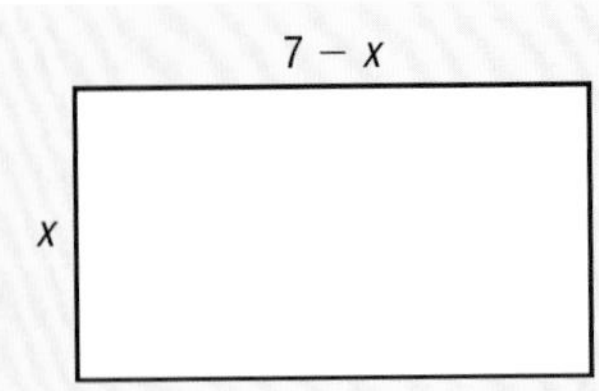

If x represents the height of the board, then $7 - x$ represents the length of its base.

The area of the whiteboard is therefore represented with the expression $x(7 - x)$, hence the following inequality to be solved:

$$x(7 - x) < 10$$
$$-x^2 + 7x < 10$$
$$-x^2 + 7x - 10 < 0 \text{ or } x^2 - 7x + 10 > 0.$$

The context suggests that you solve this inequality in the interval]0, 7[since the dimensions of the board are greater than 0 m.

Different methods can be used to solve a second-degree inequality.

The algebraic method

E.g. In the above example, in order to solve $-x^2 + 7x - 10 < 0$, it is possible to decompose the left side of the inequality into factors.

Result: $(-x + 5)(x - 2) < 0$.

When x is 5 or 2, the left side equals 0.

Value of x	]-∞, 2[	2	]2, 5[	5	]5, +∞[
Sign of $(-x + 5)$	+	+	+	0	-
Sign of $(x - 2)$	-	0	+	+	+

This type of table is called a sign chart. The product of two numbers of opposite signs produces a result that is negative.

Therefore, in order for the left side of the inequality to be less than 0, x must take on the values of]-∞, 2[∪]5, +∞[.

The graphical method

It is possible to solve an inequality by graphing the equality, defining it and analyzing the sign of the resulting representation.

E.g. In the above example, solving the inequality amounts to analyzing the sign of the function defined as $f(x) = -x^2 + 7x - 10$.

By graphically representing this function, you can see that x must take on the values of]-∞, 2[∪]5, +∞[in order for $f(x)$ to be less than 0.

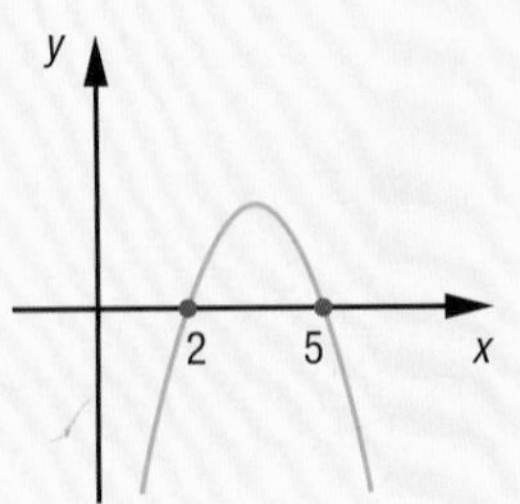

The solution must always be interpreted in relation to the context.

E.g. Thus, the rectangular whiteboard will have an area less than 10 m² if its height is less than 2 m or is between 5 and 7 m.

practice 4.2

1 Consider $f(x) = -2x^2 + 10x - 12$.

a) Draw the graph of function f.

b) For what x-values will function f be positive?

c) For what x-values is:

1) $f(x) > -4$ 2) $f(x) \leq -2$ 3) $f(x) \geq \frac{1}{2}$ 4) $f(x) < 2$

2 Complete the sign chart below in order to solve the following inequality:

$$(5 - 2x)(x + 2) \leq 0$$

Value of x	]-∞,-2[	-2	]-2,2.5[	2.5	]2.5,∞[
Sign of (5 − 2x)	+	+	+	0	−
Sign of (x + 2)	−	0	+	+	+

3 Solve the following inequalities using the algebraic method.

a) $(2x - 1)(x + 3) > 0$ b) $(1 - 2x)(4 - 2x) < 0$ c) $(4x + 10)(2x - 7) \leq 0$

d) $x^2 - 64 > 0$ e) $-x^2 + 2x - 1 < 0$ f) $5x^2 < 8x + 4$

g) $x^2 + 5x \geq -6$ h) $x(x + 6) + 9 \geq 16$ i) $(x - 1)(x + 2) > 4$

4 Solve each of the following inequalities using the graphical method.

a) $x^2 + 5x + 6 > 0$ b) $2x^2 - 4x + 2 < 0$ c) $-x^2 - 1 \leq 0$

d) $-3x^2 + 2x < 1$ e) $2(-1.5x^2 + x + 5) \geq 10$ f) $2x^2 \geq 4x + 3$

5 At the request of a car insurance company, an actuary establishes a relationship between the age of a person driving a car and the probability that he or she will have a car accident in the next five years. The actuary uses the rule $P(x) = 0.0005x^2 - 0.045x + 1.25$ where x represents the age of the driver (in years).

The insurance company decides that a person is a high risk if there is a one out of two chance that he or she will have an accident in the next five years.

a) How old are the people who are considered to be high risk by this company?

The company invites its employees to offer a discount to anyone whose chance of having an accident is less than 20%.

b) What do you think of this discount? Justify your answer.

6 A worker must design closed casings from wood panels. These casings, shown in the diagram below, will always have the "L" shape composed of a cube that links together two square-based prisms of 10 cm in height for any dimensions of the cube.

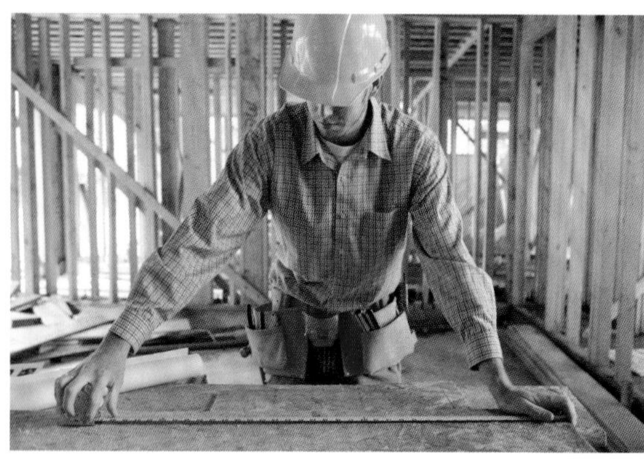

The worker has been instructed to design casings requiring no more than 600 dm^2 of wood panelling each.

a) Considering that s represents the length of an edge of the cube, show that this situation can be translated as the inequality $6s^2 + 80s - 600 \leq 0$.

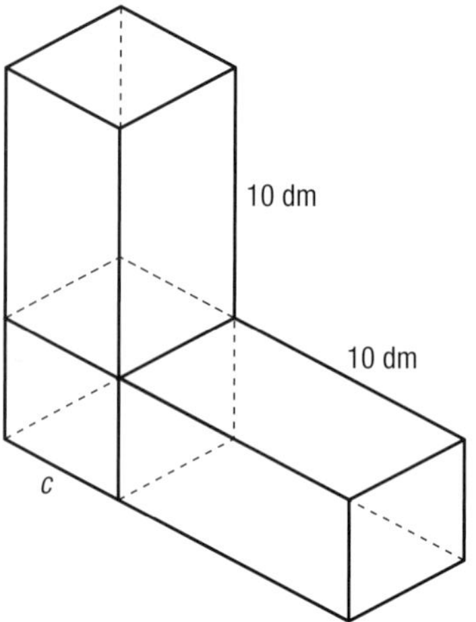

b) For each of the following lengths of the cube's edge, does the work comply with the constraint given in **a)**?

1) $s = 2$
2) $s = 3$
3) $s = 7$

c) What length should be given to the cube's edge in order to comply with the stated constraints?

7 A surveyor wants to increase the dimensions of two square-shaped lots. As illustrated below, she wants to add the same length to each side.

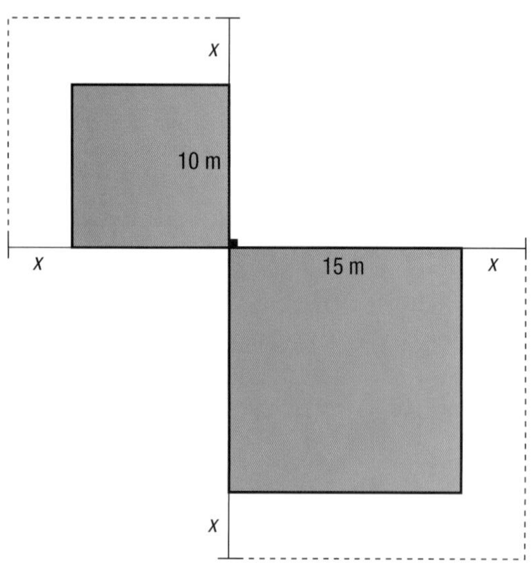

Surveyors are responsible for conducting official surveys for the purpose of assessing lot dimensions and of setting the location of property boundaries.

What lengths should be assigned to the additions so that the total area of the two lots does not exceed 1000 m^2?

8 Shaking hands is a very common ritual in many societies.

Imagine a political event where each participant, without exception, shakes hands with each of the other participants, without shaking anyone's hand twice.

a) Define, in general form, the rule of function f which makes it possible to determine the number of handshakes based on the number of people present.

b) How many people would have to attend this event in order for 10 000 handshakes to be exchanged?

It is said that the custom of shaking hands goes back to the time of chivalry. By offering his right hand, a knight showed that he would not use his weapon to attack his rival.

9 Joelle loves bungee jumping and is in fact working on developing new polymers that go into the making of a bungee cord.

A laboratory has tested a 20 cm sample of the latest bungee cord design and subjected it to a stretch s going up to 1 m. The test results showed that the force (in N) undergone by the bungee cord in relation to the stretch (in cm) is governed by the following rule:

$$F(s) = 3.2s^2 + 5s$$

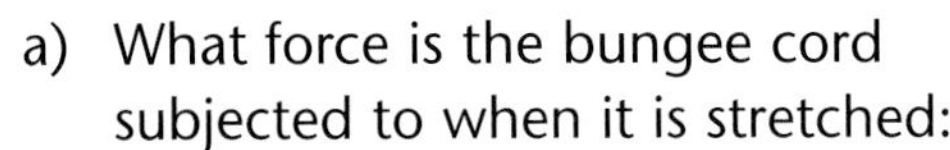

a) What force is the bungee cord subjected to when it is stretched:

1) 0 cm? 2) 10 cm? 3) 100 cm?

Before marketing the new bungee cord, Joelle must make sure that it can endure, without snapping, a force between 20 000 N and 30 000 N more than 1000 times.

b) Suggest a procedure that would allow Joelle to conduct this test. Justify it using mathematical arguments.

Bungee jumping is an extreme sport that consists of hurling oneself from the height of a crane or bridge with a bungee cord attached to one's ankles. In freefall, the jumper reaches a speed of around 100 km/h before coming back up in an ascending curve.

10 Consider the function $f(x) = ax^2 - 4x + 4$ where parameter **a** can take on any real value between 5 and 10 inclusively. What value must you assign to this parameter in order for all the x-values to be solutions to the inequality $f(x) \geq 3.4$? Justify your answer.

11 At the Science Centre, there is an exhibit on the energy efficiency of a green home that draws its energy from a small wind generator. To meet the energy needs of the household, the wind generator must be able to develop a power level greater than 2.5 kW.

After a visit to this centre, Joanne and John decide to set up a wind generator behind their house located in the Lac St-Jean region. The specifications of the wind generator state that with winds between 20 km/h and 60 km/h, the power (in W) developed by the generator is a function of wind speed x (in km/h). It is governed by the following rule:

$$f(x) = -4.2x^2 + 367x - 4967$$

a) What is the maximum power output of this wind generator?

b) What is the wind speed required in order for Joanne and John to be able to use only the energy provided by the wind generator to meet their energy needs?

12 The Safety Cone Company has received precise technical requirements to be used in the making of cone markers. Following is the diagram of these requirements:

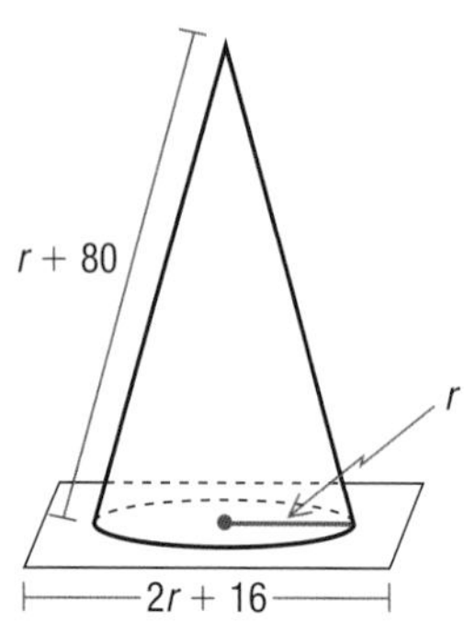

- The cone marker must sit on a square base.
- The area of the lateral surface of the cone must be at least double that of the square base.

a) Show that this situation can be represented by the inequality $(\pi - 8)r^2 + (80\pi - 128)r - 512 \geq 0$, where r is the radius of the cone (in cm).

b) Determine the possible dimensions of the cone.

c) Could you meet the requirements of the municipality if the cone's slant height measured 70 cm more than the radius, rather than 80 cm? Justify your answer.

13 The objective of a high jump is very simple: get your whole body over a horizontal bar. In order to succeed, athletes must develop sufficient vertical velocity to raise their centre of gravity higher than the height of the bar for at least 0.2 s.

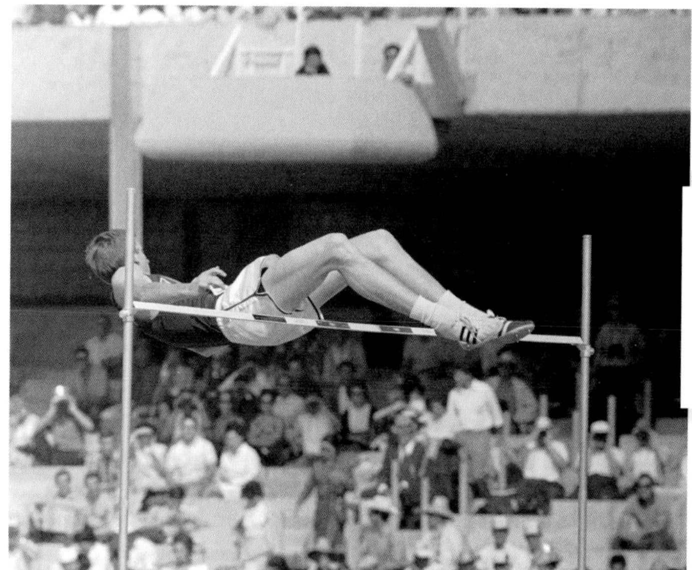

In 1968, during the Olympic Games in Mexico, Dick Fosbury jumped over a bar set at a height of 2.24 m and won the gold medal. He achieved this feat thanks to a new jumping technique that now bears his name. Nearly all high jumpers today use this technique.

The height h (in m) that Jim can reach during a jump can be represented by the rule $h(t) = -4.9t^2 + 4.6t + 1.2$, where t is the time (in s).

a) What does the value of parameter **c** represent in this rule?

b) What is the maximum height that Jim can reach during a jump?

c) During his first attempt, the bar was set at a height of 2.10 m. At what moment was his centre of gravity higher than the height of the bar?

d) Would Jim have succeeded in beating Dick Fosbury in 1968 with such a jump? Justify your answer.

14 The sign chart can be used to solve inequalities that are not of the second-degree. This method can be used to identify when the image of the function is positive or negative. This can be written in the form of a product or quotient of first-degree polynomials.

For example, below is an inequality that is in the form of a rational expression:

$$\frac{x-2}{4-x} < 0$$

a) For what values of x is this rational expression well defined?

b) If $\frac{A}{B} < 0$, what can the signs for A and B be?

c) Using a sign chart, solve the inequality.

d) Using the same strategy as above, solve the following inequalities:

1) $\frac{2x+1}{2x-1} \leq 0$ 2) $(x+1)(2x-1)(4x+2) > 0$ 3) $\frac{(5-2x)(x+4)}{x-4} \geq 0$

SECTION 4.3 Finding the rule

This section is related to LES 11.

PROBLEM A health experiment

In Physical Education and Health class, a group of students started a 5-week training program to evaluate how the intensity of training improves breathing capacity.

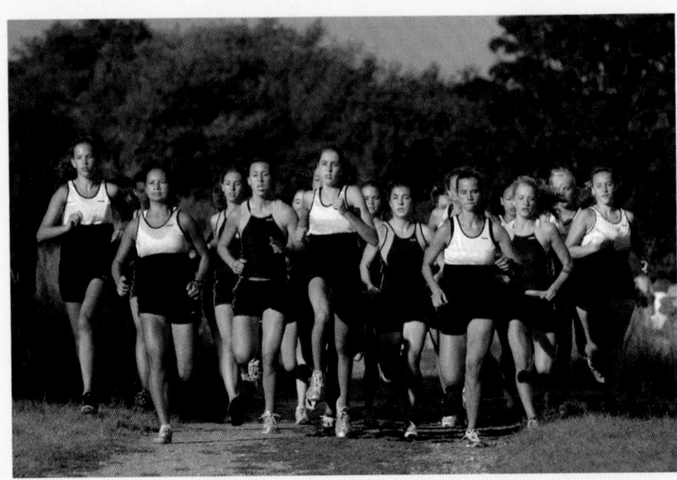

Having first tested their initial maximum breathing capacity, the students committed to training three times a week at a certain percentage of their maximum intensity, varying from 36% to 90% from student to student. The following are their results:

Improvement of VO_2 max. after a 5-week training period

Training intensity (in %)	36	37	42	48	50	53	60	62
Improvement of VO_2 max. (in %)	16	18	14	20	23	25	20	27

Training intensity (in %)	65	70	75	82	84	88	89	90
Improvement of VO_2 max. (in %)	24	28	27	28	29	28	26	24

By modelling this situation with a quadratic function, estimate the increase in breathing capacity experienced by an individual training at 100% intensity.

ACTIVITY 1 Family resemblance

Part 1

Five quadratic functions are represented in the graph below, all of which belong to the same family of functions.

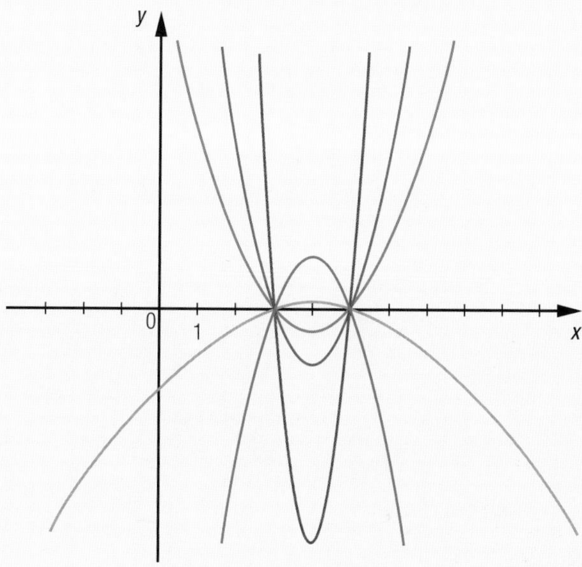

a. What characteristic do the functions belonging to this family have in common?

b. Write the rule in general form for three other functions belonging to the same family.

c. Compare the equations you have found. Formulate a conjecture and find the arguments to convince a peer of its validity.

Part 2

When a quadratic function has one or two zeros, it is possible to write its rule in factored form $f(x) = a(x - x_1)(x - x_2)$, where a, x_1 and x_2 are real numbers.
Below are three examples:

1 $f_1(x) = 2(x - 1)(x - 3)$ 2 $f_2(x) = 3(x - 2)(x + 1)$ 3 $f_3(x) = (x + 3)^2$

d. What are the zeros of these functions?

e. Write the rule of these functions in the general form.

f. Is there a link between the zeros of these functions and parameters **a**, **b** and **c** of their general form? Formulate a conjecture on this subject and state arguments to convince a peer of its validity.

ACTIVITY 2 Soothing curves

Each day, thousands visit and admire such famous fountains as the Trevi Fountain in Rome and those in the gardens of Versailles. In addition to being visually magnificent, fountains are soothing because of the movement and sound of running water.

In order to attain perfect harmony, the designer must study the trajectories of the many water jets that make up the fountain. Below are two examples:

While originally built for the city of Bordeaux in 1855, the Tourny Fountain was given to Québec City for its 400th anniversary.

The magic fountains of Barcelona were built for the 1929 World Fair. They use 3260 water jets.

A water jet from each of these fountains is represented on the Cartesian planes below. In both cases, the *x*-axis is placed at the same level as the water outlet, and the *y*-axis passes through the centre of the fountain. The metre is the unit of measure.

A water jet from the Tourny Fountain

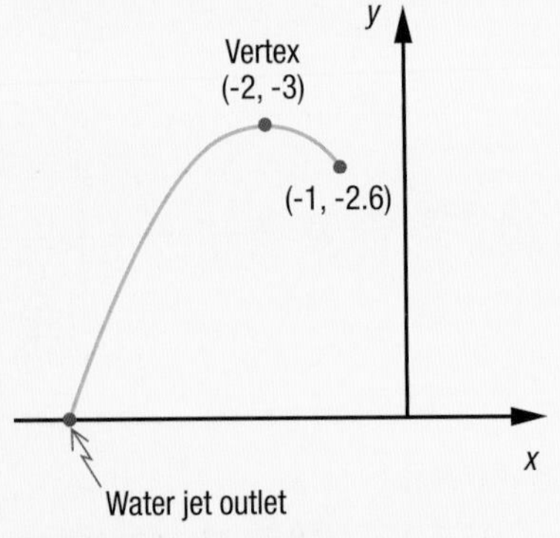

A water jet from the Barcelona Fountains

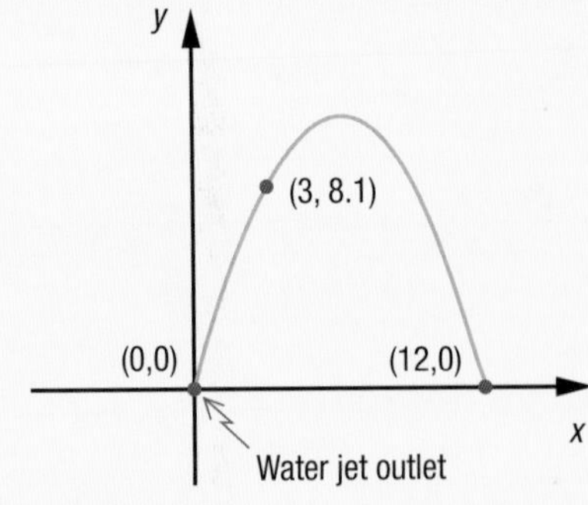

a. Determine the equation for each curve, considering that they both represent quadratic functions. Explain your approach.

b. In the Tourny Fountain, what is the position of the water jet outlet?

c. In the Barcelona Fountain, how many metres above the outlet does the jet of water rise?

ACTIVITY 3 Two graphs for a single pitch

Oliver pitches a ball to his friend Francis.

Consider y as the height of the ball (in m) and t, the elapsed time (in s). If the ball is released at a height of 2 m, and if it initially rises at a velocity of 15 m/s, then the equation showing this relationship is $y = 5t^2 + 15t + 2$.

a. Draw the graph of this function while presuming the ball thrown by Oliver will not be caught by Francis and will fall to the ground.

b. Taking the domain into account, what is the value of the only zero of this function? What does it mean in this context?

When the ball is thrown, it does not just rise upward; it also moves horizontally towards Francis at a certain constant velocity. Presume that the ball moves forward at 20 m per second. If x represents this motion, you can write: $x = 20t$.

c. In the first quadrant of a Cartesian plane, where x represents the horizontal motion of the ball and y represents its height, locate the position of the ball at each half-second over the interval 0 to 3 s. Then draw the curve that passes through these points in light of the context.

The curve drawn in **c.** represents the trajectory of the ball.

> A trajectory is a line describing the motion of a point or of the centre of gravity of an object within a certain space.

d. What is the equation of this curve?

e. Based on the equation found in **d.**, determine the x-intercept of this curve. Interpret this value based on the context.

f. Compare the graphs that you have constructed in **a.** and in **c.** In what way are they similar? In what way are they different?

Techno math

A graphing calculator allows you to display a scatter plot and to determine the equation of a quadratic function through the use of quadratic regression.

This table of values shows data collected during an experiment relating two variables.

x	-1	0	1	2	3	4
y	6	-1	-3	-1.5	5	10

This screen allows you to edit each of the ordered pairs in the table of values.

Screen 1

L1	L2	L3 3
-1	6	
0	-1	
1	-3	
2	-1.5	
3	5	
4	10	

L3(1)=

This screen allows you to display the scatter plot.

Screen 2

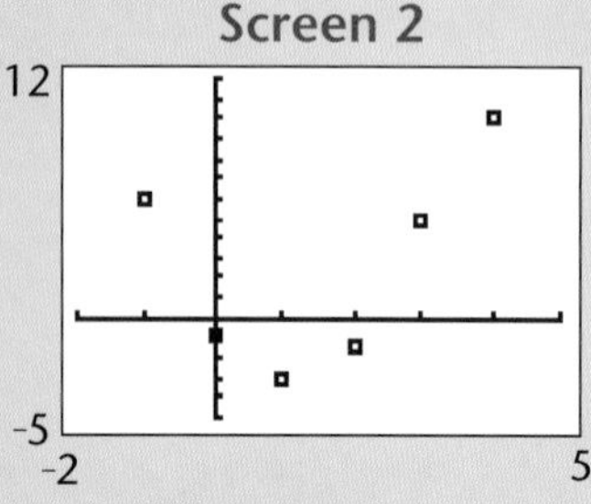

This screen allows you to use quadratic regression to determine the equation of the quadratic function.

Screen 3

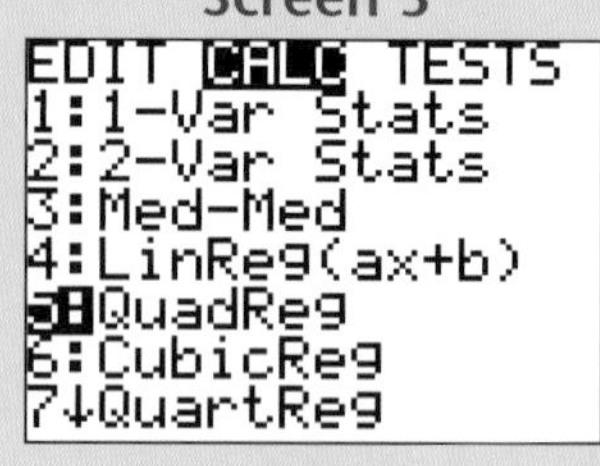

This screen allows you to place the equation of the quadratic function in the equation editor and it displays the equation obtained by the quadratic regression.

Screen 4

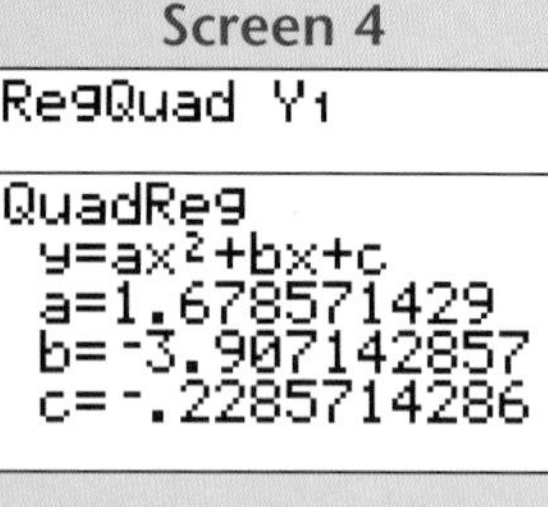

Moving the cursor allows you to display the coordinates of the points on the curve.

Screen 5

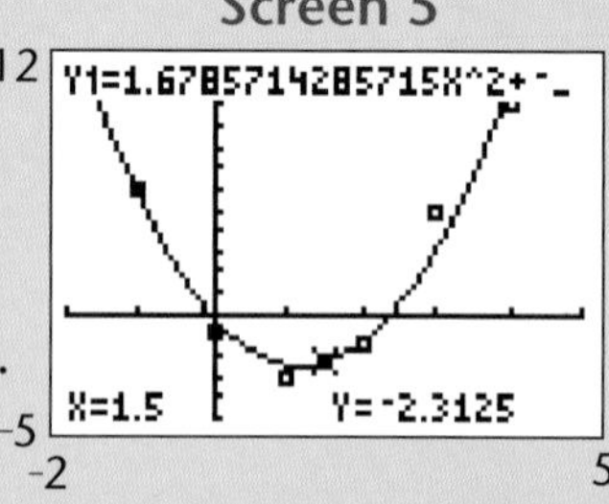

a. What is represented by a=1.678571429, b=-3.907142857 and c=-.2285714286 in Screen **4**?

b. With the help of a graphing calculator that uses the quadratic regression method, draw the parabola that represents the data in each of the tables of value below.

1)

x	7	20	33	47	60	67
y	8	15	24	26	24	21

2)

x	0	0.5	1	1.5	2	2.5
y	0	78.1	99.8	84.4	50.1	15.6

c. Based on the curves drawn in **b.**, determine, in each case, the value of y if $x = 10$.

knowledge 4.3

THE FACTORED FORM OF THE RULE OF A QUADRATIC FUNCTION

When a quadratic function has two zeros, it is possible to write its rule in the factored form $f(x) = \mathrm{a}(x - x_1)(x - x_2)$, where x_1 and x_2 are the two zeros of the function. You can then observe a relation between parameters **a**, **b** and **c** in the general form and the zeros x_1 and x_2 in the factored form:

$$\frac{\text{-b}}{\text{a}} = x_1 + x_2 \quad \text{and} \quad \frac{\text{c}}{\text{a}} = x_1x_2$$

In the case where there is just one zero, you will have $x_1 = x_2$ and the factored form can be written as: $f(x) = \mathrm{a}(x - x_1)^2$.

LOOKING FOR THE RULE OF A QUADRATIC FUNCTION

Based on the information you have on a quadratic function, you will use different strategies to try to determine the rule of this function.

Using the coordinates of the vertex and one point

If you know the vertex and another point on the curve, you will opt for writing the rule in standard form which you can then expand into the general form.

E.g. The curve that represents a quadratic function has its vertex at (3, 4) and passes through the point with coordinates (7, 2).

Proceed as follows.

- In the standard form of the rule, replace parameters **h** and **k** with the values of the coordinates of the vertex.

$f(x) = \mathrm{a}(x - \mathrm{h})^2 + \mathrm{k}$

$f(x) = \mathrm{a}(x - 3)^2 + 4$

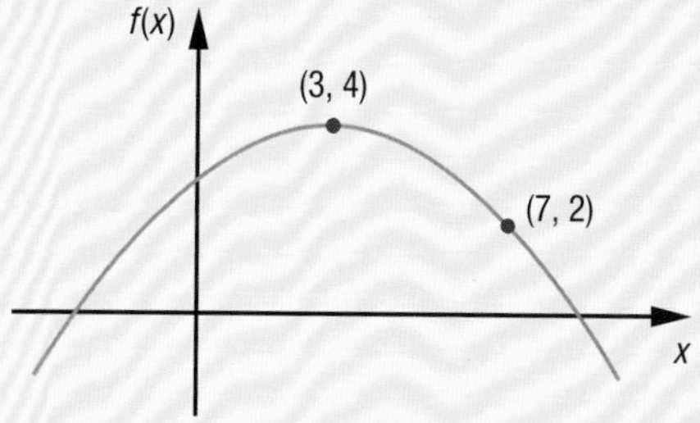

- Replace the variable x and its image $f(x)$ with the coordinates of the other point, and solve the equation obtained in order to determine the value of **a**.

$2 = \mathrm{a}(7 - 3)^2 + 4$

$2 = 16\mathrm{a} + 4$

$-2 = 16\mathrm{a}$

$\frac{-1}{8} = \mathrm{a}$

The rule is therefore:

$f(x) = \frac{-1}{8}(x - 3)^2 + 4$ or $f(x) = \frac{-x^2}{8} + \frac{3x}{4} + \frac{23}{8}$.

Using the zeros and one point

Given the zeros and one other point of the function, it is preferable to use the factored form in order to determine the rule.

Proceed as follows.	E.g. A quadratic function has two zeros, -2 and 5, and it passes through the point with coordinates (8, 3).
• In the factored form of the rule, replace parameters x_1 and x_2 with the zero values of the function.	$f(x) = a(x - x_1)(x - x_2)$ $f(x) = a(x + 2)(x - 5)$ 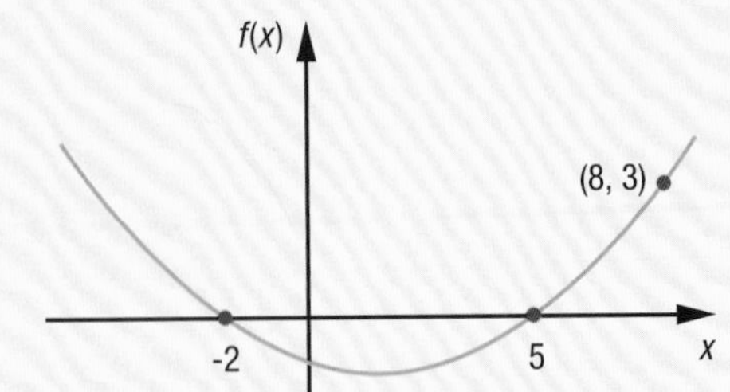
• Replace the variable x and its image $f(x)$ with the coordinates of the point (8, 3), and solve the equation thus obtained in order to determine the value of **a**.	$3 = a(8 + 2)(8 - 5)$ $3 = 30a$ $0.1 = a$ The rule is therefore: $f(x) = 0.1(x + 2)(x - 5)$ or $f(x) = 0.1x^2 - 0.3x - 1$.

MODELLING WITH A QUADRATIC FUNCTION

Sketch the curve that is most representative of the data. Then choose points on this model, such as the vertex or the points associated with the zeros in order to determine its equation.

E.g. During an experiment, the height of a ball thrown upward was measured to the nearest tenth of a metre, in relation to time.

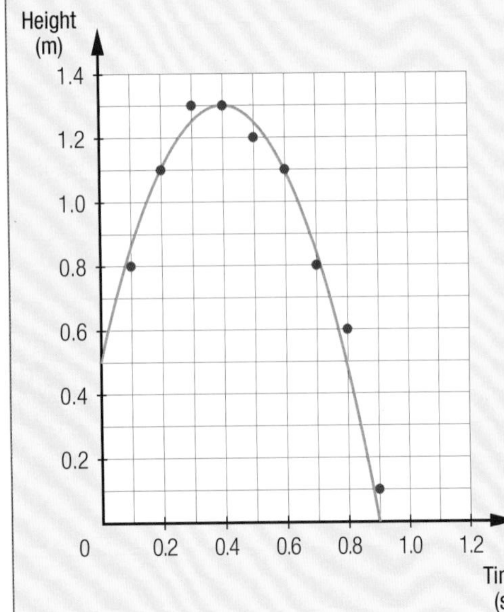

Using the coordinates of the vertex (0.4, 1.3) and those of the point (0.9, 0), estimate the equation of the parabola that best represents this scatter plot.

$$f(x) = a(x - h)^2 + k$$
$$f(x) = a(x - 0.4)^2 + 1.3$$
$$0 = a(0.9 - 0.4)^2 + 1.3$$
$$-1.3 = 0.25a$$
$$a = -5.2$$

$$f(x) = -5.2(x - 0.4)^2 + 1.3$$
or
$$f(x) = -5.2x^2 + 4.16x + 0.468$$

1 All of the functions for which the rules are given below have two zeros.

① $f(x) = x^2 + 14x + 33$ ② $f(x) = 2x^2 - 4x - 30$ ③ $f(x) = -2x^2 + 12x - 16$

④ $f(x) = 2x^2 + 5x - 12$ ⑤ $f(x) = -12x^2 - x + 6$ ⑥ $f(x) = x^2 - 4x + 1$

For each of these functions, do the following:

a) Determine the product and the sum of these zeros using the values of parameters **a, b** and **c**.

b) Determine these zeros, then show that their sum and their product are equal to the values found in **a)**.

2 Below are the graphs of three quadratic functions:

① 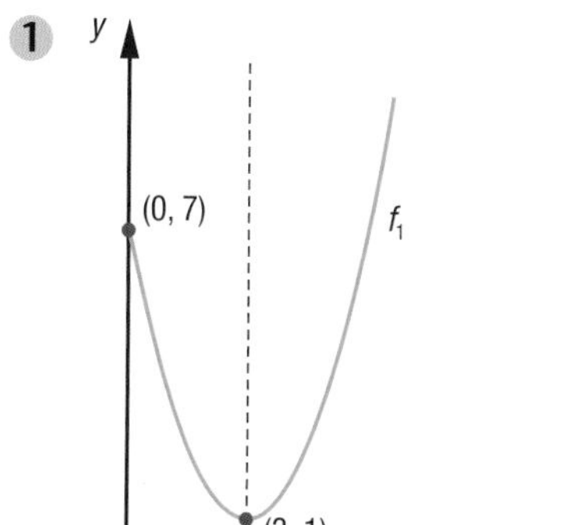

② 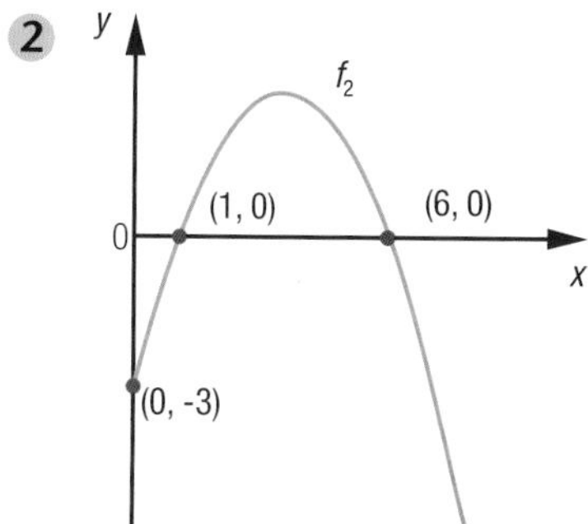

③ 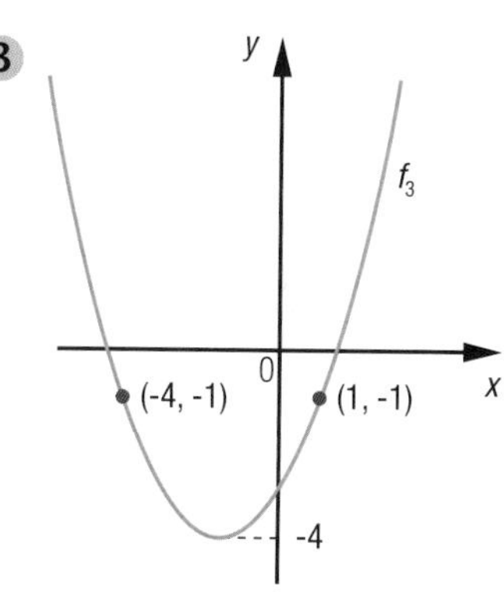

a) Determine the rule of each of these functions in general form.

b) Which of these curves pass through the point with coordinates (2, 2)?

3 Following are the zeros of different quadratic functions:

① zeros of f_1: -3 and 5 ② zeros of f_2: -8 and -4 ③ zeros of f_3: $2 - \sqrt{3}$ and $2 + \sqrt{3}$

a) What is the axis of symmetry of the curve that represents each of these functions?

b) In each case, at what distance from the axis of symmetry are each of the zeros located?

c) Answer questions **a)** and **b)** again in the case of a quadratic function of which the zeros are x_1 and x_2, with $x_1 < x_2$.

4 A quadratic function is positive over the interval $]-\infty, 2] \cup [5, +\infty[$ and its y-intercept is 5.

a) Determine the increasing and decreasing intervals of the function.

b) Determine the rule of this function.

c) Determine the range of this function.

5 During a dive, a cormorant caught a fish at a depth of 2 m which is one third the maximum depth of this dive. The cormorant then came out of the water 8 m away from the point of entry. Using the origin of the Cartesian plane as the point of entry into the water, determine the equation of the comorant's underwater parabolic trajectory.

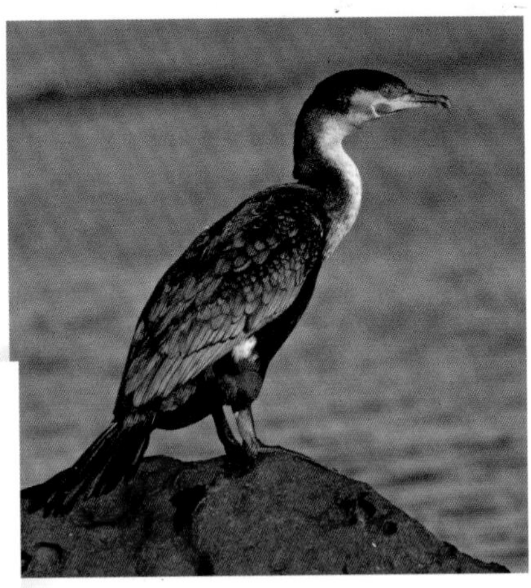

Cormorants are web-footed coastal sea birds with a dark plumage. These excellent divers hunt underwater and feed mainly on small fish varying in size from 5 cm to 15 cm, as well as certain molluscs and crustaceans. In some regions of Québec, Cormorants have a significant impact on fish stocks and, consequently, on catch quality.

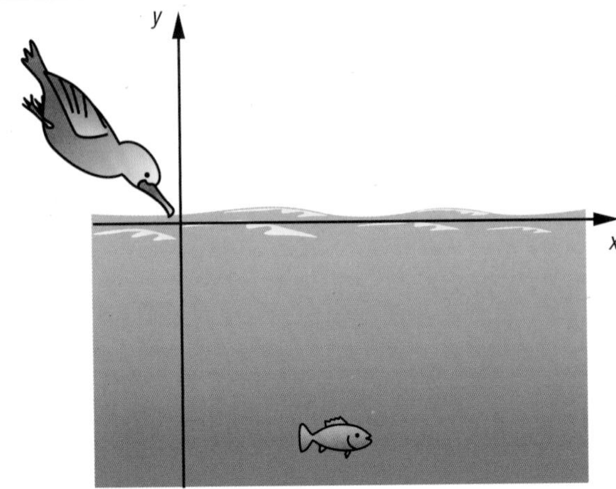

6 Determine the rule, in general form, of each of the quadratic functions described below.

a) The parabola that represents the function passes through the origin and its vertex is V(4, 5).

b) The coordinates of the vertex are V(10, 125) and the y-intercept is -275.

c) The vertex is V(-3, -2) and the parabola passes through point P(-7, -10).

d) The zeros of the function are -4 and 4, and its minimum is -12.

e) The zeros of the function are -8 and 4, and the y-intercept is 6.

f) The parabola passes through points $P_1(0, 3)$ and $P_2(1, 0)$, and its axis of symmetry is $x = 2$.

g) The function has only one zero which is 4. Its y-intercept is -4.

h) The maximum of the function is 8. Its curve passes through $P_1(1, 3)$ and $P_2(5, 3)$.

7 Based on the information provided in the table below, determine the rule of each of the functions f_1 to f_6, then complete the table.

	f_1	f_2	f_3	f_4	f_5	f_6
Zeros of the function	1 and 3	-5 and -1	-3 and 1	-1 and 4		
Coordinates of the vertex	(2, 4)	(-3, -4)	(,)	(,)	(4, -1)	(-1, 9)
y-intercept			-6	8	3	5

8 Today is a big day for Jean-Pierre. He just hit his first hole-in-one at the golf course. This happened on a par 3 with a distance of 160 yards. The ball skimmed the top of a fir tree 27 m high located 20 yards before the hole and then fell directly into the cup.

The yard is an old English measure still used in the United States. In Canada, this unit of measure is also used in certain sports such as golf and football.

a) Considering that one yard equals approximately 0.9 m and using the metre as the unit of measure, determine an equation that could represent the trajectory of Jean-Pierre's memorable shot.

b) What was the maximum height reached by the ball?

9 As a grand finale to a show, pyrotechnic devices are used to display trajectories in the shape of parabolas in the sky. Two of these devices are launched in such a way that the trajectory of the second device passes through the vertex of the trajectory of the first device before reaching its maximum height of 19 m.

a) At what distance from each other will these two pyrotechnic devices fall into the water?

b) Determine the equation of each of the two trajectories in general form.

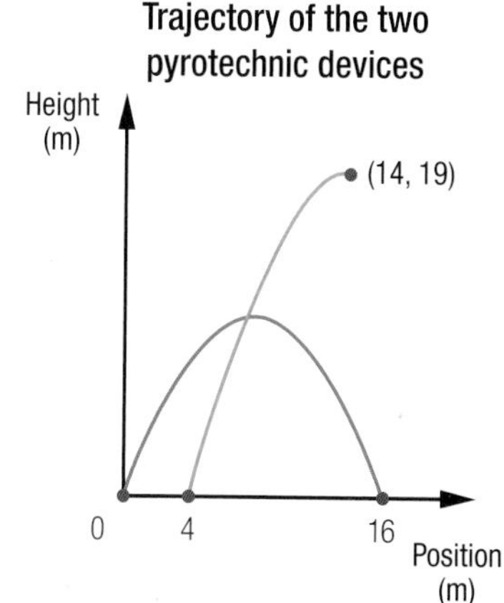

The invention of fireworks goes back to the first centuries of our era. But it was only in the 19th century, thanks to the use of metallic salts, that technicians were able to produce fireworks of various colours. Before that time, the colour of fireworks varied from yellowish white to orange.

10 A special effects team has recreated a trebuchet for a film. They filmed three trial-runs on flat ground and collected the following data.

A trebuchet is a medieval war machine. The trebuchet at *Les Baux-de-Provence* is the largest in France. Its boom measures over 11 m and it can still launch stones of more than 100 kg.

Trebuchet test shots

Height (m)

50
40
30
20
10

0 50 100 150 200

Distance (m)

a) Draw a parabola that best fits this scatter plot and determine its equation.

b) What does the *y*-intercept of the parabola represent in this context? What does the *x*-intercept of the parabola represent in this context?

c) For the making of the film, the trebuchet will be installed on the edge of a cliff 20 m higher than its target. Estimate, to the nearest metre, the distance from the cliff at which the target will have to be placed.

11 The number 1 is the value of a zero for each of the following functions.

$f_1(x) = 2x^2 - 3x + 1$ $\quad$ $f_2(x) = {}^-4x^2 + x + 3$ $\quad$ $f_3(x) = 0.5x^2 + 1.5x - 2$

a) Check that $x = 1$ is indeed a zero for each of the functions above.

b) Mentally calculate the second zero of each of these functions.
Explain how you proceeded.

c) Through trial and error, find an integer that is a zero of the function $g(x) = 3x^2 - 2x - 8$. Then mentally calculate the second zero of this function.

12 Based on the information provided, determine the second zero of each of the following functions and explain how you proceeded.

a) One of the zeros of the function $f(x) = kx^2 + kx - 6$ is 3.

b) One of the zeros of the function $g(x) = kx^2 + 3x + k$ is 2.

c) One of the zeros of the function $h(x) = x^2 + kx + k$ is 1.

13 The table of values below shows the American records set for the women's 100 m dash according to the age of the runners.

American records set for women's 100 m dash

Age (years)	10	15	20	27	29	30	38	42	47	51	58	61
Record time (s)	13.2	11.5	11.2	10.9	10.5	11.5	11.2	12.5	12.7	13.1	14.6	15.8

a) Draw the scatter plot associated with this data as well as the parabola of best fit.

b) Determine the rule of the quadratic function that models this data.

c) Based on this model, what could be the record time for a 70-year-old runner in the 100 m race?

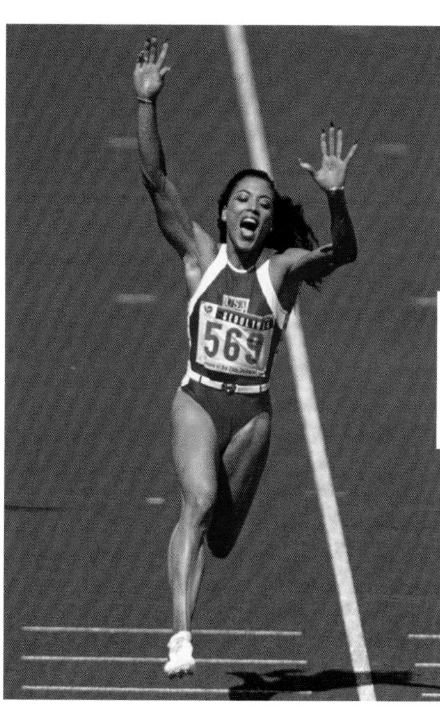

In 1988, Delorez Florence Griffith Joyner, 29, smashed previous women's-100-m record by 0.27 s with a time of 10.49 s. Her record still stands more than 20 years later.

14 On February 7, 1971, at the end of the Apollo 14 Lunar Mission, Astronaut Alan Shepard hit a golf ball with a number 6 iron he had brought along without anyone's knowledge. It is not known exactly what the result of this memorable shot was, but that the height of the ball (in m) is described by the quadratic function $h(t) = -0.8t^2 + 8t$ where t is the time (in s).

a) Draw the graph of this function.

b) What are the zeros of this function? What do they represent in this context?

c) Presuming that the horizontal speed of displacement of the ball is 12 m/s, plot the trajectory of the ball in a Cartesian plane.

d) What is the equation of this trajectory?

e) According to this data, at what distance from the astronaut did the golf ball hit the lunar surface?

15 Bianca and Sarah are playing catch and throwing the ball over the roof of their house. With each throw, they try to throw the ball to the lowest possible height.

A few measurements are recorded in the adjacent illustration. Among other things, you can see that the ball is released and caught 1.6 m above the ground.

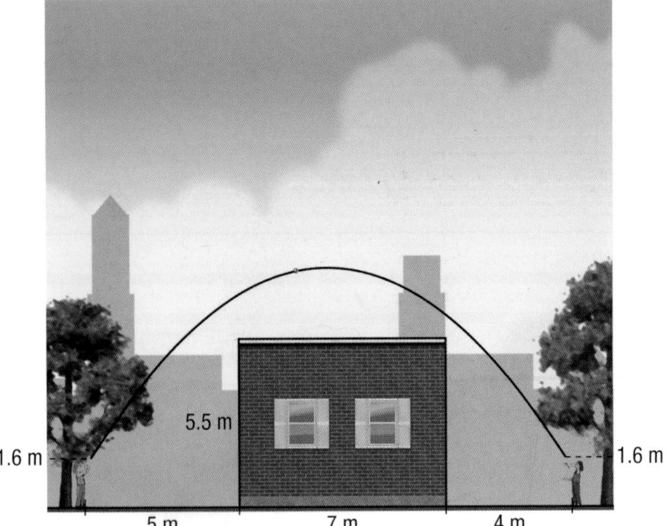

a) Represent this situation in a Cartesian plane while carefully situating the axes.

b) Based on your representation, determine the equation for the trajectory the ball should follow in order to reach a minimal height without requiring the girls to move.

c) What is this minimal height?

16 The surface of a liquid rotating in a cylinder-shaped container takes the shape of a parabolic revolution. The diagram under the illustration represents a cross-section through the axis of revolution at the centre of the surface and of the container for a given rotational velocity.

a) The height reached by the liquid at a point on its surface is a quadratic function of the distance that separates this point from the axis of revolution. What is the rule of this function?

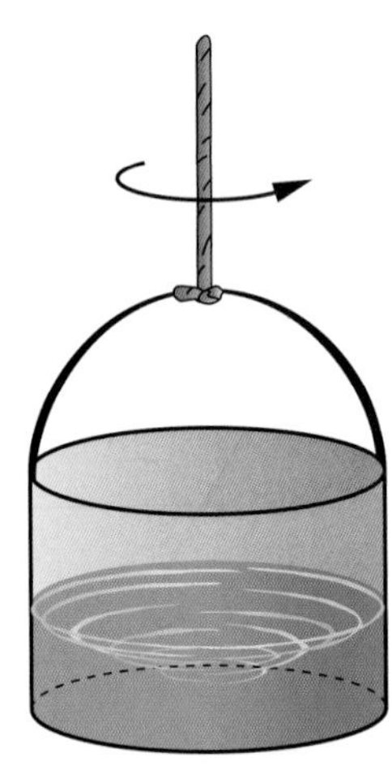

By increasing the rotational velocity, you can make the vertex of the parabola reach the bottom of the container. In this case, parameter **a** of the rule of the function will be multiplied by 6.

b) At what distance from the edge of the container will the liquid then rise?

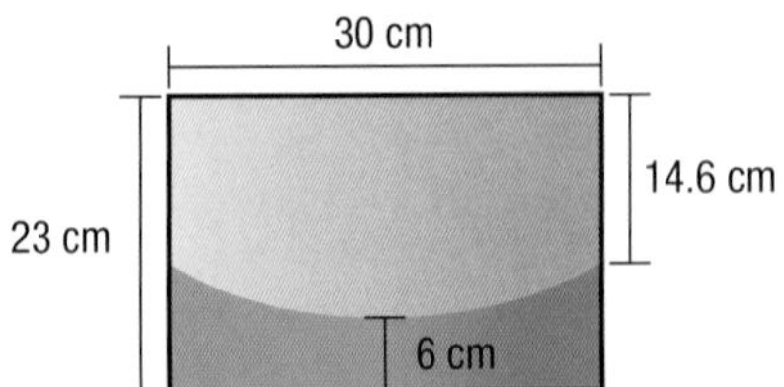

SECTION 4.4 Distance and the quadratic function

This section is related to LES 12.

PROBLEM The furthest point

In the game of golf, the trajectory of the ball through the air is almost perfectly parabolic. All along this trajectory, the ball is generally the furthest away from its starting point when it touches the ground for the first time.

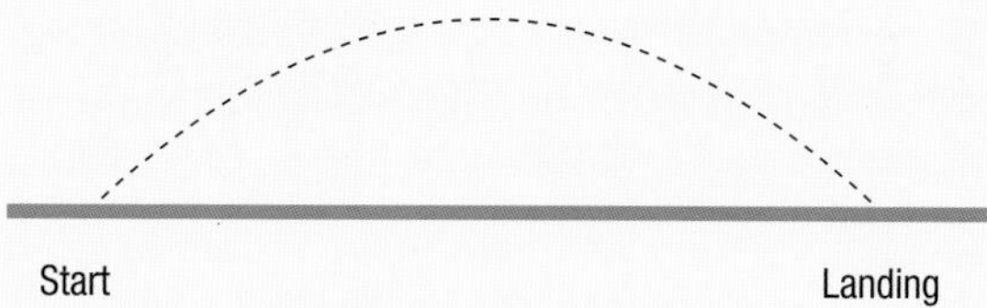

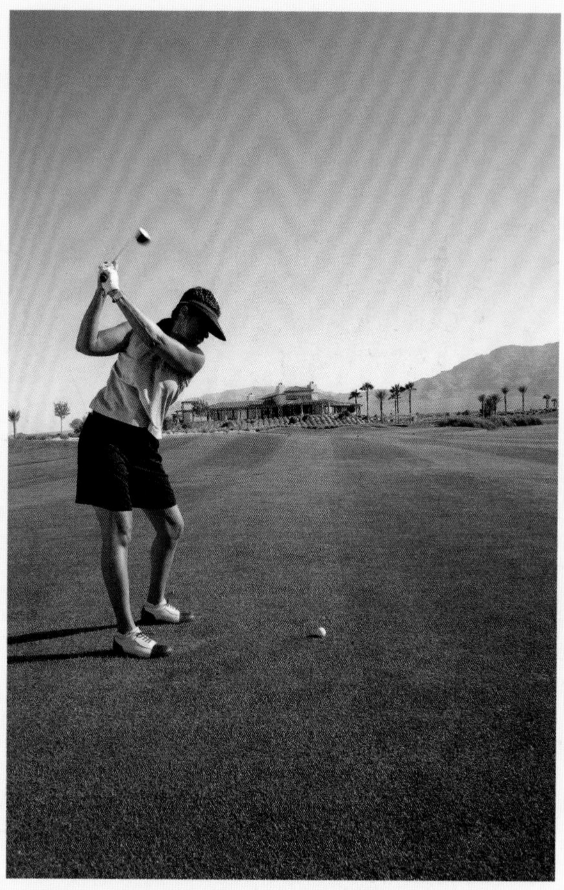

Occasionally, for certain shots, the vertex of the parabola is further away than the landing point in relation to the starting point.

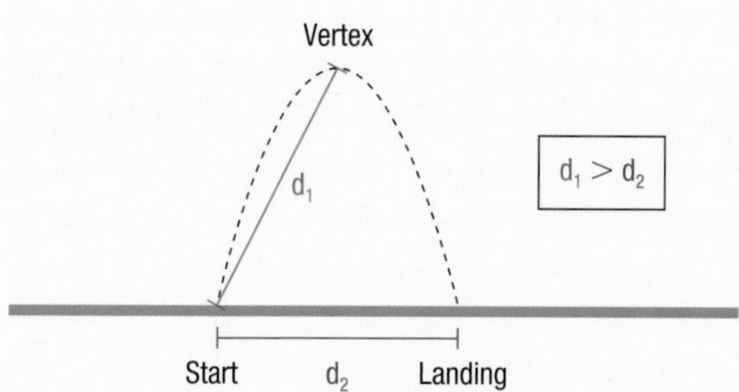

If this trajectory is represented on a Cartesian plane by locating the starting point at the origin, the equation of the trajectory takes the form:

$$y = ax^2 + bx$$
with $a < 0$ and $b > 0$.

In the case where the vertex is further away from the landing point in relation to the starting point, what can you say regarding the value of parameters a and b? Formulate a conjecture, and prove it.

Situation 1

A 7.5 m foot bridge joins the roof of two buildings that are separated by a 6 m space. One of the buildings has a height of 21.5 m, and the other is 19 m high.

a. Represent this situation in a diagram.

b. Prove that it would be possible to set up a shorter bridge to join the two roofs. Determine the minimum length of this bridge.

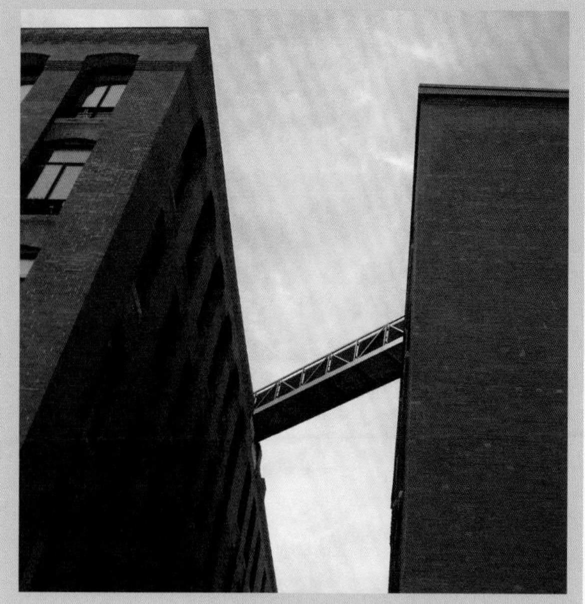

Situation 2

Observe this representation of two poles joined by a cable.

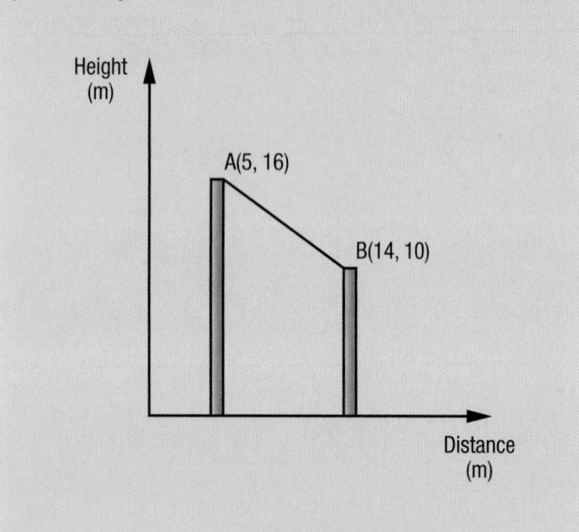

c. What is the length of the cable?

Situation 3

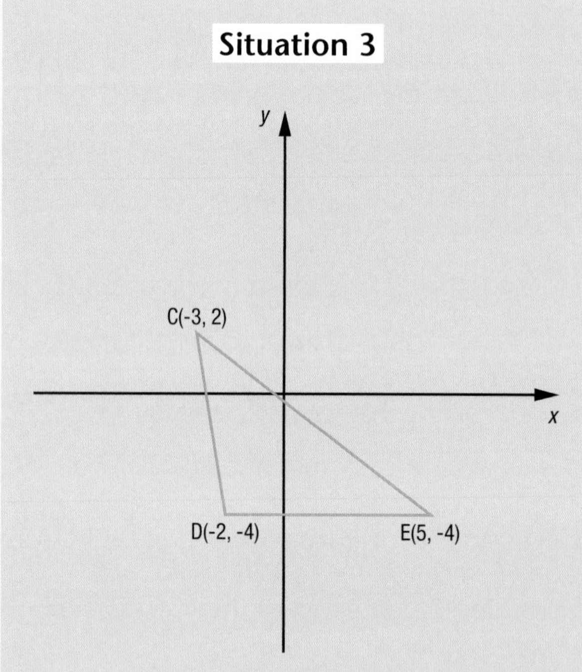

d. What is the perimeter of triangle CDE?

Situation 4

Consider points $P_1(x_1, y_1)$ and $P_2(x_2, y_2)$ in a Cartesian plane.

e. Explain how you might determine the distance between P_1 and P_2. In your explanations, use the expression $d(P_1, P_2)$ to designate this distance when necessary.

ACTIVITY 2 Chasing the coach

Is there anyone who has not, at some point, missed a boat, or a bus?

As Teresa walks towards the main road, she sees her coach bus in the distance. At that moment, she needs to walk 90 m in order to get to the point nearest to the bus on the main road. The coach bus is 255 m away from that same point.

The bus is moving three times faster than she is. Teresa starts to run because she fears missing the bus.

Below is a representation of the situation in a Cartesian plane where the *x*-axis represents the main road:

A coach is a type of bus used for public transportation from one city to another or for tourist excursions.

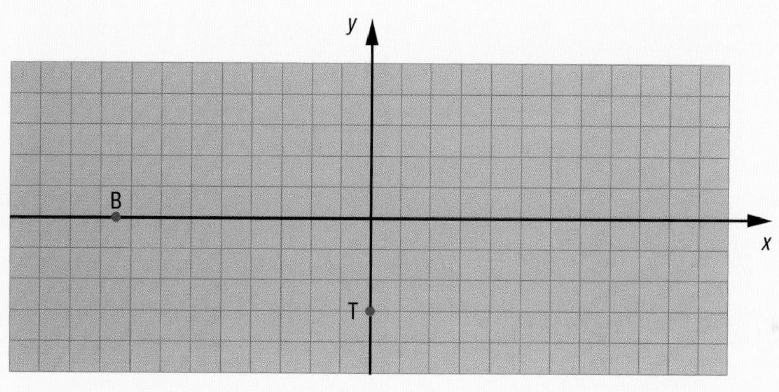

There is still hope however. Teresa (T) could arrive in time to board the bus (B) if she heads for a point P on the main road so that:

$$d(\text{B, P}) = 3 \times d(\text{T, P}).$$

a. Consider $(x, 0)$ as the coordinates of this point P. What algebraic expression represents:

1) $d(\text{B, P})$?   2) $d(\text{T, P})$?

b. By squaring each side of the above equality, translate this situation into a second-degree equation.

c. Show the location of a point on the main road towards which Teresa should be heading.

ACTIVITY 3 At equal distance

A teacher stands 2 m away from a wall in his classroom. He asks ten students to stand up and he gives them the following assignment.

a. Represent this situation with a diagram. Plot the ten points on your diagram to indicate the students' positions.

b. What can you say about the set of points you have plotted? Describe the characteristics of the line that the set of points seems to define.

In a Cartesian plane, you can represent the teacher's position with point P(0, 2) while the x-axis will represent the classroom wall.

c. Presuming that three students placed themselves at points with x-coordinates respectively at -2, 0 and 2, what is the y-coordinate of each of these points?

d. Determine the y-coordinate of the following points so that they are equidistant from point P and the x-axis:

1) A(4, y) 2) B(-5, y) 3) C(-9, y) 4) D(12, y)

e. Two students placed themselves 3 m from the wall. What distance separates them from each other?

knowledge 4.4

THE CONCEPT OF DISTANCE IN A CARTESIAN PLANE

Certain geometric concepts can be expressed algebraically when the figures concerned are drawn on a Cartesian plane. For example, this holds true for the concept of **distance.**

Distance between two points

To calculate the distance between two points P_1 and P_2, identified as $d(P_1, P_2)$, use the Pythagorean theorem.

This relation can be expressed in the following form:

$$d(P_1, P_2) = \sqrt{(x_2 - x_1)^2 + (y_2 - y_1)^2}$$

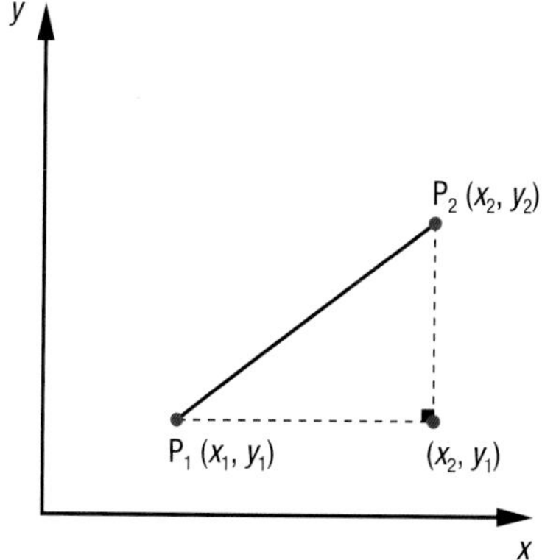

Note that the distance between two points is always greater than or equal to 0.

E.g. What is the length of segment AB whose endpoints are A(-1, -7) and B(2, -3)?

$\text{m}\ \overline{AB} = d(A, B) = \sqrt{(2 - (-1))^2 + ((-3) - (-7))^2} = \sqrt{25} = 5$

The length of segment AB is therefore 5 units.

Special cases

1. If the two points P_1 and P_2 have the same *y*-coordinate, then the expression $y_2 - y_1$ equals 0 and the above relation becomes $d(P_1, P_2) = \sqrt{(x_2 - x_1)^2}$.

   This last equality can be simplified to $d(P_1, P_2) = x_2 - x_1$, if $x_2 \geq x_1$. In the opposite case, if $x_2 < x_1$, write $d(P_1, P_2) = x_1 - x_2$ so that the result remains positive.
2. If the two points P_1 and P_2 have the same *x*-coordinate, you get $d(P_1, P_2) = \sqrt{(y_2 - y_1)^2}$ which can be simplified as:

   $d(P_1, P_2) = y_2 - y_1$, if $y_2 \geq y_1$

   or as $d(P_1, P_2) = y_1 - y_2$, if $y_2 < y_1$

The distance between a point and a vertical or horizontal line

The distance between a point P and a vertical line (or horizontal line) is equal to the distance between point P and the point on the line that has the same *y*-coordinate (or *x*-coordinate) as this point P.

E.g. Point A on line *l* has the same *y*-coordinate as point P. The distance between point P and line *l* equals 3 since $d(P, A) = 6 - 3 = 3$.

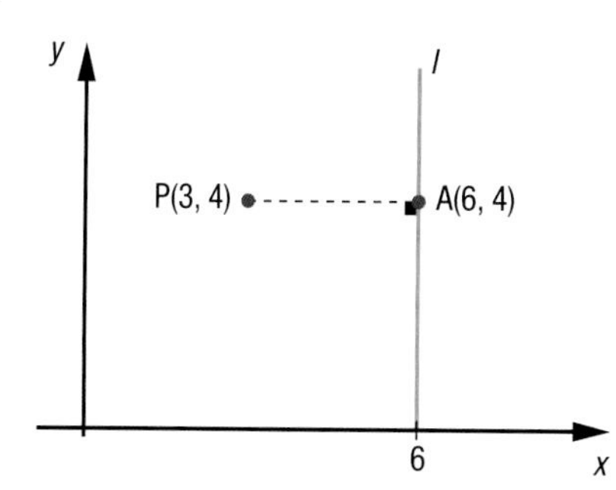

APPLYING THE CONCEPT OF DISTANCE

Some problems regarding trajectories or positions related to the concept of distance in the Cartesian plane are translated into an equation that includes a square root. This type of equation can be transformed into a first- or second-degree equation by squaring each side of the equality.

E.g. What point on the x-axis is equidistant from points A(1, 2) and B(5, 8)?

Consider C(x, 0), as the point you are seeking. You have:

$$d(A, C) = d(B, C)$$

$$\sqrt{(x - 1)^2 + (0 - 2)^2} = \sqrt{(x - 5)^2 + (0 - 8)^2}$$

By squaring each side of the equality, you get the equation:

$$(x - 1)^2 + (0 - 2)^2 = (x - 5)^2 + (0 - 8)^2$$

And after simplifying:

$$x^2 - 2x + 5 = x^2 - 10x + 89$$

By subtracting x^2 from each side, you get the first-degree equation:

$$-2x + 5 = -10x + 89$$

Solving this, you get:

$$x = 10.5$$

Point C (10.5, 0) is equidistant from points A and B.

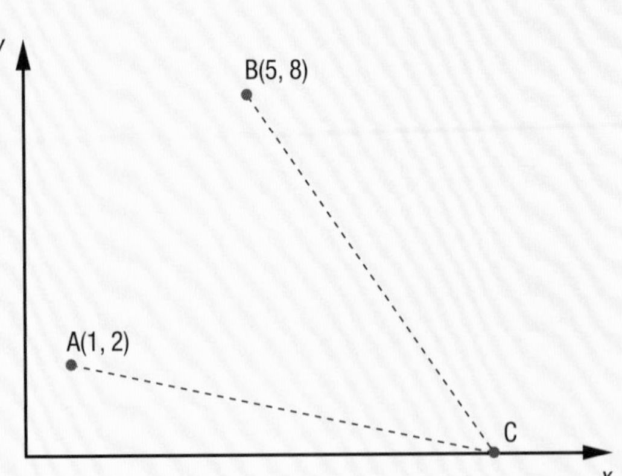

DISTANCE AND PARABOLA

The graphical representation of quadratic functions, and that of certain trajectories, uses a curve called a parabola. It is possible to precisely define a parabola in relation to the concept of distance.

> A parabola is a curve formed by all the points that are equidistant from a line and a specific point outside of this line. This point outside of the line is called the focus of the parabola.

E.g. The parabola shown in the adjacent graph is the locus of points equidistant from point F(0, 2) and line l with equation $y = -2$.

The vertex V of the parabola is located at the midpoint of point F and the line.

You can verify, for example, that the distance between point P(6, 4.5) and line l is 6.5, that is, 4.5 − (-2).

In the same way, the distance between F and P is $d(F, P) = \sqrt{(6 - 0)^2 + (4.5 - 2)^2}$
$= \sqrt{42.25} = 6.5$.

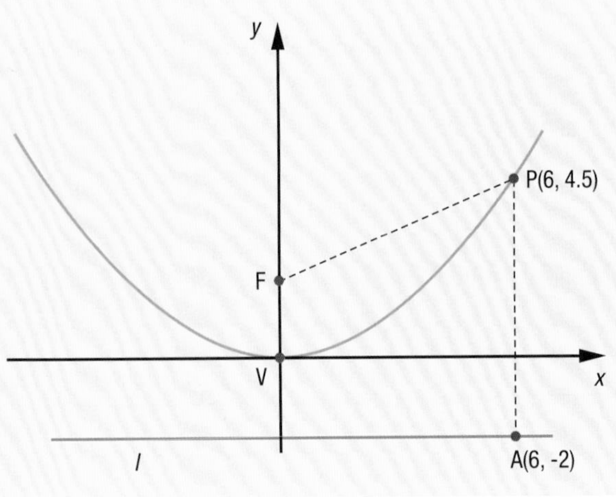

practice 4.4

1 The endpoints of the segments represented below have integer coordinates. Determine the length of each of these segments.

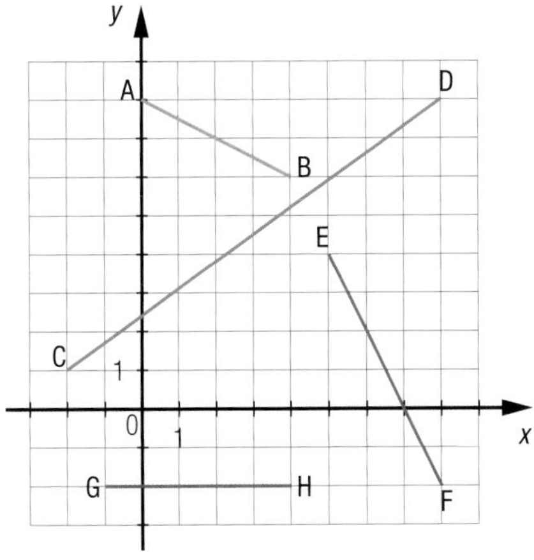

2 The quadrilateral ABCD shown in the adjacent illustration is a rectangle.

a) What is the area of this rectangle?

b) What is its perimeter?

c) Show that the diagonals of this rectangle are congruent.

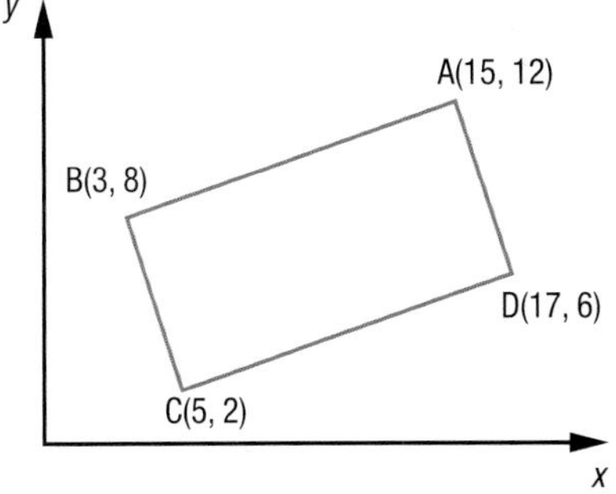

3 Calculating the exact length of a curved line is generally quite complex, yet it is possible to find an approximation by modelling the curve with a broken line.

Take the example of a trajectory defined by the equation $y = -x^2 + 6x$ with x varying from 0 to 6. In the adjacent graph, the parabola is approximated with a broken line passing through points A to G whose x-coordinates are the integers from 0 to 6.

a) Determine the y-coordinate of each of these points.

b) Estimate the length of the trajectory by calculating the total length of the broken line. Round off to the nearest hundredth.

c) How might you improve this estimated distance? Provide an example.

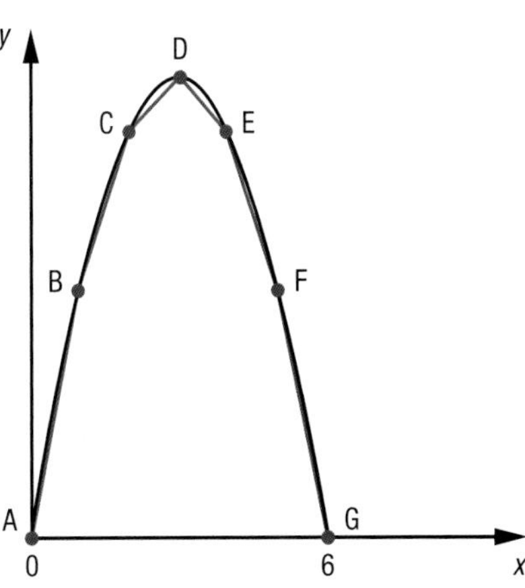

4 Fabian is very proud of a snowboard jump he was able to accomplish. The trajectory of this spectacular jump can be represented by the following equation with the x-values varying from 0 to 9:

$$y = \frac{-2}{9}x^2 + \frac{4}{3}x$$

a) Represent this trajectory in a Cartesian plane.

b) Using the metre as unit, determine the distance he covered from the starting point at $x = 0$, to the landing point at $x = 9$.

c) Determine the distance between the vertex of the trajectory and the landing point of this jump.

5 In a Cartesian plane, construct triangle ABC whose vertices have the following coordinates: A(0, 0), B(4, 6), and C(14, 0).

a) Determine the lengths of the sides of this triangle.

b) Which is its longest side? Which is the shortest?

c) Draw the three medians AD, BE and CF of this triangle, then determine their length.

d) Which is the longest median? Which is the shortest?

e) Is there a relation between the answers found in **b)** and in **d)**? Explain your answer.

6 To find the coordinates of the midpoint of a segment, Julie calculated the mean value of the x-coordinates and the mean value of the y-coordinates using its endpoints. She got (6, 5). But is this really the midpoint? To make sure, Julie tells herself that if M is the midpoint of $\overline{AB}$, then you must have:

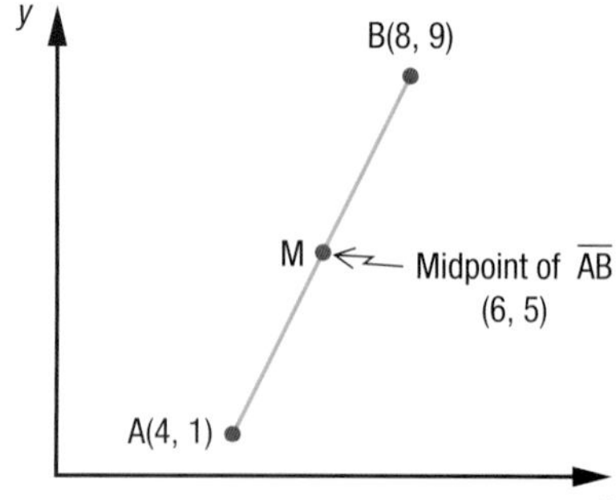

$$d(A, M) = d(B, M) = \frac{1}{2} \times d(A, B)$$

a) Does the point M found by Julie satisfy this equality? Justify your answer.

b) Determine the coordinates of the midpoint of the segment whose endpoints are C(-9, -12) and D(15, -2). Using the concept of distance as in **a)**, prove that these coordinates are indeed those of the midpoint.

7 **SYDNEY BRIDGE** The famous Sydney Harbour Bridge in Australia features an arch in the shape of a parabola.

In the representation below, the x-axis represents the bridge deck, and the y-axis is located at the pillar at the end of the arch.

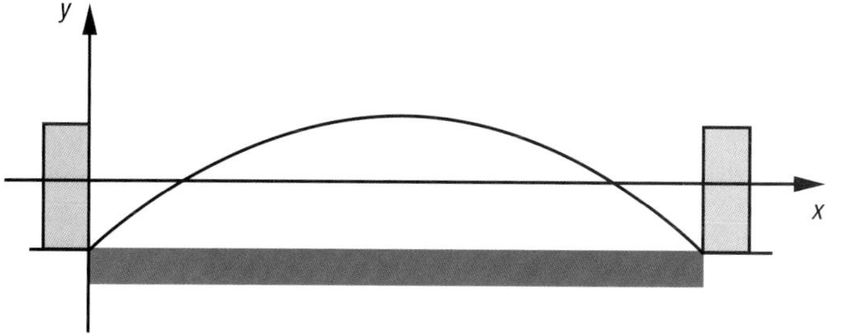

Distance between the two pillars	500 m
Distance between the vertex of the arch and the bridge back	50 m
Distance between the bridge deck and the water	50 m

a) In this representation, what are the coordinates:
   1) of the vertex of the parabola?
   2) of the two ends of the arch?

b) Determine the equation of this parabola in standard form.

c) Determine the coordinates of the intersection points of the arch and the bridge deck. What is the distance between these two points?

d) The two sections of the arch under the bridge deck are only slightly curved; they could almost be considered segments. Estimate the length of these sections.

e) Considering that the pillars have a height of 90 m above the water level, what distance must a bird fly to get from the top of a pillar to the vertex of the arch?

8 The locations of the entrances to the three most popular rides of an amusement park are identified in the grid below. The owners of the park decide to set up a new ride that would be equidistant from these three entrances. Where should the new ride be located?

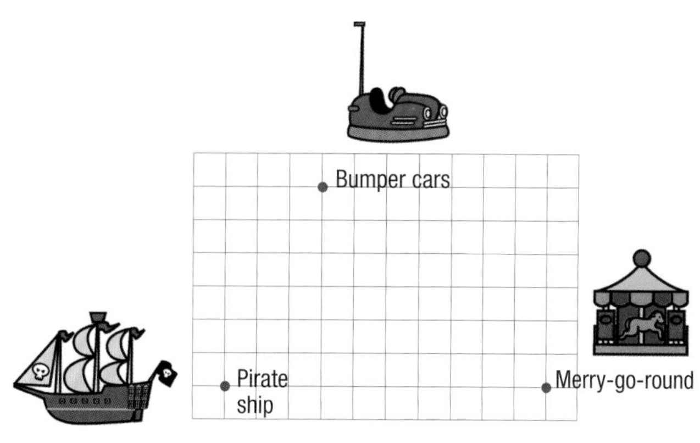

9 The coordinates of point A are (3, 5) and the x-coordinate of point B is 6. Determine the y-coordinate of point B considering that the measure of segment AB is 5 units.

10 Vilma drew a square with sides measuring 1 unit on a Cartesian plane. Inside this square, she inscribed the largest possible equilateral triangle.

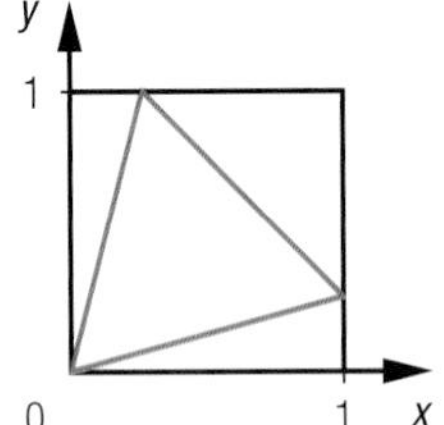

a) What are the lengths of the sides of this triangle?

b) What is the area of this triangle?

11 The adjacent diagram depicts Mary and Anthony on a beach. They decide to meet at the water's edge at a place that is equidistant from their respective starting points.

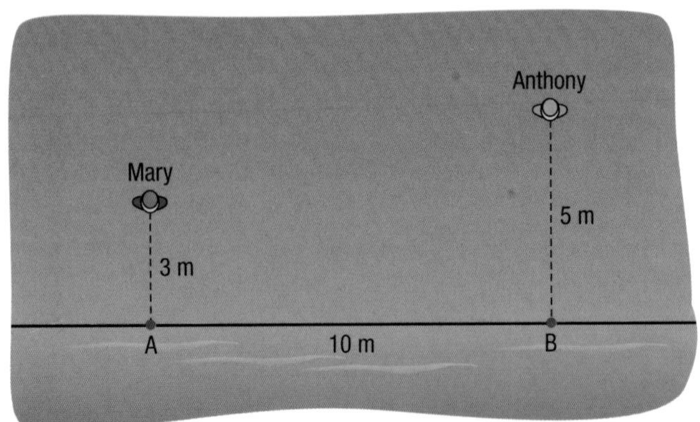

a) Determine their meeting point and locate it in relation to point A.

b) What distance separates them from this point?

c) Where would their meeting point be located if they decided instead to meet at a place by the water two times closer to Mary than to Anthony?

d) In this case, what is the total distance separating them from the meeting point?

e) Is there another meeting point by the water for which the total distance to be covered by Mary and Anthony would be shorter than for the others? Justify your answer.

12 Walking through an airport, Patrick steps onto a moving walkway. At that very moment, his girlfriend Nancy does the same at the other end of the corridor, taking the adjacent walkway moving in the opposite direction. The corridor measures 30 m. The velocity of the walkways, which are 0.5 m away from each other, is 1 m/s.

a) Represent this situation in a Cartesian plane.

b) After t seconds, what will Patrick's and Nancy's positions be according to the graph you made in **a)**?

c) Presuming their arms are 65 cm long, at what moment will they be able to reach out and touch each other's hands?

13 **RADIO TELESCOPE** With its 100 m diameter, the Effelsberg radio telescope in Germany is one of the largest parabolic-shaped radio telescopes in the world. The following is a representation of a cross section of this radio telescope drawn on a Cartesian plane.

The Effelsberg radio telescope

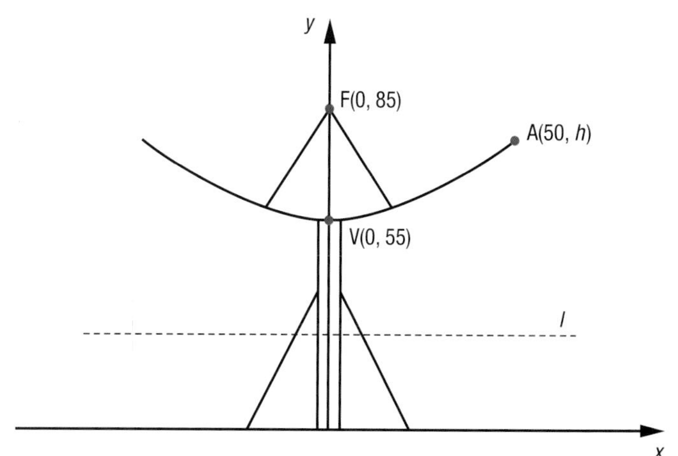

The x-axis represents ground level. One unit on the Cartesian plane corresponds to 1 m. In this representation, each point on the parabola is equidistant from the focus F and a dotted line l represented by the equation $y = 25$.

Determine the height h of point A.

14 The vertex V of the parabola represented by the equation $y = x^2$ is located at the origin of the Cartesian plane. This parabola also passes through the point with coordinates (1, 1). All the points on the parabola are equidistant from focus F and from a horizontal line l drawn in red.

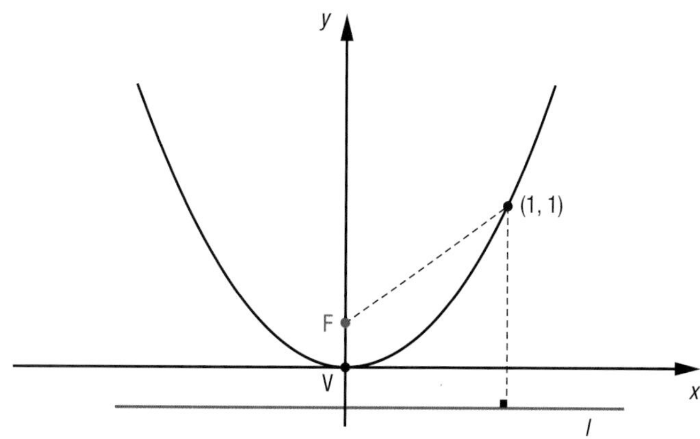

a) If F(0, c) is the focus of the parabola, you can show that the equation of the line drawn in red is $y = -c$. Based on this information, determine the value of **c**.

b) A line is drawn parallel to the x-axis and passes through the focus. This line intersects with the parabola at points A and B. What is the length of segment AB?

c) What is the ratio of the length of segment AB to the distance between the focus and the vertex of the parabola?

d) Would the ratio found in **c)** be the same for another parabola? Justify your answer.

Chronicle of the

past Jerome Cardano

Jerome Cardano (1501-1576)

A Renaissance scientist

Jerome Cardano is the anglicized name of Gerolamo Cardano, born in Pavia, in 1501. As a mathematician, physician, and scientist, he had interests in many fields. He is credited for the invention of cryptography and the U-joint; a device still found in cars today. In mathematics, his main contribution resulted from his interest in solving equations.

Solving equations of the third-degree

At the time of Cardano, it was common to see mathematicians challenge each other for the sake of honour and money. One such challenge consisted of solving third-degree equations.

From the work of Arab mathematician Al Khawarizmi, we knew how to solve second-degree equations, but no one thus far had succeeded in finding a general algorithm for third-degree equations.

A mathematician named Niccolo Fontana, better known as Tartaglia, was famous for his ability to solve such equations. He frequently won all the challenges given to him.

An intrigued Cardano met with Fontana and managed to obtain the secret which he promised not to divulge. Cardano did not keep his promise. Having broadened the scope of Tartaglia's method, Cardano published his results in 1545 in his master work, *Ars Magna* (*The Great Art*). In this work, he proved that one of the solutions to the equation $x^3 = px + q$, where p and q are positive numbers, can be obtained through the following formula:

$$\sqrt[3]{\frac{q}{2} + \sqrt{\left(\frac{q}{2}\right)^2 - \left(\frac{p}{3}\right)^3}} + \sqrt[3]{\frac{q}{2} - \sqrt{\left(\frac{q}{2}\right)^2 - \left(\frac{p}{3}\right)^3}}$$

Niccolo Fontana, a.k.a. Tartaglia (ca. 1499 - ca. 1557). It is possible that Tartaglia did not actually discover the method that made him famous. This method was allegedly developed by Scipione del Ferro (1465-1526), another Italian mathematician.

1. The equation $x^3 - 39x - 200 = 0$ has only one real solution.

a) Express this equation in the form of $x^3 = px + q$, then use Cardano's formula to find the solution. If necessary, round off to the nearest ten thousandth.

b) Prove that this equation has no other real solutions.

Imaginary numbers

It sometimes seems that Cardano's formula is impossible since it requires finding the square root of a negative number. For example, this is the case if you try to solve the equation $x^3 = 12x + 14$. In this case, p = 12 and q = 14. Note that the expressions under the radicals of the square roots are respectively $7 + \sqrt{-15}$ and $7 - \sqrt{-15}$.

Without totally solving this problem, Cardano still had the idea, which even he found somewhat bizarre, of doing the calculations with these imaginary numbers as if they truly existed. He then noted that the sum of the two expressions above is 14, and their product is 64. He discovered to his amazement that ordinary operations performed on two imaginary numbers can yield perfectly real answers!

A *complex number* is a number in the form of a + bi, where a and b are real numbers and $i^2 = -1$.

Now these "imaginary" numbers, which today are called "complex numbers," are of great significance in mathematics, and they have many applications, particularly in physics. Cardano had the great merit of being the first to dare to manipulate them.

Multiple solutions

Cardano also had the merit of understanding the importance of negative solutions to equations.

For example, in his book *Ars Magna*, he draws attention to the fact that there are two square roots of a number, one positive and one negative. More generally speaking, he shows that equations above the first-degree can have several solutions and that these solutions can be positive or negative.

Cardano's work is considered a major step towards the full and thorough recognition of negative quantities as numbers.

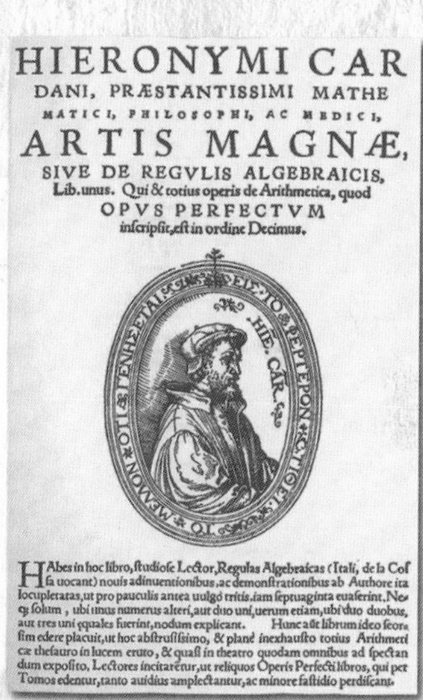

HIERONYMI CAR
DANI, PRÆSTANTISSIMI MATHE
MATICI, PHILOSOPHI, AC MEDICI,
ARTIS MAGNÆ,
SIVE DE REGVLIS ALGEBRAICIS,
Lib. unus. Qui & totius operis de Arithmetica, quod
OPVS PERFECTVM
inſcripſit, eſt in ordine Decimus.

HAbes in hoc libro, ſtudioſe Lector, Regulas Algebraicas (Itali, de la Coſſa uocant) nouis adinuentionibus, ac demonſtrationibus ab Authore ita locupletatas, ut pro pauculis antea uulgò tritis, iam ſeptuaginta euaſerint. Neq; ſolum, ubi unus numerus alteri, aut duo uni, uerum etiam, ubi duo duobus, aut tres uni æquales fuerint, nodum explicant. Hunc aũt librum ideo ſeorſim edere placuit, ut hoc abſtruſiſſimo, & planè inexhauſto totius Arithmeticæ theſauro in lucem eruto, & quaſi in theatro quodam omnibus ad ſpectandum expoſito, Lectores incitarẽtur, ut reliquos Operis Perfecti libros, qui per Tomos edentur, tanto auidius amplectantur, ac minore faſtidio perdiſcant.

2. a) Show that the product of $7 + \sqrt{-15}$ and $7 - \sqrt{-15}$ is indeed 64. Explain your reasoning.

b) Applying this reasoning once again, calculate the product of complex numbers 2 + 3i and 2 − 3i.

3. Cardano also took an interest in fourth-degree equation. Some of these equations are easier to solve than others. For example, take the equation $x^4 - 13x^2 + 36 = 0$.

a) By replacing $y = x^2$, convert this equation into a second-degree equation.

b) Deduce from **a)** the four solutions to the initial equation.

c) Using a graphing calculator, graphically represent the function $f(x) = x^4 - 13x^2 + 36$.
For what x values is this function negative?

In the
workplace
Interpretative scientists

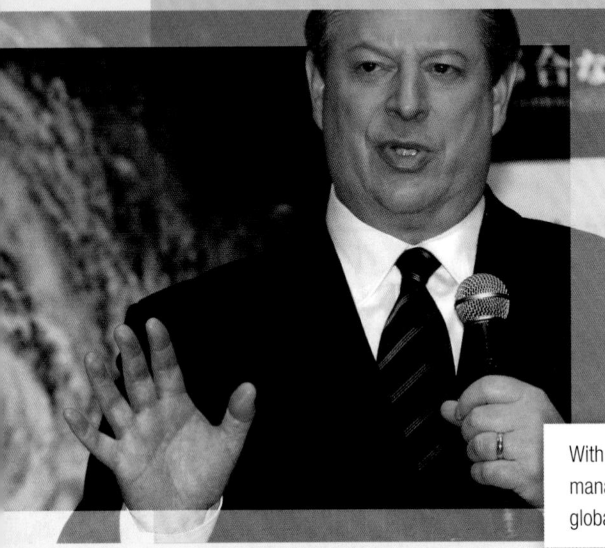

Science for everyone

Popularizing scientific phenomena is not always a simple task. Interpretative scientists must be able to convey accurate information while making it accessible to the audience. Therefore it is not enough for these professionals to have a thorough knowledge of the topic at hand; they must also excel in the art of communication. Astrophysicist Hubert Reeves; politician Al Gore; and biologist Claude Benoît are considered brilliant interpretative scientists and excellent communicators.

With the film entitled *An Inconvenient Truth*, Al Gore has managed to bring public awareness to the problem of global warming.

Science, a bridge towards interpretative science

The scope of science is not confined to laboratories. Sciences such as chemistry, physics and biology can lead to the field of communication. The media (television, Internet, newspapers, magazines, etc.) often serve as a means of popularizing science.

For her part, biologist Claude Benoît tapped into her skills as an interpretative scientist to set up such places as the *Biodôme*, the *Montréal Science Centre*, and the *Musée de la civilisation* in Québec City.

In 2004, Claude Benoît was awarded the McNeill prize for having shown outstanding skill in promoting and spreading scientific knowledge among students and the general public.

1. At the *Biôdome*, plans are being made to create a new living environment for river otters. The plan calls for four dens arranged around a water hole with the following specifications.

- The four dens must be located 30 m from the water hole.
- Each of the dens must be located at a distance of at least 20 m from the boundaries of the lot and over 30 m away from each other.

Propose locations for these four dens. Show that your proposal is well within the specifications by clearly explaining your approach.

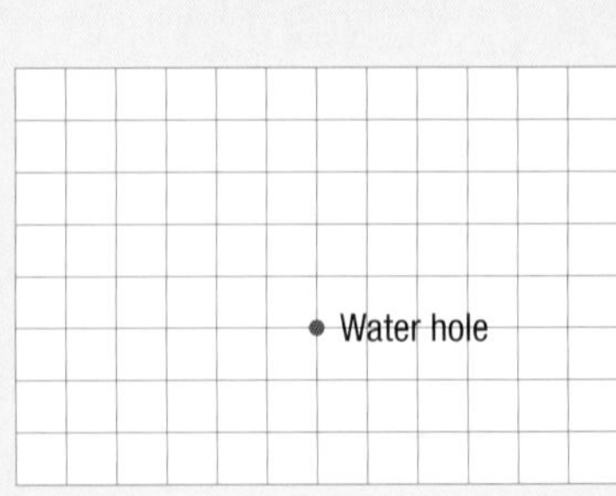

In the workplace

> « I believe that communicating knowledge is at least as important as furthering this knowledge: it is unsavory, and sometimes dangerous to maintain this lofty secrecy around science. »
>
> Hubert Reeves

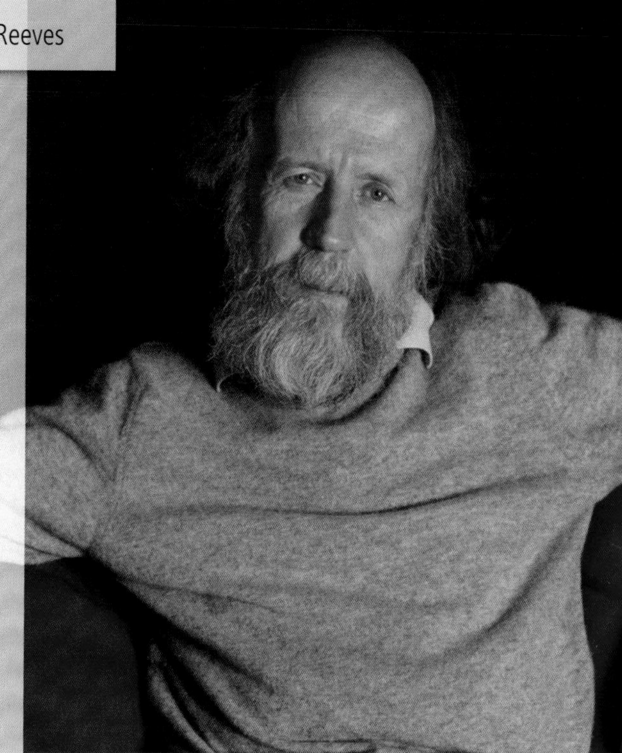

An astrophysicist becomes an interpretative scientist

Global warming is one of Hubert Reeves' major concerns. For many years now, he has been using forums to draw the public's attention to the fact that our planet is facing global warming. During interviews posted on the Internet, he indicated that the temperature of the planet has increased by approximately 1°C over the last 50 years. He also noted that as predicted through mathematical models the main effect of this warming trend is climate destabilisation.

In particular, this climate destabilization will have an impact on agriculture and, consequently, on human beings.

2. An American team analyzed the quality of grape production (recorded in %) in relation to the mean temperature (°C) observed during vine growth. They noted that the mean temperature had an impact on grape quality.

Model this scatter plot with a quadratic function. Then using this function to explain the effect that temperature variations can have on the quality of grape production, write a 100 to 150-word article, for a scientific journal intended for young people aged 12 to 18. Be sure to justify your statements with relevant numerical data taken from your model.

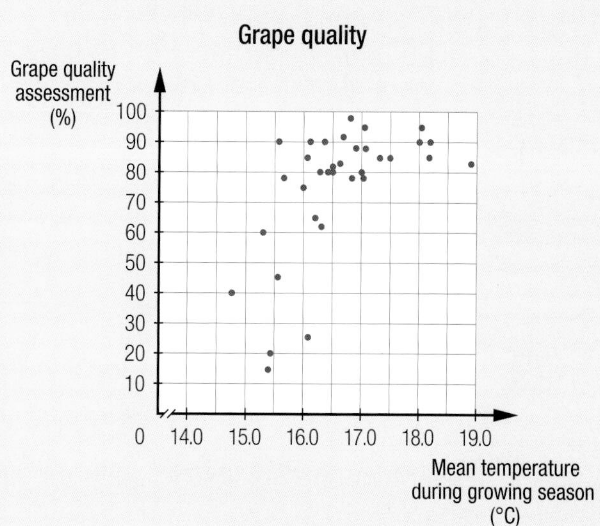

overview

1 Rachel has displayed the graph of the function $y = 2x^2 - 7x + 3$ on her calculator. Determine, in general form, the equation of the curves obtained by applying the following geometric transformations to Rachel's graph:

a) a reflection across the x-axis

b) a reflection across the y-axis

c) a 180° rotation about the origin

d) a 3-unit translation towards the left

e) a 2-unit translation downwards

f) a translation of 4 units towards the right and 3 units upwards

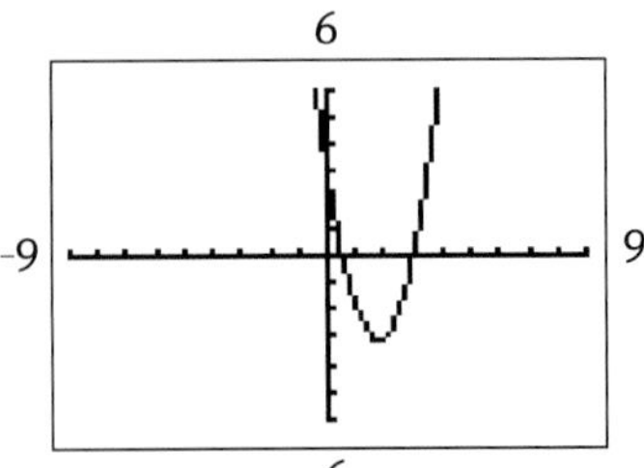

2 During a chess tournament, the number of matches played in relation to the number of players follows the rule of a quadratic function. In a tournament involving 12 players, 132 matches were played. If there had been two more players, the tournament would have involved 50 additional matches.

a) Determine the rule of this function, considering that it is valid regardless of the number of players. Explain your answer with the help of a diagram.

b) How many players were present at a tournament where 380 matches were played?

c) During a tournament where no more than 10 players were present, more than 40 matches were played. How many matches could they have played?

Alexandre Lesiège is the international chess Grand Master. In his younger years, he won the world title three times in the Cadet category.

3 Consider the following quadratic functions:

① $f(x) = x^2 + kx + 1$ ② $f(x) = x^2 + kx + (k + 3)$ ③ $f(x) = kx^2 + x + (k + 2)$

Determine the possible **k** values for which these functions have:

a) two zeros b) only one zero c) no zeros

4 At the *Parc national des Grands-Jardins*, six new sections for hiking and camping are being planned. The drawing below shows the location of the sites.

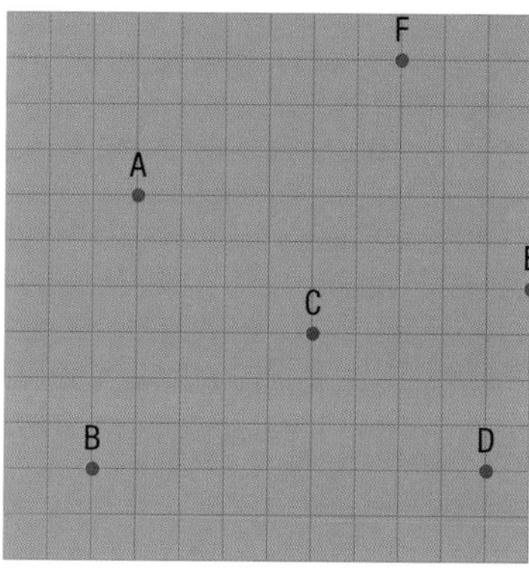

1 km

The park's managers want the environmental impact to be minimal. For this reason, they want the path joining these sites to be as short as possible.

With respect for the managers' concerns, propose a path that would allow hikers to go from one site to the next. What is the length of your proposed path?

5 A pyrotechnic rocket is launched from the ground and explodes at a height of 60 m. The height of the fireworks above the ground (in m) is shown in relation to the elapsed time (in s) after launching. The rule of the function is $h(t) = -5t^2 + 40t$.

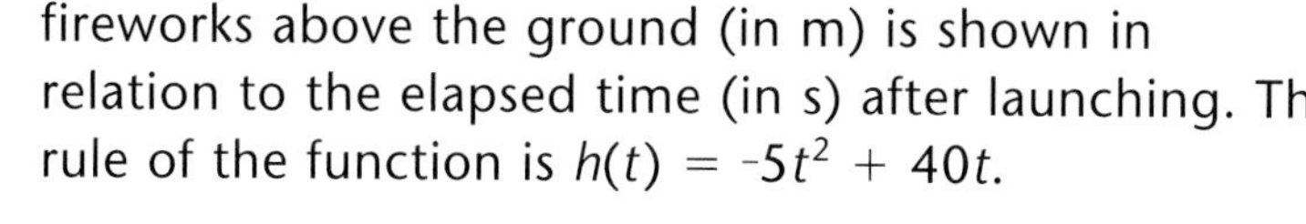

a) If the rocket exploded during its ascent:
   1) what was the elapsed time before it exploded?
   2) how high was it after 0.5 s, after 1 s, after 2 s?

b) If, instead, the rocket exploded during its descent:
   1) what was the elapsed time before it exploded?
   2) what was the maximum height reached by the rocket?

6 Consider $f(x) = x^2 + \text{b}x + 3$.

a) Determine the coordinates of the vertex representing the function for the following **b** values.

   1) b = -4 2) b = -2 3) b = 0 4) b = 2 5) b = 4

b) What is the equation of the curve passing through these different vertices?

c) Is there a relation between the equations found in **b)** and the rule of the function?

d) What if the rules of the functions were different? Formulate a conjecture and prove it.

7 Practising the extreme sport of parkour, a traceur must jump from the roof of a building to another roof below. On the ground, this traceur can jump over a distance of 4 m while reaching a height of 1 m in the middle of his trajectory.

Parkour is the art of displacement from point A to point B while efficiently overcoming obstacles along the way. Individuals who practise this sport are called *traceurs* or *traceuses* for females.

a) Can a traceur safely perform this jump between two buildings if they are 5 m apart and if the second building is 3 m lower than the first? Justify your answer.

b) What is the distance between his starting point and his landing point?

8 The Harlem Globetrotters are a team of players who have turned basketball into a show. During a spectacular routine, one of the players performs field goal shots from the centre of the court. His extremely precise shots always reach the height of 6.1 m, and he sinks the ball into the basket through the centre of the hoop.

It is partly thanks to the Harlem Globetrotters that the general public discovered basketball. The team, which has existed for over 80 years, holds the best performance in this professional sport. Out of 22 500 games played, the Globetrotters have lost a mere 345.

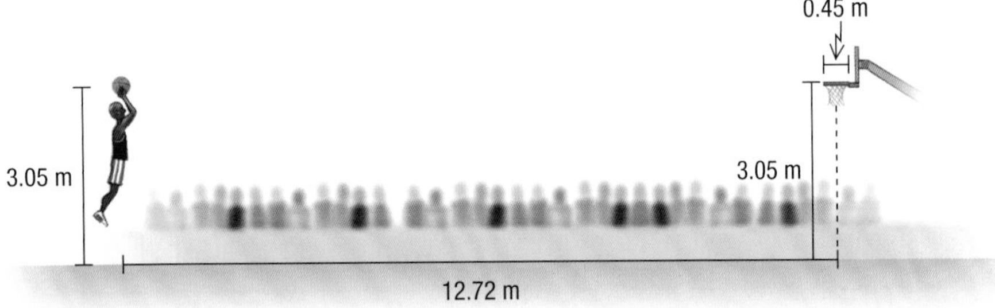

a) At what distance from the centre of the court does the ball reach its maximum height?

b) Taking the centre of the court as the origin in a Cartesian plane, determine the equation that describes the ball's trajectory.

c) The ball has a diameter of 24 cm. At the moment when the centre of the ball comes over the hoop, what distance separates the ball from the hoop?

9 An airline company charges $1,000 for each ticket to carry 200 passengers from one city to another. The company calculated that for each additional group of 5 passengers, it can offer a $10 discount for each ticket. Despite this discount, the company wants to generate over $225,000 in revenue for this flight.

Considering that n represents the number of additional groups of 5 people, answer the following questions.

Revenues of an airline company

Number of passengers	Ticket price ($)	Company revenue ($)
200	1,000	200 × 1,000
205	990	205 × 990
210	980	210 × 980
215	970	215 × 970
220	960	220 × 960

a) Show that this situation can be expressed as $-50n^2 + 3000n - 25\,000 > 0$.

b) With this discount policy, could the airline company reach the desired revenue of $225,000? Determine the number of passengers it must carry in order to achieve this objective. If not, explain why it cannot reach its objective.

10 Amelia attended a public conference on undersea life. She learned that the temperature at the bottom of the sea is 4°C. Why? The answer is simple: this is the temperature at which water density is highest. Thus, at 4°C, water tends to "sink."

After this conference, Amelia researched water density further and found the results shown in the adjacent table.

Water density

Temperature (°C)	Density (g/mL)
4.0	0.999 973
4.5	0.999 972
5.0	0.999 965
5.5	0.999 955
6.0	0.999 941
6.5	0.999 924
7.0	0.999 902
7.5	0.999 877
8.0	0.999 849
8.5	0.999 817
9.0	0.999 781
9.5	0.999 742
10.0	0.999 700

a) Represent this data as a scatter plot and draw the parabola that seems to best fit the data.

b) Determine the rule of this quadratic function in general form.

c) What does parameter **c** represent in this rule?

d) Is your model valid at any temperature?

A number of deep-sea species of fish and marine animals have bioluminescent organs that are capable of producing light. This small squid, called *cranchia scabra*, lives in the waters of the Gulf of Mexico. On each eye, it has 14 luminescent cells that emit greenish or bluish light.

11 The technique used for tennis drop shots depends on the distance that separates the player from the net. For a short drop shot, the ball must reach its maximum height at the moment when it goes over the net. For a long drop shot, the ball must reach its maximum height long before it reaches the net.

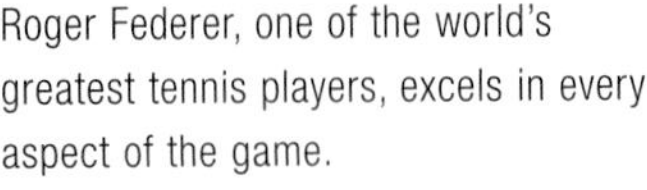

Roger Federer, one of the world's greatest tennis players, excels in every aspect of the game.

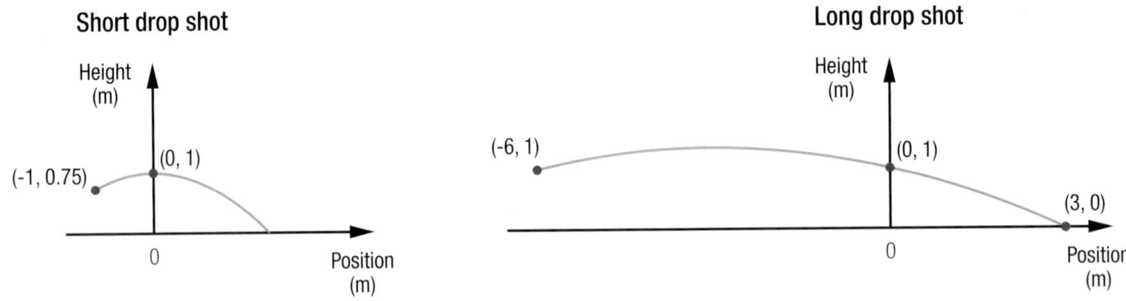

In the two graphs above, the trajectory of the ball is defined in relation to the position of the net which is associated with the vertical axis.

a) Determine the equation of each trajectory in general form.

b) At what distance from the net did the short drop shot land?

c) What was the maximum height reached by the ball in the long drop shot?

d) For each type of drop shot, calculate the distance between the point of impact of the ball with the racket and the falling point of the ball on the court. How many times longer is the distance in the long drop shot?

12 Presuming that variable x represents a positive number, solve each of the following inequalities.

a) $\sqrt{x} > x$ b) $\sqrt{x} \leq \frac{x}{2}$ c) $\sqrt{x} \leq \frac{x + 1}{2}$

13 A cube-shaped reservoir has walls 0.5 cm thick. Consider x as the length of the outside edges.

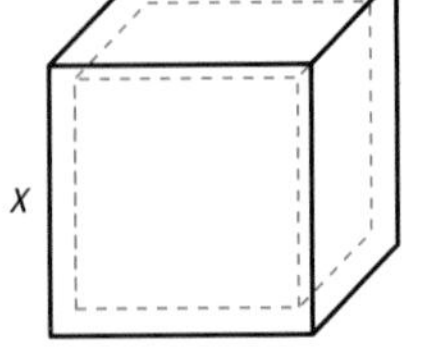

a) What algebraic expression represents the reservoir's capacity expressed in cubic centimetres?

b) What must the length of the outside edges be so that the capacity of this cube is between 1 and 2 L?

14 Dax is in the gondola of a hot air balloon that has been rising for 2 s at a velocity of 2 m/s. His friend Raoul realizes that Dax forgot his water bottle on the ground. He throws it to Dax vertically at a velocity of 12 m/s. This situation can be represented by the function $d(t) = 5t^2 - 10t + 4$ where $d(t)$ represents the distance (in m) separating Dax from the bottle and t, the elapsed time since Raoul's throw.

a) Will it be possible for Dax to catch the bottle? Justify your answer.

b) If the bottle had been thrown 3 s after lift-off, would your answer in **a)** have been the same? Justify your answer.

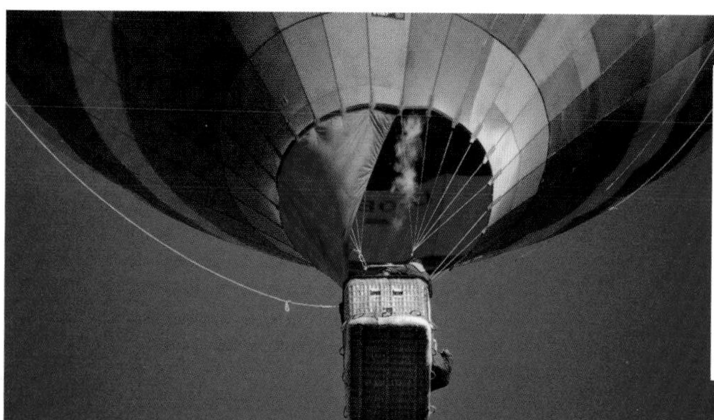

The hot air balloon was invented by the Montgolfier brothers. After completing several tethered flights, they decided to try a manned flight. A volunteer offered to go, but the endeavour was deemed too risky because the effects of altitude variations on the human body were unknown. Thus, for that first flight, in 1783, a rooster, a duck and a sheep were chosen. The animals landed safe and sound.

15 A fire hose nozzle can propel a water jet to a maximum height of 18 m. When the nozzle is placed 50 m away from the burning building, the water hits the wall 3 m above the ground, at the same height as the end of the nozzle. The building has a height of 16 m and a width of 8 m.

a) At what distance from the building should the nozzle be placed in order for the water to hit the wall?

b) At what distance from the building should the nozzle be placed in order for the water to hit the roof?

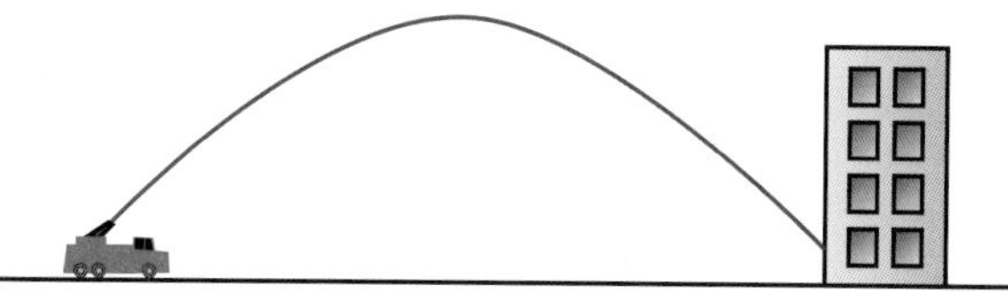

16 Donna represented two quadratic functions that had the same axis of symmetry and the same opening on the same graph. She then joined the two intersection points and the two vertices of the parabolas so as to form a rhombus.

$$f_1(x) = 0.5x^2 - 4x + 8$$

$$f_2(x) = -0.5x^2 + 4x$$

a) Write the rules of functions f_1 and f_2 in standard form.

b) Determine the coordinates of the points that represent the vertices of the quadrilateral.

c) Calculate the perimeter and the area of this rhombus.

bank of problems

17 At an amusement park, a game of skill consists of bouncing a ball on the ground so that it lands in a basket and stays there. The game's difficulty is due to the fact that the ball can easily bounce out. Below is a depiction of the winning shot performed by Cecilia.

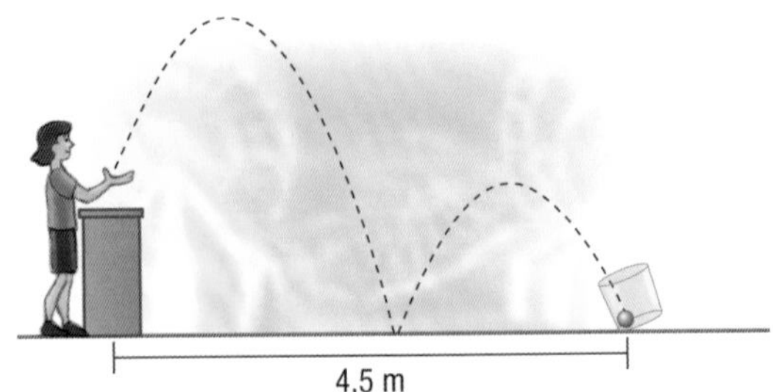

The ball was thrown at a height of 1.5 m. One metre further, it reached its maximum height of 2.7 m. Considering that the trajectory consists of two parabolic curves with the same opening, determine the maximum height reached by the ball following the rebound.

18 A train with panoramic windows is moving in a straight line at a uniform speed of 20 m/s. A person standing in the train throws a ball vertically in the air and catches it at the same height 1.2 s later. At the same moment, a farmer in his field is watching the train go by.

Considering that the height of the ball (in m) in relation to the windowsill is given by the function $h(t) = -5t^2 + 4t + 0.2$, where t is the elapsed time (in s), as precisely as possible describe the farmer's view of the trajectory of the ball.

19 **ODEILLO** The solar oven in Odeillo, in southern France, is one of the largest solar ovens in the world. By concentrating the Sun's energy onto its focus, it can quickly reach a temperature above 3000°C.

Solar ovens are used to study and develop materials intended for the aerospace industry and are capable of withstanding very high temperatures.

As shown in the diagram below, the adjustable mirrors reflect the solar rays toward the parabolic mirror which in turn redirects the rays toward the focus.

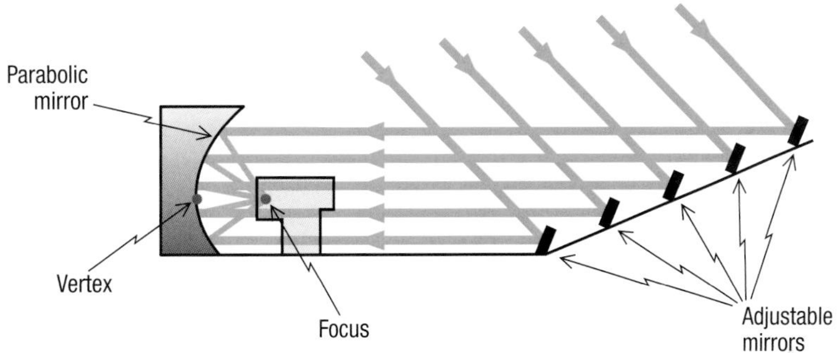

The following is an estimation of some of the characteristics of the parabolic mirror:

- The height of the vertex and the focus is 12 m.
- The height of the highest point of the mirror is 32 m.
- The distance between the vertex and the focus is 18 m.

Based on the properties of a parabola, determine the distance between the highest point and the lowest point of the mirror.

20 By definition, the product of a number and its reciprocal always equals 1. For example, $\frac{2}{3}$ is the reciprocal of $\frac{3}{2}$ and $\frac{2}{3} \times \frac{3}{2} = 1$. What can you say regarding the sum of a number and its reciprocal? Formulate a conjecture about this and prove it.

21 Lee lives in a cottage by a river with a beach that is located 60 m downstream. During the summer, when the river's current is weak, his canoe trip to the beach takes 1 minute. In the spring, the current is stronger than in the summer, and the time for the trip to the beach is shorter, but the time required to get back is much longer.

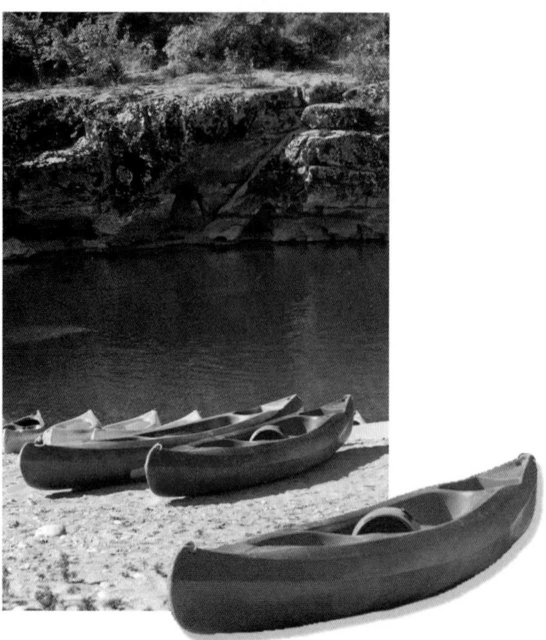

What must the speed of the current be for Lee to be able to make a round trip to the beach in less than 3 minutes?

22 Garen is struggling with the following problem.

> What are the coordinates of the vertex of the curve that represents the quadratic function of which the *y*-intercept is 3 and the zeros are 2 and 6?

Following extensive calculations, Garen found the right answer, that is (4, -1). As he is not that keen on calculations, he tells himself that it would be nice to have a formula to determine these coordinates.

What formula would yield the coordinates of the vertex based on the *y*-intercept **c** and the zeros x_1 and x_2 of a quadratic function?

23 Consider s and t which are two irrational numbers of a quadratic function whose coefficients are integers. Considering that $s < t$ and that $s^2 + 2t = 6$, show that $t^2 + 2s = 6$.

24 A woman is driving a car at 90 km/h (or 25 m/s) when she sees the adjacent sign by the side of the road. The sign's blinking lights warn that the traffic light 300 m ahead has turned red. She estimates that the light will turn green in 20 s. She takes her foot off the accelerator and, without braking, allows the car to decelerate. She hopes that the light will turn green before she gets to the intersection and that no other vehicle will be stopped there.

Presuming the deceleration is constant, the distance (in m) that separates the car from the intersection will be described as a function in the form $d(t) = at^2 - 25t + 300$ where t is the elapsed time (in s). Parameter **a** depends on the car's deceleration.

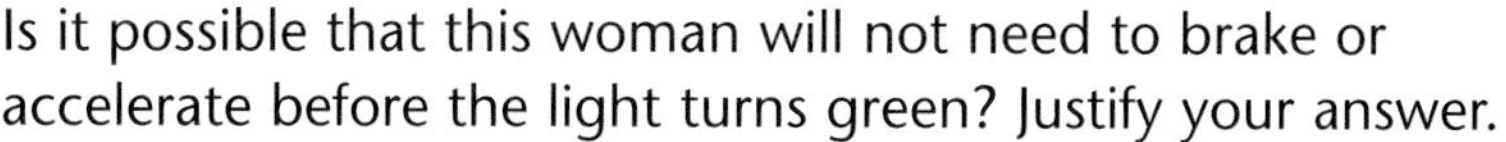

Is it possible that this woman will not need to brake or accelerate before the light turns green? Justify your answer.

25 On a pool table, two balls are hit simultaneously in perpendicular directions. The initial distances between the centre of the balls and the intersection point of their trajectories are respectively 2.1 m and 1.2 m.

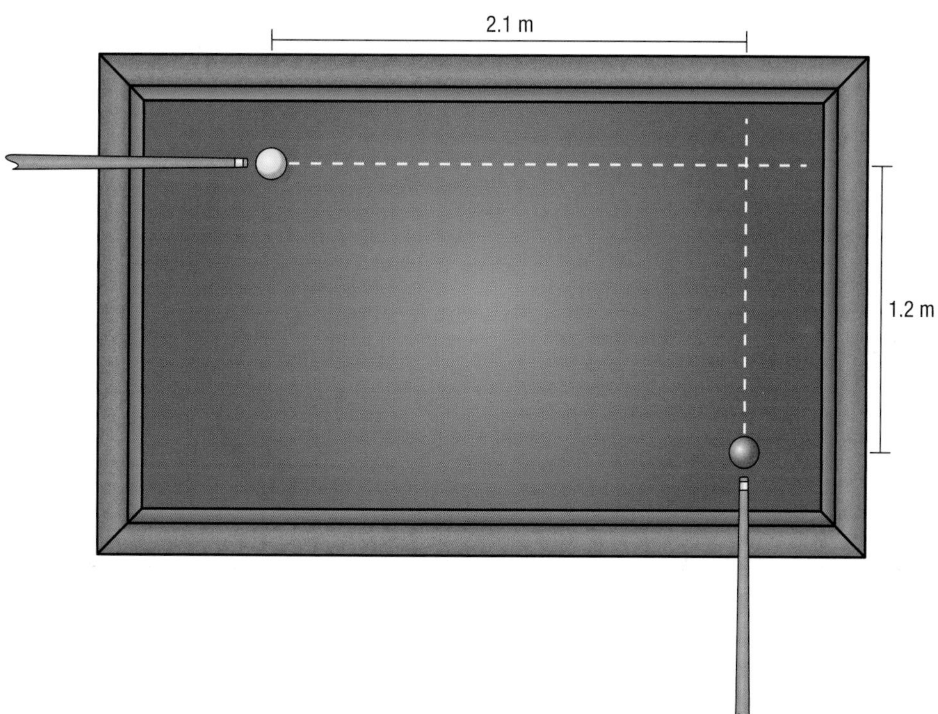

The two balls have a diameter of 6 cm. The velocity of the white ball is 0.8 m/s and that of the red ball is 0.5 m/s.

Before they reach the edge of the table, will the two balls touch each other? If not, at what moment will they be closest to each other?

LEARNING AND EVALUATION SITUATIONS

TABLE OF CONTENTS

Are we really happy?

Learning context

For a long time we have evaluated countries by demographics, religions, population growth, life expectancy, revenue, education and levels of happiness. But isn't happiness the ultimate goal of every person on earth?

Happiness has been a subject of reflection since antiquity. Nevertheless it is only recently that happiness is being explored scientifically. Biologists, psychologists, chemists and even economists are now studying this subject.

Do you personally think it is possible for everyone to be happy? Do you believe that you have an influence on your own path to happiness? Do you think that one day, science will be able to explain happiness?

This LES is related to section 1.1.

LES 1

Planetary happiness

In Western countries, happiness is often associated with consumption. When we say consumption we mean the use of the planet's resources that are limited. If each person on the planet consumed as much as the average Canadian, it would take 3.6 planets like ours to supply the demand. This is why we say that the *ecological footprint* of Canada is 3.6.

By comparison, the ecological footprint of Bhutan is 0.7. If the whole world lived like the average Bhutanese, we would use only 70% of our natural resources. But this raises the question: Are Bhutanese less happy than Canadians?

Studies are being conducted to measure the happiness levels in different countries. Using the sheet that you will receive, look at the indicators relating to the ecological footprint of 178 countries.

Write a report which addresses the following questions:

- Globally, is there a relationship between the ecological footprint of a country and the level of happiness of its inhabitants?
- If so, what are the characteristics of this relationship and how would you explain them?

Compare your conclusions with those of a peer.

LES 2

C1

This LES is related to section 1.2.

Variables of happiness

Feelings of happiness are related to your experiences. However, look at your peers. Most of them say they are happy, but for some, happiness seems to be inaccessible. Would you like to help them? In fact, wouldn't you like to make everyone happier? But what steps could you take to accomplish this?

Ask yourself the question as a doctor or a psychologist would: What determines whether or not you are happy? Below are a variety of quantitative characteristics that could have a positive or negative effect on the happiness level of any teenager.

- disposable income
- number of friends
- time devoted to work
- academic success
- physical activity

Do you believe that there are other variables that influence happiness? Discuss this question in class.

Choose at least two variables from those mentioned in class. Your task is to decide which of these variables has the greatest correlation with happiness according to the questionnaire given to your classmates. Interpret these results and try to explain them.

Propose ways to improve the level of happiness for your classmates.

Answer the questionnaire anonymously. It will help you quantify your own level of happiness and provide insight into the happiness of those around you.

LES 3

This LES is related to section 1.3.

Does money buy happiness?

There is a well known saying that "Money cannot buy happiness." Some people say money contributes to happiness. Others say money cannot bring everything you wish for and, in fact, money may cause you a lot of distress. Economists try to understand this. Let's look at what is happening in the USA, considered by many to be the richest country in the world.

Revenue and happiness in the USA (1996)*

Mean annual income ($)	Index of happiness (1 to 3) (3 being the happiest)
3,300	1.94
7,000	2.03
10,000	2.07
13,400	2.15
17,100	2.19
20,600	2.29
24,300	2.20
29,600	2.24
39,700	2.30
70,900	2.32

* Data obtained from a sample of the population grouped according to income level into 10 groups of the same size.

Evolution of revenue and happiness in the USA

Year	Annual income per capita ($)	Percentage of people who say they are happy (%)
1946	1,200	31
1951	1,500	38
1956	1,900	43
1961	2,200	40
1966	2,800	37
1971	3,900	36
1976	5,900	34
1981	9,900	32
1986	14,400	31
1991	19,200	31
1996	23,600	30

Your task is to establish a possible relationship between money and happiness using data from one of the tables above. You must write a report and clearly describe this relationship that addresses the following:

- Is it possible to form a mathematical linear equation describing this relationship?
- Would another model be more suitable?

Justify your statements by using mathematical reasoning.

Citius, altius, fortius

Learning context

Swifter, higher, stronger! is the motto of the Olympic Games. One-hundredth of a second, a centimetre or a kilogram can make the difference between a gold, silver or bronze medal and between glory and anonymity.

Today science can be used to create new champions. The top sports nations systematically use science for better planning, better execution, and better control of training and competition. Math serves not only to measure performance levels; it also uses models to analyze physical performance, the goal being to push the limits of the human machine as far as possible.

How do you think the different fields of science can contribute to improving the performance of athletes?

LES 4

This LES is related to section 2.1.

A real machine

While observing athletes, we get the impression that the human body is truly a performance machine. However, we must be in tune with this machine and know how to use it effectively. This is where modelling and science enter the game!

1. Ian Thorpe's "bent elbow recovery" technique

Notice that the height of the elbow changes over time.

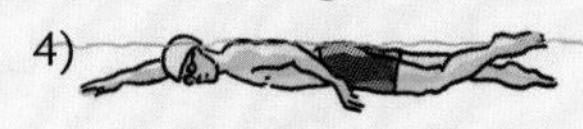

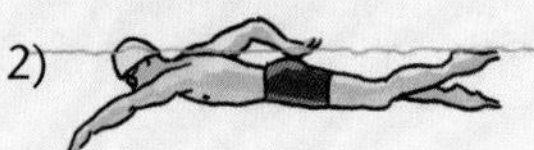

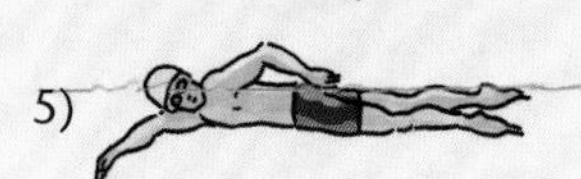

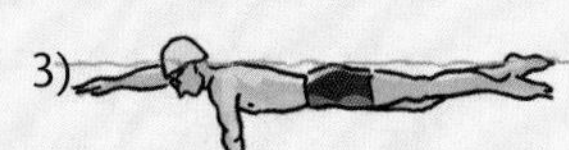

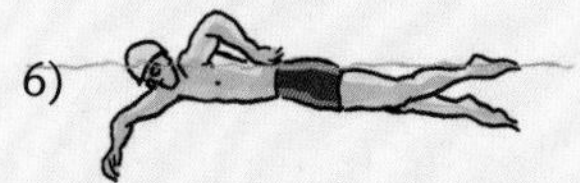

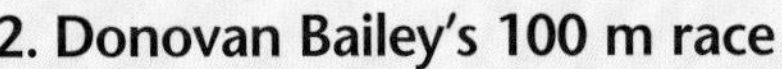

2. Donovan Bailey's 100 m race

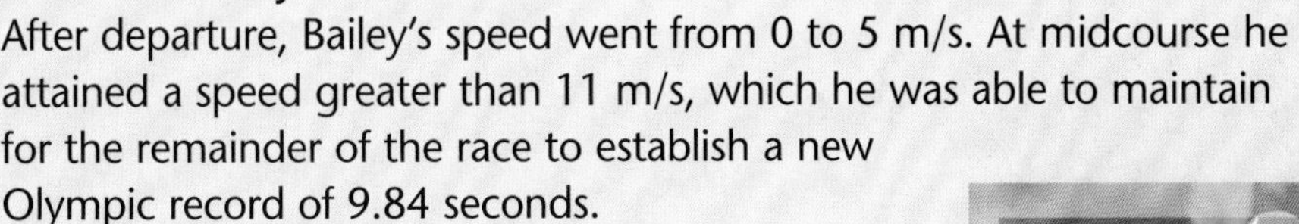

After departure, Bailey's speed went from 0 to 5 m/s. At midcourse he attained a speed greater than 11 m/s, which he was able to maintain for the remainder of the race to establish a new Olympic record of 9.84 seconds.

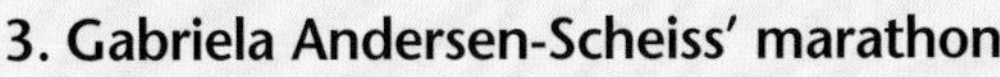

3. Gabriela Andersen-Scheiss' marathon

At the Los Angeles Olympic Games, in 1984, she barely crossed the finish line. Her determination shows evidence of the relationship existing between the quantity of energy expended and speed.

Speed (m/min)	105	125	185	225	305	345	385
Energy expenditure (kcal/kg/km)	1.06	1.046	1.028	1.027	1.038	1.049	1.062

Find the graphical model most appropriate to describe the existing relationship between the variables considered in each of the situations described above. Then choose another sporting event that introduces two variables, and research the pertinent data in order to answer the following questions:

- Can any of the models used for the three situations described above also be used to model the new situation that you have chosen? Justify your response.
- How does the model of best fit for this situation differ from those given above?

LES 5

This LES is related to section 2.2.

Planning a perfect dive

The degree of difficulty of a dive depends on the number and variety of positions it involves. The ability to perform these positions quickly and gracefully, accompanied by a straight and vertical water entry, is the mark of a great champion.

The time to complete the dive is very short when diving from the 10 m tower.

This picture depicts a 1½ tuck somersault with a ½ twist. A photographer took a series of photos of this dive in rapid succession. The interval between each pose is 0.2 s. The red dot is the diver's centre of gravity.

Canadian diver Alexandre Despatie won the silver medal at the 2004 Athen's Olympic Games.

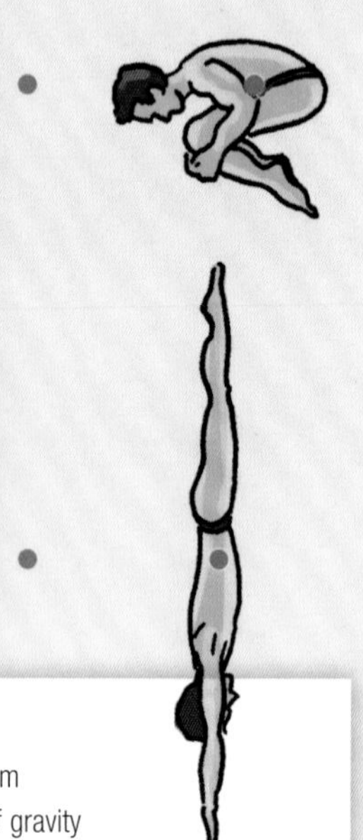

Positions and execution times

Position	Time
Tuck somersault	0.35 s
Jacknife somersault	0.40 s
Open jackknife	0.50 s
Extended somersault	0.60 s
Twist*	0.10 s
Opening	0.10 s

Your task is to design another dive to be performed from a 10 m platform and to describe the positions to be assumed in the dive. In order to design a perfect dive, leave nothing to chance. Indicate the diver's centre of gravity and the time that should elapse at the end of each position.

Legend

2.5 cm ≙ 1m

● Centre of gravity

* The twist is executed during an extended somersault. Each twist adds 0.1 seconds to the dive. A diver can execute a maximum of 3 twists during an extended somersault.

LES 6

This LES is related to section 2.3

The mathematics of endurance

Training is an essential component of the development of an athlete. To prepare a personalized training program, we first measure the athlete's physical ability during a sustained effort. Several endurance tests allow us to make such measurements.

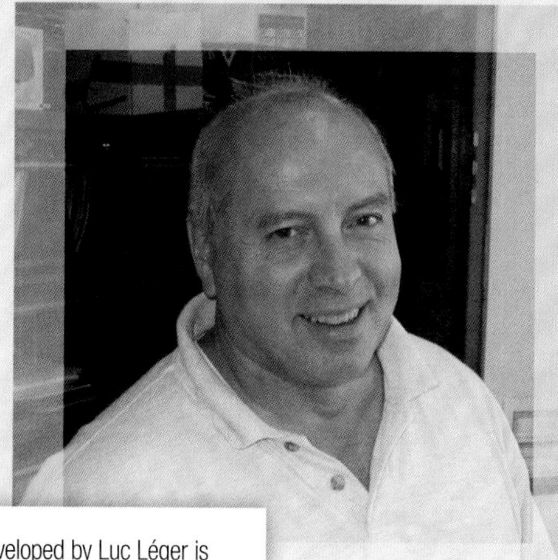

The test developed by Luc Léger is used to measure the maximal aerobic capacity of a person (VO_2 max).

A well-known test on the treadmill was first suggested by Québec physiologist, Luc Léger. A person taking this test is asked to run at a constant rate for each distance. At regular intervals the speed is increased. The runner must keep up as long as possible. When the runner can no longer continue he or she is considered to be at maximal aerobic capacity.

Design an endurance test in units that could be programmed for a treadmill just as Luc Léger did. The test must meet the following conditions:

- During each stage of equal duration, the speed of the treadmill is constant.
- The acceleration will be the same for each interval.
- The test will include at least 12 intervals of increasing difficulty, from beginner to expert level.
- The test will take a maximum of 20 minutes, and the total distance run by the athlete must not exceed 4 km.

Describe the characteristics of your test, indicating the duration and speed during each interval with the help of a table of values, a graph or an equation. Then explain how your test meets the conditions listed above.

A world of calculations

Learning context

The elevators we take, the lights that control traffic in our cities, the GPS that we use when hiking, the airplane that whisks us to our travel destination and the Canadarm used to repair the International Space Station are all examples of modern society's ingenuity.

When we look at the achievements of engineers, we can clearly see that they are the result of many mathematical calculations. These calculations allow us to choose the best solutions, solutions that on one hand minimize costs, energy or space, and on the other, increase precision, efficiency and strength.

Are you intrigued by machines and their mechanisms?

Aside from competent calculation skills, what else do you think characterizes a good engineer?

Aeronautical engineers have drawn inspiration for their designs from the wings of bats: maximum speed that requires minimum energy.

This LES is related to section 3.1.

Nature's contribution

Engineers design and solve problems in the production of products, systems and services. Nature is often a source of inspiration for finding the best solution.

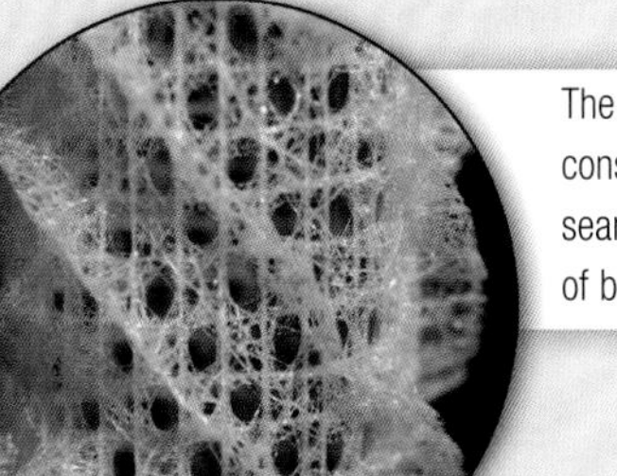

The marine sponge inspired construction engineers in their search for rigidity and stability of buildings.

For example, what form having the smallest possible surface allows us to define a given space? To analyze this problem, an engineer might think of observing the shape that a soap bubble forms in a state of zero gravity.

Imagine you are part of the crew of the International Space Station performing the following experiment. You place a soap bubble having a volume of 100 cm^3 in a transparent cube with a 10 cm edge. The bubble sticks to the wall of the cube in such a way that the surface in contact with the air is reduced to a minimum in order to reduce surface pressure.

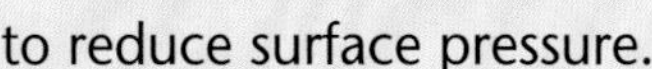

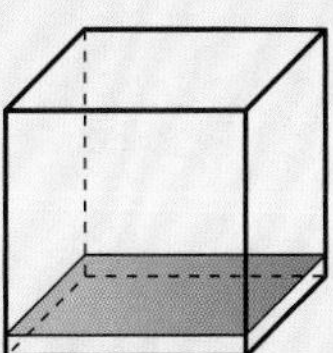

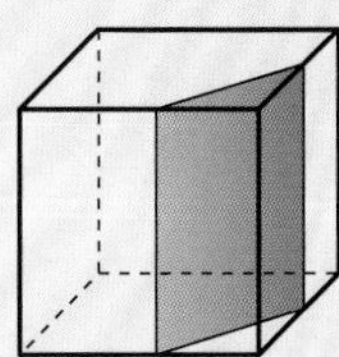

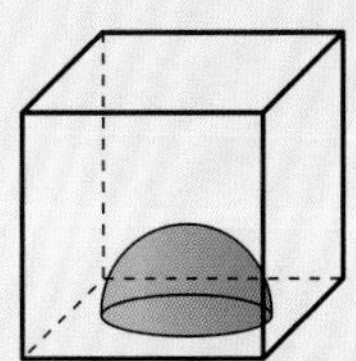

What shape should the bubble take on the cube's wall: a prism with a square base, a prism with a triangular base or perhaps a hemisphere?

In the examples above, the form created is not the most optimal. The surface of the soap bubble could be smaller. What shape could the bubble take on the cube's wall in order for its surface to appear smaller than those in the above examples?

If we wanted to confine a 200 cm^3 space, would the shape you chose above still result in the soap film covering the smallest area?

LES 8

This LES is related to section 3.2.

C3

Ingenuity in reserve

In mathematics, the surface of a solid has no thickness. However, engineers working on a design for a reservoir of a given capacity must include the thickness of its walls in their calculations. They select different forms, thicknesses and dimensions depending on the intended use of the reservoir. To avoid having to recalculate each time, it is useful to establish a general formula for a given type of reservoir.

For example, the capacity of all cubic reservoirs can be calculated using the formula $(a - 2x)^3$ where a is the measurement of the edge of a reservoir wall and x is its thickness.

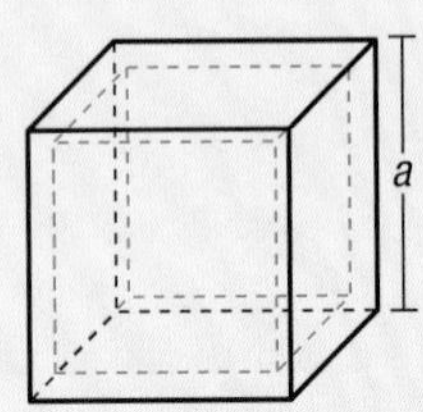

The two reservoirs below having x units of thickness are composed of hemispheres, cylinders and right prisms.

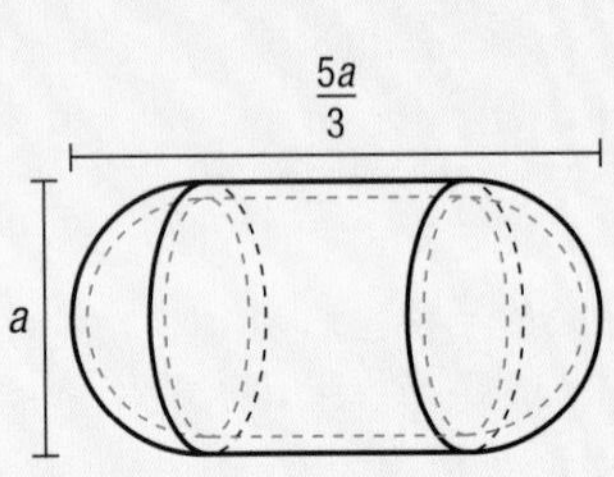

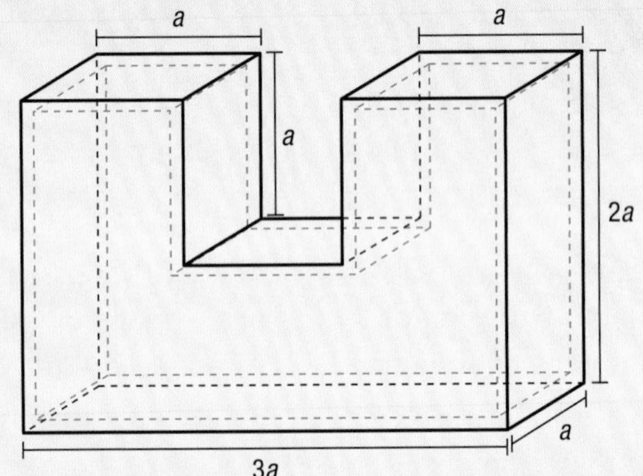

With your peers, discuss other reservoirs of this type where all of the exterior dimensions are expressed using the variable a.

Your task is to choose one of these reservoirs and show as clearly as possible its capacity, the wall volume and the relationship between the capacity of this reservoir and that of the cubic reservoir.

Compare your data with that of a peer who chose the same reservoir as you. Is the data you both obtained equivalent? Do you understand each other's calculation process? After this discussion, improve upon your solution.

LES 9

This LES is related to section 3.3.

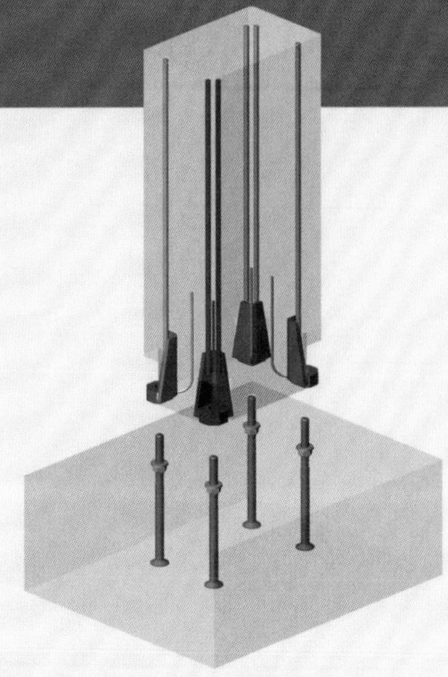

Concrete bases

When a pole is placed on a concrete base, anchor points are attached around this base to keep everything in place. The anchor points must be positioned far enough away from the edge to ensure their stability in the event of cracking or crumbling. This concrete base can be designed in many shapes but is generally a prism or cylinder with its sidewalls buried in the ground.

Visualize the following situation. You are working for a civil engineering firm that asks you to design a base to be used to support a street lamp. There are four anchor points located on top of a square with side lengths measuring 1 m.

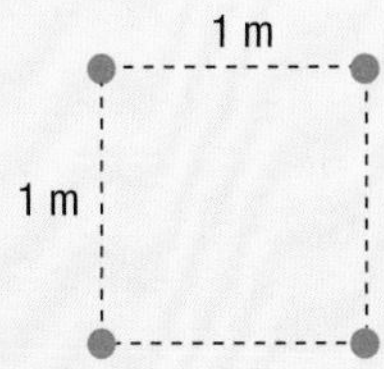

After taking into account the various constraints, you determine that the concrete base will have a volume of 12.5 m^3 and a height of 2 m. You have the choice between a square-based prism and a circular cylinder shape.

Which of these two shapes should you choose if you want to maximize the distance between each anchor point and the edge of the platform? Would the answer be the same if the area of the platform base were larger? Is there another shape that would allow you to increase this distance even more for a volume of 12.5 m^3? If so, design a diagram for the base, indicating the relevant measurements.

A visit to the Science Centre

Learning context

Every major city in the world has a museum dedicated to science which provides an overview of the progress made by science and technology by presenting popular interactive exhibitions for visitors of all ages.

The job of setting up these exhibits requires the talent of a skilled scientific writer. The person must have in-depth knowledge of the subject being presented and be able to express the facts in language that is clear and easily understood by the general public. But sometimes a problem arises: scientific language is primarily of a mathematical nature. In order to properly explain scientific phenomena, it may be necessary to present geometric figures, formulas or equations that are not understood by all.

Have you ever had difficulty fully grasping explanations of a scientific nature because you did not have the required mathematical knowledge?

Do you feel that you have the skills required to become a good scientific writer?

LES 10

This LES is related to sections 4.1 and 4.2.

C2

Road safety

Speeding is one of the main causes of highway accidents. The Science Centre has set up a speed simulator for its visitors so that they can experience a "lead foot" with no risk to themselves.

The adjacent sign can be found alongside a highway in France. The pictogram indicates that it is safer to reduce speed in rainy conditions when the road surface is wet.

However, we can ask ourselves the following: Is it necessary to doubt this information about the maximum speed of a car on a wet road?

The Science Centre provides the following information to help visitors properly understand the context of the question.

A vehicle's stopping distance (D_A) is composed of 2 parts: the reaction distance (D_R) and the braking distance (D_F).

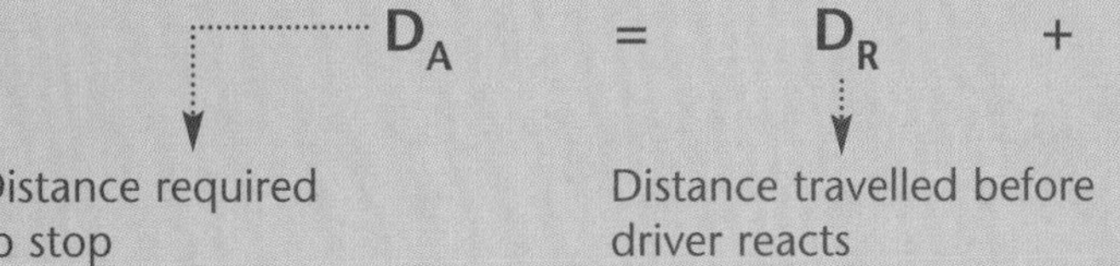

- Once an obstacle is observed, a driver's average reaction time before braking is 1.3 seconds.
- The braking distance (D_F) is proportional to the square of the initial speed and the coefficient of proportionality is $\frac{1}{2a}$ where a represents the deceleration of the vehicle, which varies from:
  - 5 to 8 m/s^2 on a dry road surface
  - 3.4 to 5.5 m/s^2 on a wet road surface

Nearly 40% of highway deaths are speed-related.

If a highway road sign in Québec indicates that the maximum speed allowed is 90 km/h on a dry road surface, what should the maximum speed be on a wet road surface? What conjecture can represent this situation? Prove it.

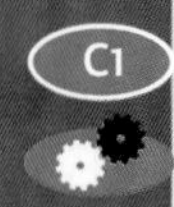

LES 11

This LES is related to section 4.3.

C1

Science of the circus

At an exhibition on the science of the circus, the Science Centre offers its visitors a human cannonball display. This dangerous specialty act requires a lot of preparation to ensure that a safe execution is properly calculated.

During his shows at the Ontario Science Centre, human cannonball David Smith was launched more than 21 metres into the air before falling into a net positioned 45 metres away from the cannon.

While quite spectacular, the human cannonball show has not been repeated often since it was first performed in 1871. To spice up the performance, a human cannonball wants to fly through a flaming hoop when shot out of the cannon. To simulate this situation, a science centre offers its young visitors the following activity.

Can you help the human cannonball fly through a flaming hoop?

Place the ring and net wherever you want in their respective zones and, standing behind the red line, try to throw the ball through the hoop into the net simulating the human cannonball event.

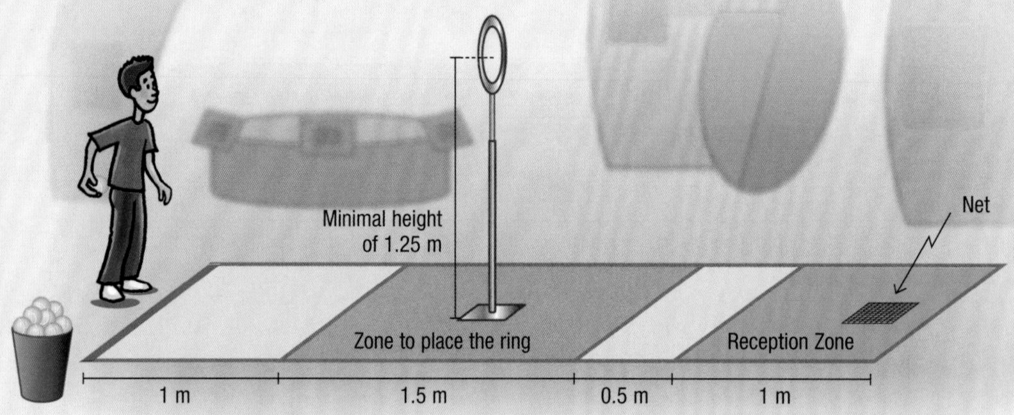

Your task is to determine the proper placement of the ring, the height at the centre as well as the position of the net. Describe the ideal trajectory of the ball as it passes through the ring and lands in the net. Test your theory by throwing the ball exactly as you've described it. Then recommend how the equipment should be set.

This LES is related to section 4.4.

LES 12

Parabolas and whispers

At the Science Centre there is a room dedicated to sound, and in this room there are two identical parabolic-shaped disks facing each other. Someone who whispers in front of one of the disks, will be clearly heard by another person standing in front of an identical disk even if these two people are facing backwards and are separated by a great distance. How is this possible?

Below are a few measurements used for this installation which is comprised of two parabolic reflectors and an explanatory sign:

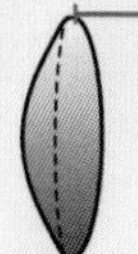

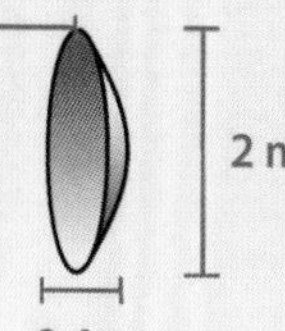

When you whisper into one of the disk's centres, you emit a sound wave that emanates towards the parabolic reflector.

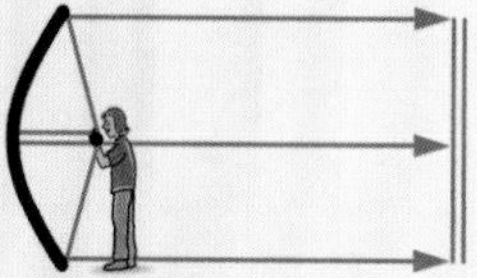

All parts of the sound wave that touch the reflector are reflected back in a straight line to the second parabolic reflector.

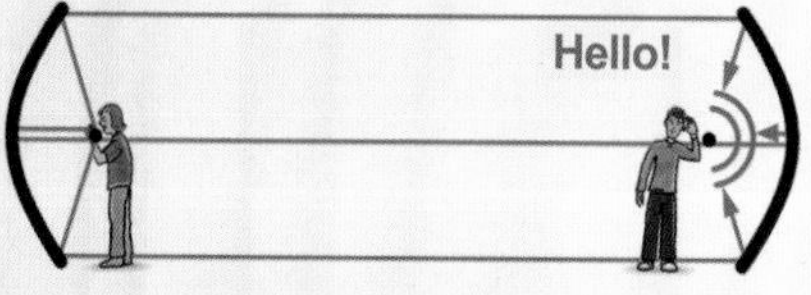

The sound wave is then reflected towards the centre of this reflector. The sound is recreated exactly at this precise point because all parts of the sound wave arrive at the same time.

If all of the sound waves arrive at the centre of the second reflector at the same time, it is because the total distance they travel is exactly the same. Your task is to prepare a document that provides a mathematical explanation for this phenomenon by restating everything in terms of distance travelled, given the properties of the parabolas. In your plan, you must accurately indicate where the two people must stand in order for one to clearly hear the whispering of the other.

REFERENCE

TABLE OF CONTENTS

Graphing calculator

TECHNOLOGY

Sample Calculations

It is possible to perform scientific calculations and to evaluate both algebraic and logical expressions.

Display screen

Graphic keys

Cursor keys

Editing keys

Menu keys

Scientific calculation keys

Scientific calculations

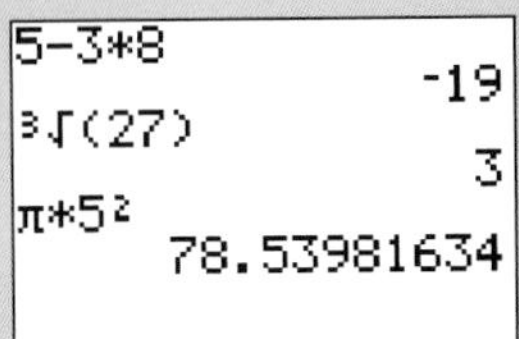

Logical expressions

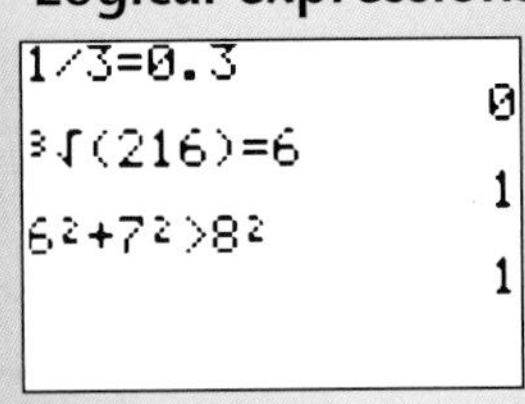

Algebraic expressions

```
5→X
                5
-2→Y
               -2
5X-2Y²
               17
```

Display a table of values and a graph

1. Define the rule.

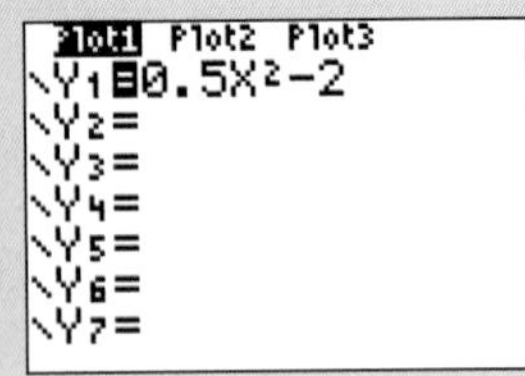

- This screen allows you to enter and edit the rule for one or more functions where Y is the dependent variable and X is the independent variable.

2. Define the viewing window.

```
TABLE SETUP
 TblStart=-3
 ΔTbl=1
Indpnt: Auto Ask
Depend: Auto Ask
```

- This screen allows you to define the viewing window for a table of values indicating the starting value of X and the step size for the variation of X.

3. Display the table of values.

X	Y1
-3	2.5
-2	0
-1	-1.5
0	-2
1	-1.5
2	0
3	2.5

X=-3

- This screen allows you to display the table of values of the rules defined.

4. Define the viewing window.

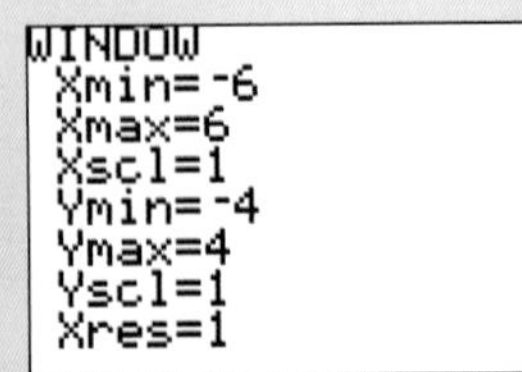

- This screen allows you to define the viewing window by limiting the Cartesian plane: Xscl and Yscl correspond to the step value on the respective axes.

5. Display the graph.

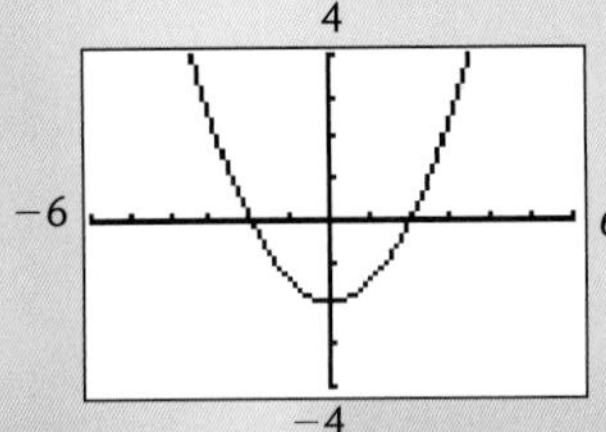

- This screen displays the graph of the defined rule.

6. Analyze the function.

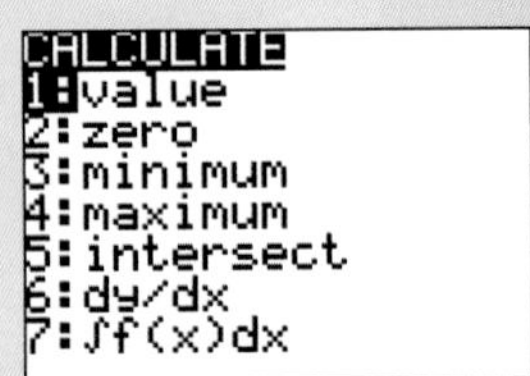

- This screen allows you to display some of the properties associated with the function.

Display several curves

1. Define the rules.

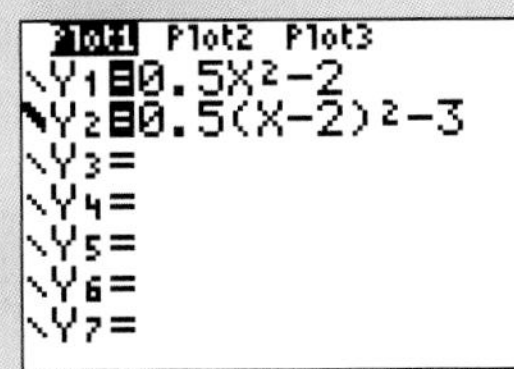

- It is possible to define several rules on the same screen. If desired, the thickness of the curve (E.g. normal, thick or dotted) can be adjusted for each rule.

2. Display the graph.

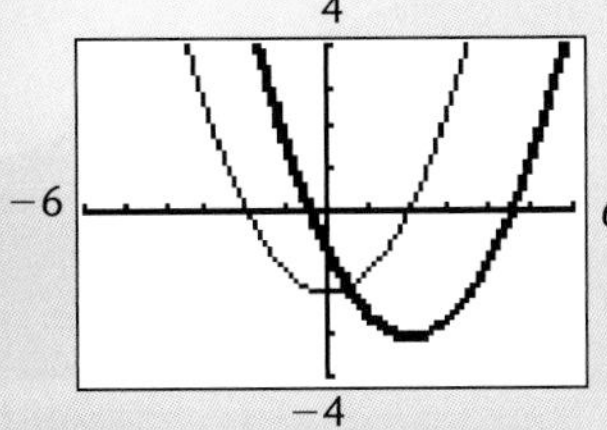

- The graphs of all the previously defined rules are displayed in a single window.

3. Compare the curves.

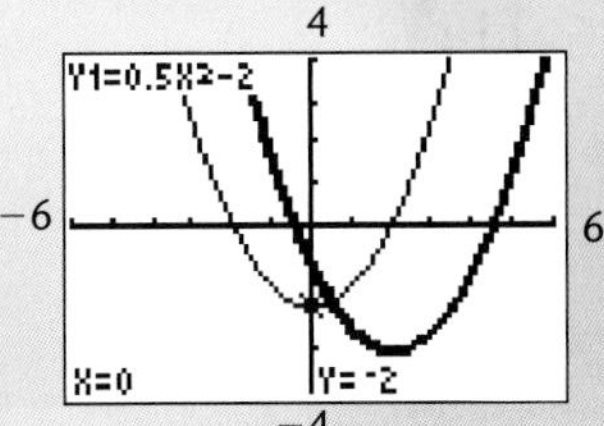

- If necessary, it is possible to move the cursor along the curves while viewing the coordinates.

Display a scatter plot, a regression line and correlation coefficient

1. Enter the data.

L1	L2	L3
1	9	
2	5	
3	6	
4	4	
5	4	
6	2	

L3(1)=

- This screen allows you to enter the data from a distribution. For a two-variable distribution, data entry is done in two columns.

2. Select a graph.

- This screen allows you to choose the type of statistical diagram.

3. Display the graph.

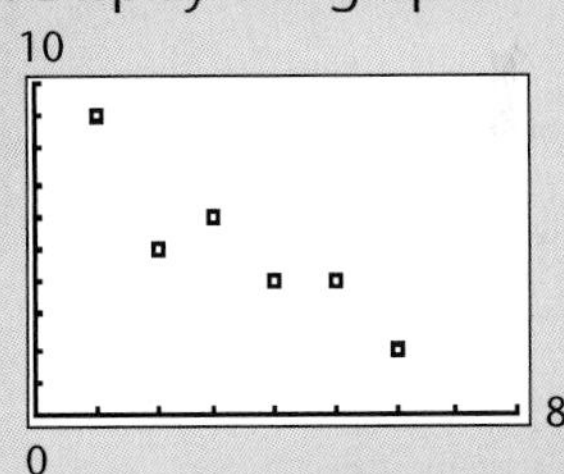

- This screen allows you to display the scatter plot.

4. Perform statistical calculations.

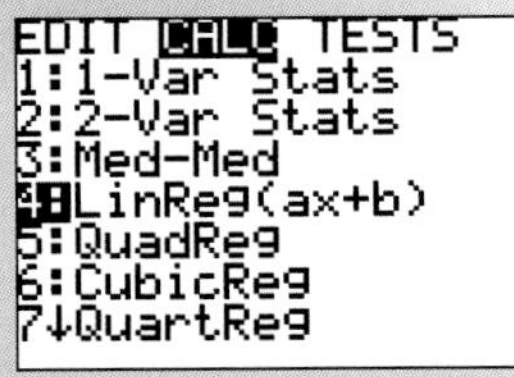

- This menu allows you to access different statistical calculations, in particular that of linear regression.

5. Determine the regression and correlation.

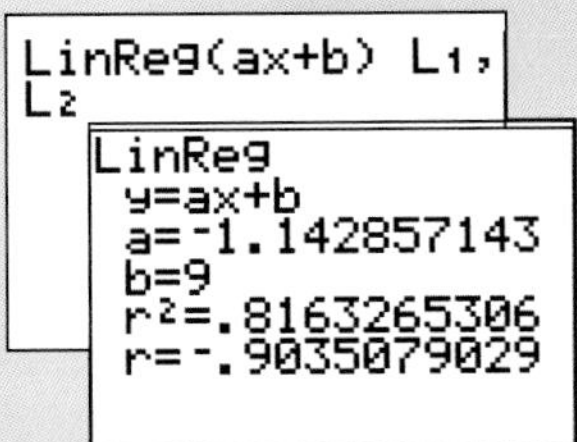

- These screens allow you to obtain the equation of the regression line and the value of the correlation coefficient.

6. Display the line.

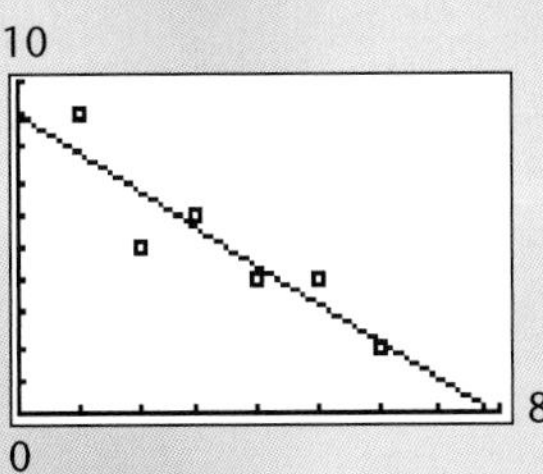

- The regression line can be displayed on the same graph as the scatter plot.

Spreadsheet

A spreadsheet is software that allows you to perform calculations on numbers entered into cells. It is used mainly to perform calculations on large amounts of data, to construct tables and to draw graphs.

Spreadsheet Interface

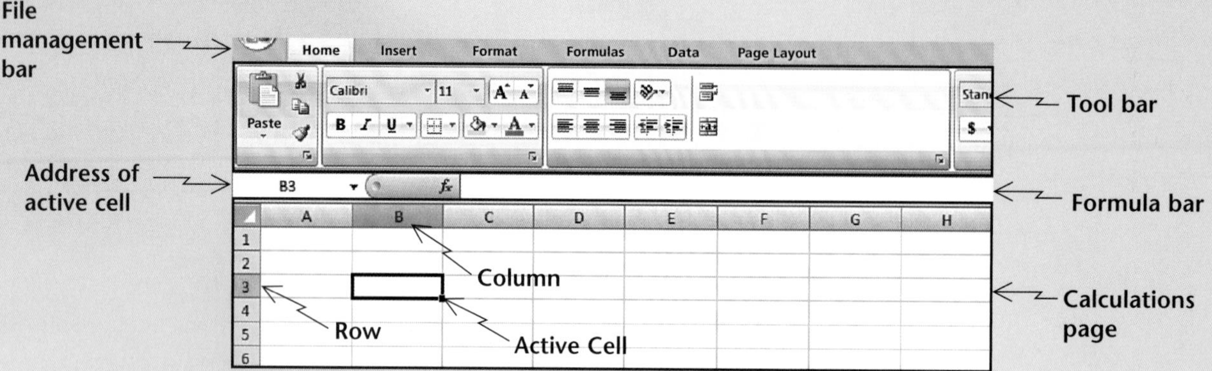

What is a cell?

A cell is the intersection of a column and a row. A column is identified by a letter and a row is identified by a number. Thus, the first cell in the upper right hand corner is identified as A1.

Entry of numbers, text and formulas in the cells

You can enter a number, text or a formula in a cell after clicking on it. Formulas allow you to perform calculations on numbers already entered in the cells. To enter a formula in a cell, just select it and begin by entering the "=" symbol.

Example:
Columns **A** and **B** contain data from a two-variable distribution which you wish to analyze.

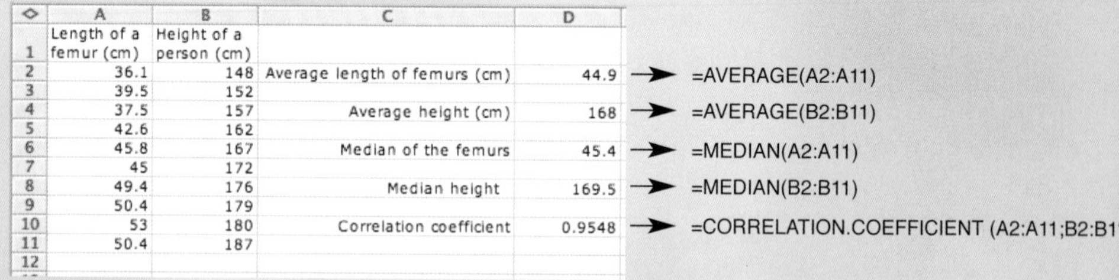

	A	B	C	D	
1	Length of a femur (cm)	Height of a person (cm)			
2	36.1	148	Average length of femurs (cm)	44.9	→ =AVERAGE(A2:A11)
3	39.5	152			
4	37.5	157	Average height (cm)	168	→ =AVERAGE(B2:B11)
5	42.6	162			
6	45.8	167	Median of the femurs	45.4	→ =MEDIAN(A2:A11)
7	45	172			
8	49.4	176	Median height	169.5	→ =MEDIAN(B2:B11)
9	50.4	179			
10	53	180	Correlation coefficient	0.9548	→ =CORRELATION.COEFFICIENT (A2:A11;B2:B11
11	50.4	187			
12					

In a spreadsheet, predefined functions exist to calculate the sum, the mean, the median and the correlation coefficient of a distribution.

How to construct a graph and a regression line

1) Select the range of data.

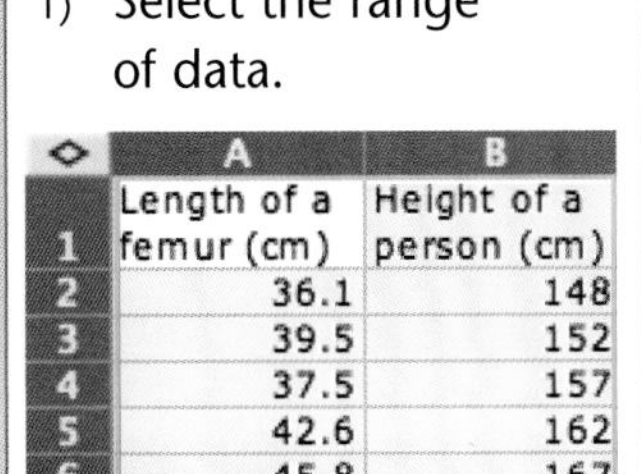

	A	B
1	Length of a femur (cm)	Height of a person (cm)
2	36.1	148
3	39.5	152
4	37.5	157
5	42.6	162
6	45.8	167
7	45.0	172
8	49.4	176
9	50.4	179
10	53.0	180
11	50.4	187

2) Choose the graph type.

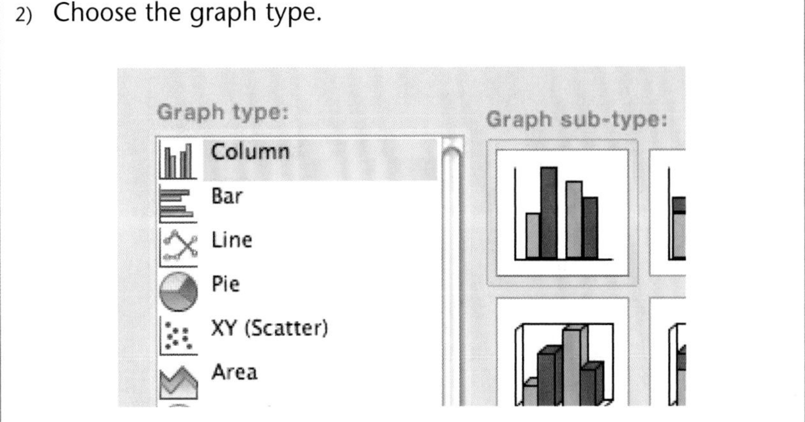

3) Choose the graph options.

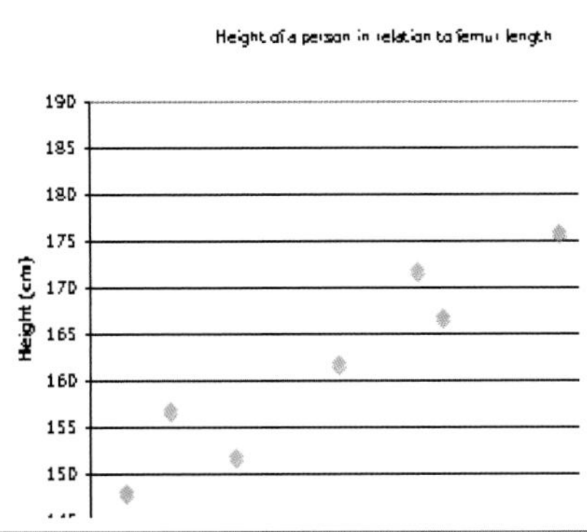

After drawing the graph, the different elements can be modified by using the appropriate menus or clicking on the graph.

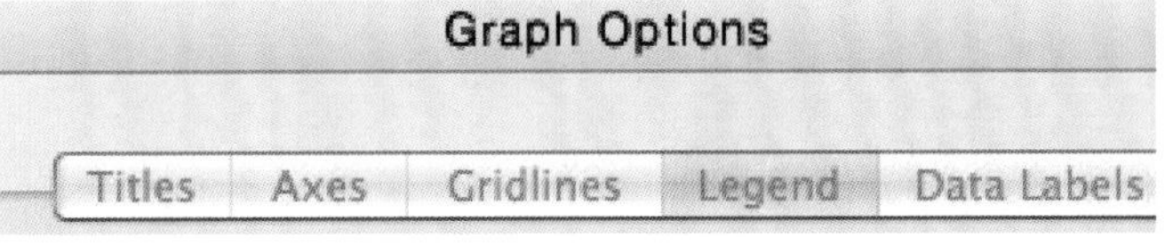

4) Add a regression line and display the equation on the graph.

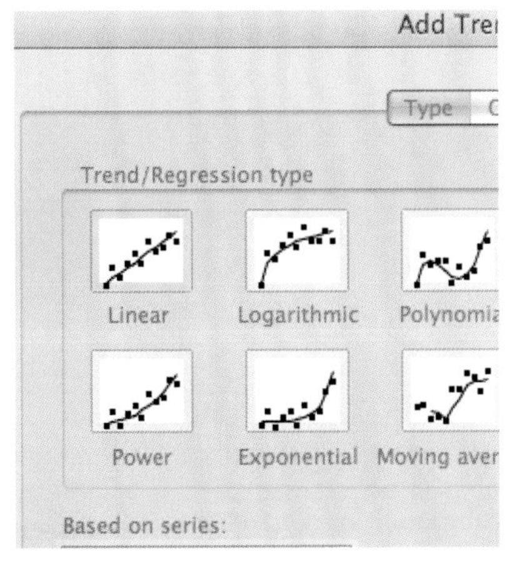

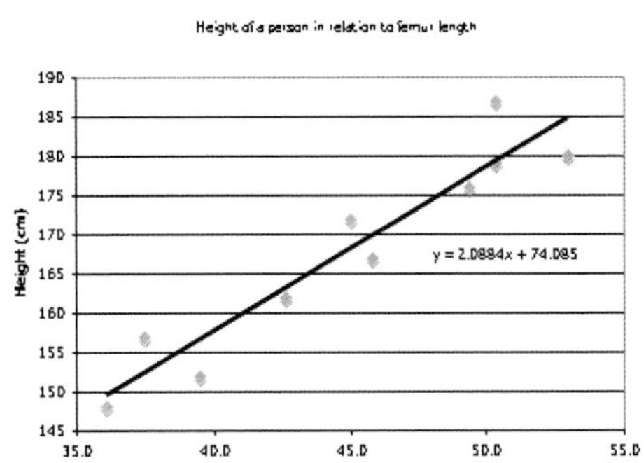

The option "Trendline" from the Layout menu allows you to add the regression line and to display the equation.

Dynamic geometry software

TECHNOLOGY

Dynamic geometry software allows you to draw and move objects in a workspace. The dynamic aspect of this type of software allows you to explore and verify geometric properties and to validate constructions.

The workspace and the tools

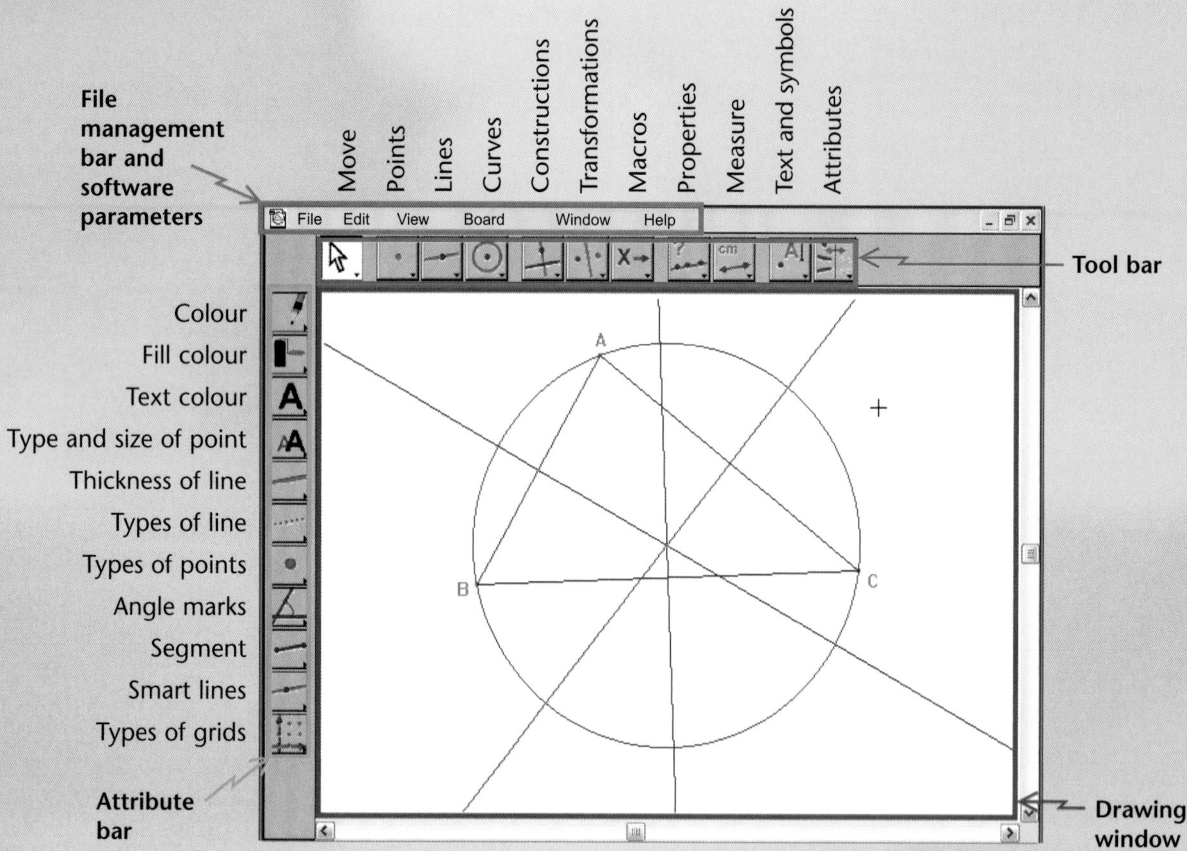

A geometric exploration

A triangle is inscribed in a circle. One of the sides of the triangle corresponds to a diameter of the circle. In order to explore the properties of this triangle, perform the following construction. To determine if triangle ABC is a right triangle, display the measurement of angle C, verify that the Pythagorean theorem holds true for the lengths of the sides of the triangle or use the software to confirm that sides AC and BC are perpendicular. By moving the point C on the circle or by modifying the size of the circle, note that angle C remains a right angle.

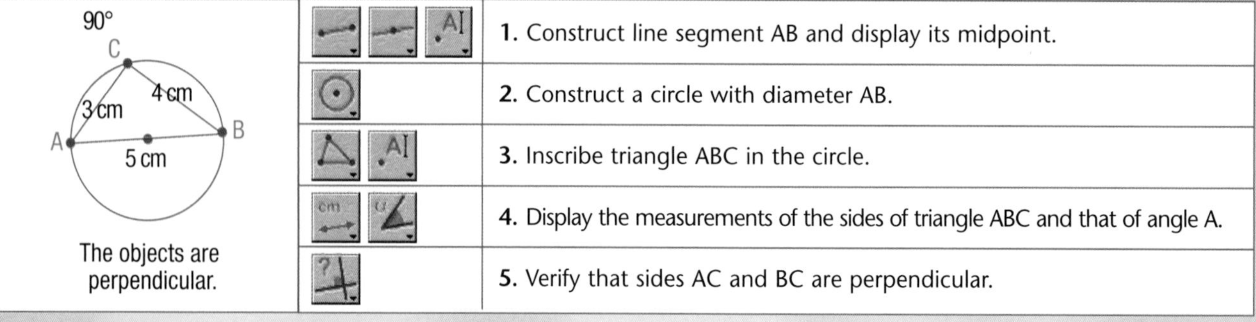

The objects are perpendicular.

Step
1. Construct line segment AB and display its midpoint.
2. Construct a circle with diameter AB.
3. Inscribe triangle ABC in the circle.
4. Display the measurements of the sides of triangle ABC and that of angle A.
5. Verify that sides AC and BC are perpendicular.

A graphical exploration

In order to discover the relationship between the parameters of a quadratic function and the properties of its graph, perform the following construction. Steps **1** to **3** of this construction are designed to represent the graph of the function for the parameters **a, h** and **k** that can be varied later. Step **4** displays the *y*-intercept. Steps **5** and **6** allow you to draw the axis of symmetry and to determine the coordinates of the vertex. To vary the parameters, select one of the numbers created. A window with arrows appears. By modifying the value of the parameter, you can observe the resulting changes in the shape and position of the curve.

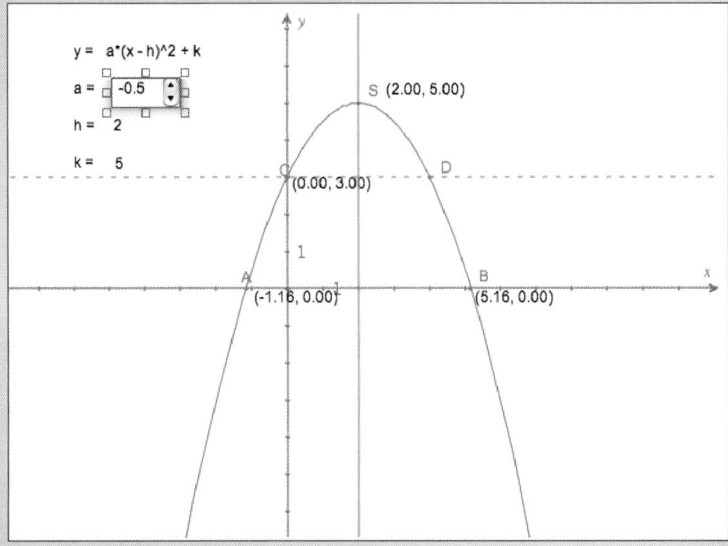

	1. Display the axes on the Cartesian plane and establish a scale.
	2. Enter the expression $a(x - h)^2 + k$. Select three numbers and add the labels "y =" , "h =" and "k =".
	3. Select the expression $a(x - h)^2 + k$ and display the curve using the values selected above for **a**, **h** and **k**.
	4. Place the points A and B at the intersection of the curve and the *x*-axis. Place point C at the intersection point of the curve and the *y*-axis. Display the coordinates of these points.
	5. Construct a line parallel to the *x*-axis passing through point C. Place point D at the intersection of the curve and the straight line.
	6. Construct the bisector of segment CD. Place point S at the intersection point of the bisector and the curve. Display the coordinates of this point.

Notations and symbols

Notation & symbols	Meaning
{ }	Brace brackets, used to list the elements in a set
$\mathbb{N}$	The set of Natural numbers
$\mathbb{Z}$	The set of Integers
$\mathbb{Q}$	The set of Rational numbers
$\mathbb{Q}'$	The set of Irrational numbers
$\mathbb{R}$	The set of Real numbers
$\cup$	The union of sets
$\cap$	The intersection of sets
$\varnothing$ or { }	The empty set (or the null set)
$\neq$	… is not equal to … or … is different from …
$<$	… is less than …
$>$	… is greater than …
$\leq$	… is less than or equal to …
$\geq$	… is greater than or equal to …
$[a, b]$	Interval, including a and b
$[a, b[$	Interval, including a but excluding b
$]a, b]$	Interval, excluding a but including b
$]a, b[$	Interval, excluding both a and b
∞	Infinity
(a, b)	The ordered pair a and b
$f(x)$	Is read as f of x or the value (image) of the function f at x
$x \mapsto f(x)$	x has as its image $f(x)$
Δy	Variation or growth of y
$[x]$	Greatest-integer less than or equal to x

Notation & symbols	Meaning
( )	Parentheses show which operation to perform first
$-a$	The opposite of a
$\frac{1}{a}$ or a^{-1}	The reciprocal of a
a^2	The second power of a or a squared
a^3	The third power of a or a cubed
$\sqrt{a}$	The square root of a
$\sqrt[3]{a}$	The cube root of a
%	Percent
$a : b$	The ratio of a to b
$\approx$	…is approximately equal to…
π	Read "pi," it is approximately equal to 3.1416
$^\circ$	Degree, unit of angle measure
m $\overline{AB}$	Measure of segment AB
d(A,B)	The distance from A to B
m $\angle$	The measure of an angle
m $\overset{\frown}{AB}$	The measure of the arc of the circle AB
//	… is parallel to …
$\perp$	… is perpendicular to …
∟	Indicates a right angle in a geometric plane figure
Δ ABC	Triangle ABC
$\cong$	… is congruent to …
$\sim$	… is similar to …
$\triangleq$	… corresponds to …
Med	The median of a distribution
$\overline{X}$	The arithmetic mean of a distribution

Geometric statements

KNOWLEDGE

	Statement	Example
1.	If two lines are parallel to a third line, then they are all parallel to each other.	If $l_1 // l_2$ and $l_2 // l_3$, then $l_1 // l_3$. 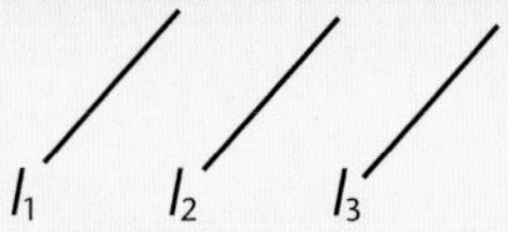
2.	If two lines are perpendicular to a third line, then the two lines are parallel to each other.	If $l_1 \perp l_3$ and $l_2 \perp l_3$, then $l_1 // l_2$. 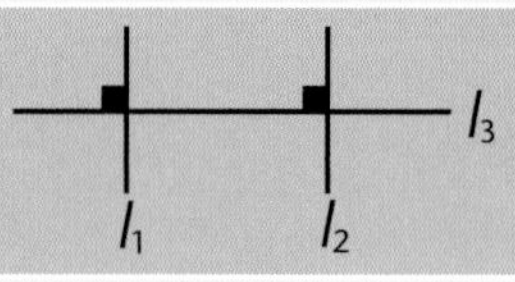
3.	If two lines are parallel, then every line perpendicular to one of these lines is perpendicular to the other.	If $l_1 // l_2$ and $l_3 \perp l_2$, then $l_3 \perp l_1$. 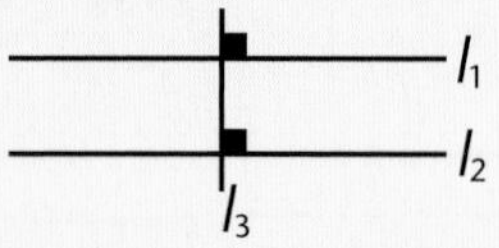
4.	If the exterior arms of two adjacent angles are collinear, then the angles are supplementary.	The points A, B and D are collinear. ∠ ABC & ∠ CBD are adjacent and supplementary. 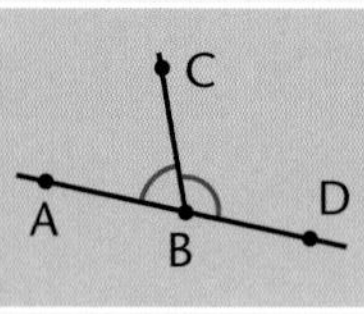
5.	If the exterior arms of two adjacent angles are perpendicular, then the angles are complementary.	$\overline{AB} \perp \overline{BD}$. ∠ ABC and ∠ CBD are adjacent and complementary. 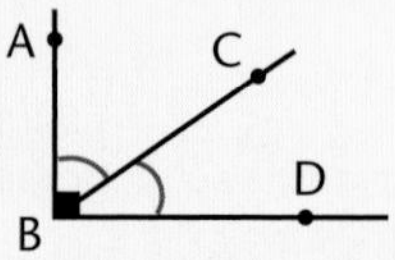
6.	Vertically opposite angles are congruent.	∠ 1 ≅ ∠ 3 ∠ 2 ≅ ∠ 4 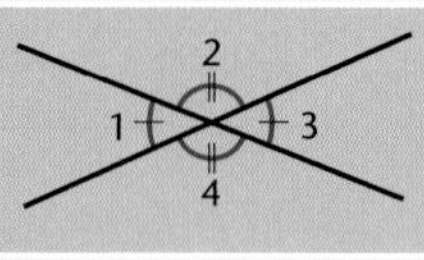
7.	If a transversal intersects two parallel lines, then the alternate interior, alternate exterior and corresponding angles are respectively congruent.	If $l_1 // l_2$, then angles 1, 3, 5 and 7 are congruent as are angles 2, 4, 6 and 8. 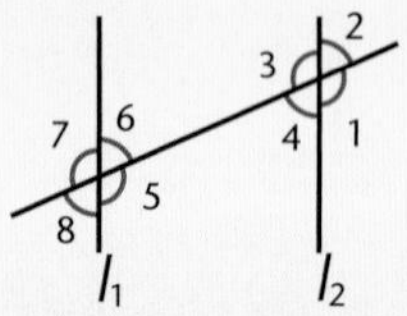
8.	If a transversal intersects two lines resulting in congruent corresponding angles (or alternate interior angles or alternate exterior angles), then those two lines are parallel.	In the figure for statement 7, if the angles 1, 3, 5 and 7 are congruent and the angles 2, 4, 6 and 8 are congruent, then $l_1 // l_2$.
9.	If a transversal intersects two parallel lines, then the interior angles on the same side of the transversal are supplementary.	If $l_1 // l_2$, then m ∠ 1 + m ∠ 2 = 180° and m ∠ 3 + m ∠ 4 = 180°. 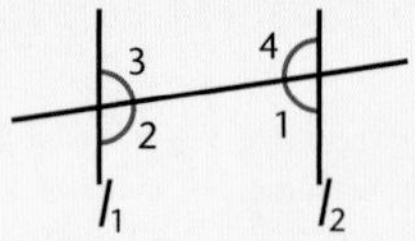

	Statement	Example
10.	The sum of the measures of the interior angles of a triangle is 180°.	$m\angle 1 + m\angle 2 + m\angle 3 = 180°$
11.	Corresponding elements of congruent plane or solid figures have the same measurements.	$\overline{AD} \cong \overline{A'D'}$, $\overline{CD} \cong \overline{C'D'}$, $\overline{BC} \cong \overline{B'C'}$, $\overline{AB} \cong \overline{A'B'}$ $\angle A \cong \angle A'$, $\angle B \cong \angle B'$, $\angle C \cong \angle C'$, $\angle D \cong \angle D'$
12.	In an isosceles triangle, the angles opposite the congruent sides are congruent.	In the isosceles triangle ABC: if if $\overline{AB} \cong \overline{AC}$ then $\angle C \cong \angle B$
13.	The axis of symmetry of an isosceles triangle represents a median, a perpendicular bisector, an angle bisector and an altitude of the triangle.	Axis of symmetry of triangle ABC. Median from point A Perpendicular bisector of the side BC Bisector of angle A Altitude of the triangle
14.	The opposite sides of a parallelogram are congruent.	In the parallelogram ABCD: $\overline{AB} \cong \overline{CD}$ and $\overline{AD} \cong \overline{BC}$
15.	The diagonals of a parallelogram bisect each other.	In the parallelogram ABCD: $\overline{AE} \cong \overline{EC}$ and $\overline{DE} \cong \overline{EB}$
16.	The opposite angles of a parallelogram are congruent.	In the parallelogram ABCD: $\angle A \cong \angle C$ and $\angle B \cong \angle D$
17.	In a parallelogram, the sum of the measures of two consecutive angles is 180°.	In the parallelogram ABCD: $m\angle 1 + m\angle 2 = 180°$ $m\angle 2 + m\angle 3 = 180°$ $m\angle 3 + m\angle 4 = 180°$ $m\angle 4 + m\angle 1 = 180°$
18.	The diagonals of a rectangle are congruent.	In the rectangle ABCD: $\overline{AC} \cong \overline{BD}$
19.	The diagonals of a rhombus are perpendicular.	In the rhombus ABCD: $\overline{AC} \perp \overline{BD}$
20.	The measure of an exterior angle of a triangle is equal to the sum of the measures of the interior angles at the other two vertices.	$m\angle 3 = m\angle 1 + m\angle 2$

	Statement	Example
21.	In a triangle the longest side is opposite the largest angle.	In triangle ABC, if the largest angle is A, then the longest side is BC.
22.	In a triangle, the smallest angle is opposite the smallest side.	In triangle ABC, if the smallest angle is B, then the smallest side is AC.
23.	The sum of the measurements of two sides in a triangle is larger than the measurement of the third side.	$2 + 5 > 4$ $2 + 4 > 5$ $4 + 5 > 2$ 2 cm, 5 cm, 4 cm
24.	The sum of the measures of the interior angles of a quadrilateral is 360°.	$m\angle 1 + m\angle 2 + m\angle 3 + m\angle 4 = 360°$
25.	The sum of the measures of the interior angles of a polygon with n sides is $n \times 180° - 360°$ or $(n-2) \times 180°$.	$n \times 180° - 360°$ or $(n-2) \times 180°$
26.	The sum of the measures of the exterior angles (one at each vertex) of a convex polygon is 360°.	$m\angle 1 + m\angle 2 + m\angle 3 + m\angle 4 + m\angle 5 + m\angle 6 = 360°$
27.	The corresponding angles of similar plane figures or of similar solids are congruent and the measures of the corresponding sides are proportional.	The triangle ABC is similar to triangle A'B'C': $\angle A \cong \angle A'$ $\angle B \cong \angle B'$ $\angle C \cong \angle C'$ $\frac{m\,\overline{A'B'}}{m\,\overline{AB}} = \frac{m\,\overline{B'C'}}{m\,\overline{BC}} = \frac{m\,\overline{A'C'}}{m\,\overline{AC}}$
28.	In similar plane figures, the ratio of the areas is equal to the square of the ratio of similarity.	In the above figures, $\frac{m\,\overline{A'B'}}{m\,\overline{AB}} = \frac{m\,\overline{B'C'}}{m\,\overline{BC}} = \frac{m\,\overline{A'C'}}{m\,\overline{AC}} = k$ ← Ratio of similarity $\frac{\text{area of triangle A'B'C'}}{\text{area of triangle ABC}} = k^2$
29.	Three non-collinear points define one and only one circle.	There is only one circle which contains the points A, B and C.
30.	The perpendicular bisectors of the chords in a circle intersect at the centre of the circle.	l_1 and l_2 are the perpendicular bisectors of the chords AB and CD. The point of intersection M of these perpendicular bisectors is the centre of the circle.

	Statement	Example
31.	All the diameters of a circle are congruent.	$\overline{AD}$, $\overline{BE}$ and $\overline{CF}$ are diameters of the circle with centre O. $\overline{AD} \cong \overline{BE} \cong \overline{CF}$
32.	In a circle, the measure of the radius is one-half the measure of the diameter.	$\overline{AB}$ is a diameter of the circle with centre O. $m\ \overline{OA} = \frac{1}{2}\ m\ \overline{AB}$
33.	In a circle, the ratio of the circumference to the diameter is a constant represented by π.	$\frac{C}{d} = \pi$
34.	In a circle, a central angle has the same degree measure as the arc contained between its sides.	In the circle with centre O, $m\ \angle\ AOB = m\ \overset{\frown}{AB}$ is stated in degrees.
35.	In a circle, the ratio of the measures of two central angles is equal to the ratio of the arcs intercepted by their sides.	$\frac{m\angle\ AOB}{m\ \angle COD} = \frac{m\ \overset{\frown}{AB}}{m\ \overset{\frown}{CD}}$
36.	In a circle, the ratio of the areas of two sectors is equal to the ratio of the measures of the angles at the centre of these sectors.	$\frac{\text{Area of the sector AOB}}{\text{Area of the sector COD}} = \frac{m\angle\ AOB}{m\ \angle COD}$
37.	For two similar solids: • the ratio of the surface areas is equal to the square of the ratio of similarity • the ratio of the volumes is equal to the cube of the ratio of similarity	If two solids are similar: The ratio of similarity = k = 2 The ratio of the areas = $k^2 = 2^2$ The ratio of the volumes = $k^3 = 2^3$
38.	In a right triangle, the square of the measure of the hypotenuse is equal to the sum of the measures of the squares of the other two sides.	In the right triangle ABC, $c^2 = a^2 + b^2$.
39.	If in a triangle, the square of the measurements of the hypotenuse is equal to the sum of the measures of the squares of the other two sides, then it is a right triangle.	A triangle with sides of 5 cm, 12 cm, and 13 cm is a right triangle since $13^2 = 12^2 + 5^2$.

A

Algebraic demonstation, p. 155

Altitude of a triangle
Segment from one vertex of a triangle, perpendicular to the line containing the opposite side. The length of such a segment is also called a height of the triangle.

Apothem of a regular polygon
Segment (or measure of segment) from centre of the regular polygon perpendicular to any of its sides. It is determined by the centre of the regular polygon and the midpoint of any side.

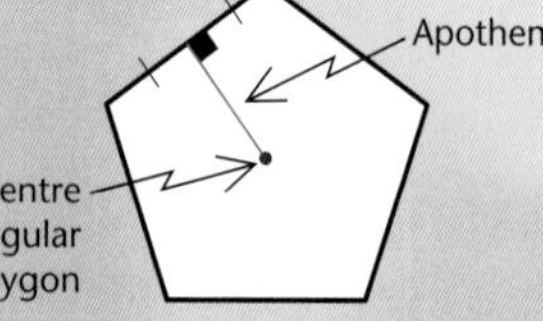

Area of a circle

$A_{circle} = \pi r^2$

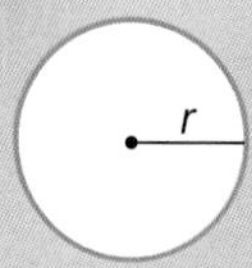

Area of a parallelogram

$A_{parallelogram} = b \times h$

Area of a regular polygon

$$A_{regular\ polygon} = \frac{((perimeter) \times (apothem))}{2}$$

Area of a rhombus

$$A_{rhombus} = \frac{D \times d}{2}$$

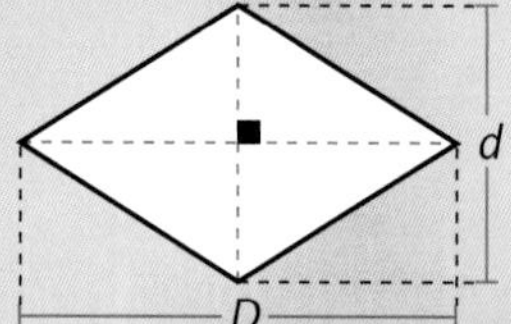

Area of a right circular cone

$A_{right\ circular\ cone} = \pi r^2 + \pi ra$

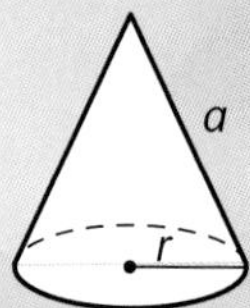

Area of a sphere

$A_{sphere} = 4\pi r^2$

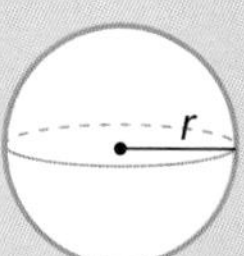

Area of a trapezoid

$$A_{trapezoid} = \frac{(B + b) \times h}{2}$$

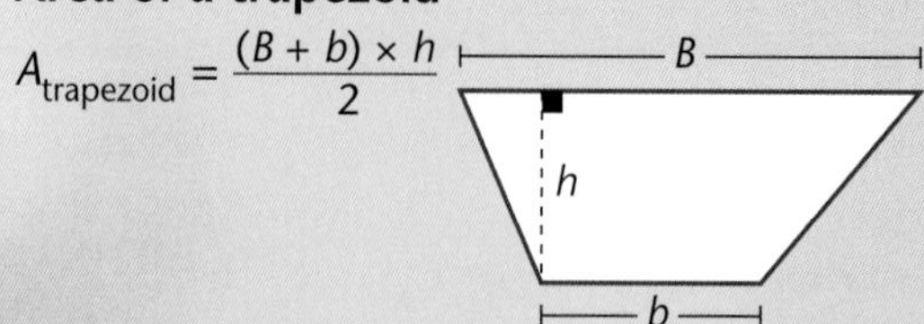

Area of a triangle

$$A_{triangle} = \frac{b \times h}{2}$$

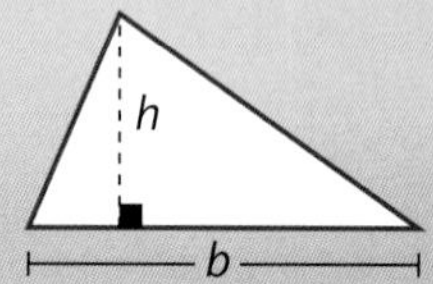

Asymptote, p. 79

Axis of symmetry
A line is an axis of symmetry for a figure if and only if a reflection of the figure over that line is the mirror image.

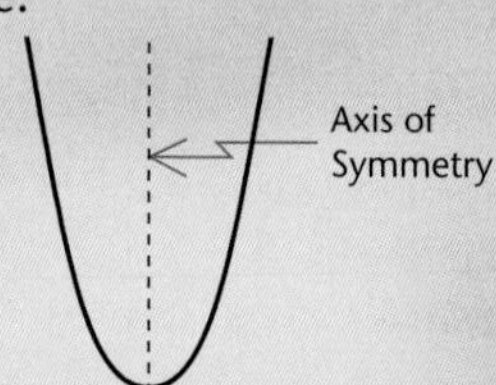

B

Binomial
A polynomial with exactly two terms.

C

Capacity
Volume of a fluid which a solid can contain.

Cartesian plane
A plane formed by two scaled perpendicular lines. Each point is located by its distance from each of these lines respectively.

Central angle
Angle formed by two radii in a circle. The vertex of the angle is the centre of the circle.

Circle
The set of all points in a plane at an equal distance from a given point called the centre.

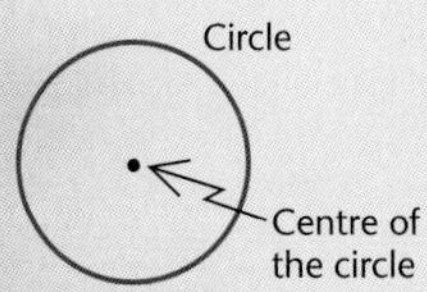

Circumference
The perimeter of a circle. In a circle whose circumference is C, diameter is d and radius is r:
$C = \pi d$ and $C = 2\pi r$.

Contingency table, p. 14

Coordinates of a point
Each of the two numbers used to describe the position of a point in a Cartesian plane.

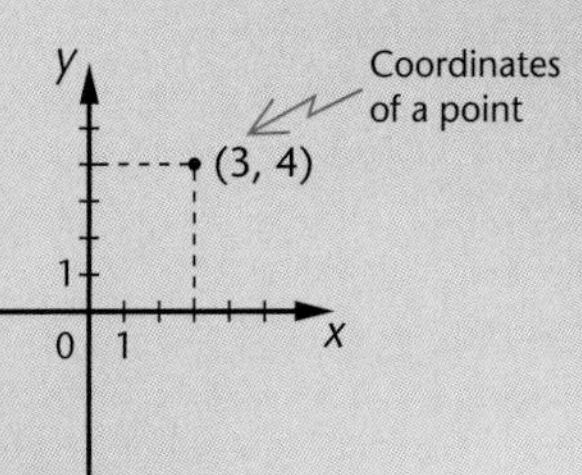

Correlation, p. 14

Linear correlation, p. 15

Correlation coefficient, p. 28, 29

Non-linear correlation, p. 42

Cube root of a number
The number a is a cube root of the number b, if $a^3 = b$. Every real number has one and only one real cube root written $\sqrt[3]{b}$.
E.g. In "$\sqrt[3]{125} = 5$", 3 is the index, $\sqrt{}$ is a radical sign, 125 is the radicand and $\sqrt[3]{125}$ is a radical.

Decreasing function, p. 70

Degree of a monomial
The sum of the exponents of the monomial.
E.g. 1) The degree of the monomial 9 is 0.
2) The degree of the monomial $-7xy$ is 2.
3) The degree of the monomial $15a^2$ is 2.

Degree of a polynomial in one variable
The largest exponent of that variable in the polynomial.
E.g. The degree of the polynomial $7x^3 - x^2 + 4$ is 3.

Diameter
Segment (or length of segment) which is determined by two points on a circle passing through the centre of the circle.

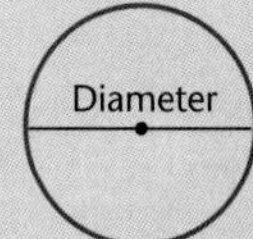

Discriminant, p. 206

Distance between two points, p. 239

Domain of a function, p. 70

Edge
Segment formed by the intersection of any two faces of a solid.

Equation
Mathematical statement of equality involving one or more variables. E.g. $4x - 8 = 4$

Equivalent algebraic expressions, p. 153

Equivalent equations, p. 169

Equivalent inequalities, p. 196

Equivalent figures, p. 141, 142

Extremes of a function, p. 79

Face
Plane or curved surface bound by edges.

Factoring
Writing an expression as a product of factors.

Removing a common factor, p.133

Factoring by grouping, p.168

Factoring by trinomial, p.168

Completing the square, p.169

Function
A relation between two variables in which each value of the independent variable is associated to at most one value of the dependent variable.

Basic quadratic function, p. 91

Direct variation function, p. 71

First-degree polynomial function, p. 78

Greatest-integer function, p. 71

Inverse variation function, p. 71

Piecewise function, p. 78

Rule of a function
An equation of a function that describes the link between the dependent and independent variables.

Rule of a first-degree polynomial function, p. 78

Rule of a piecewise function, p. 106
(standard form)

Rule of a quadratic function
- **Factored form,** p. 227
- **General form,** p. 205
- **Standard form,** p. 91, 205

Second-degree polynomial function, p. 78
(quadratic function)

Step function, p. 105

Zero-degree polynomial function, p. 78
(constant function)

Hypotenuse
The side opposite the right angle in a right triangle. It is the longest side of a right triangle.

Hypotenuse

Image
In geometry, figure obtained by a geometric transformation performed on an initial figure.

Increasing function, p. 70

Initial figure
Figure on which a geometric transformation is performed.

Integer - see Numbers.

Interquartile range, p. 6

Interval
A set of all the real numbers between two given numbers called the endpoints. Each endpoint can be either included or excluded in the interval.
E.g. The interval of real numbers over -2 included, to 9 excluded, is [-2, 9[.

Irrational number - see Numbers.

Lateral area of a solid
Sum of the areas of the lateral faces (not bases) of a solid.

Laws of Exponents, p. 133

Legs (or arms) of a right triangle
The sides that form the right angle in a right triangle.

Like terms - see Terms.

Linear correlation coefficient, p. 28, 29

Mathematical model, p. 70
Representing mathematical relationships with equations, tables or graphs as a means of analyzing the information being examined.

Maximum of a function, p. 70

Median, p. 6

Mean, p. 6

Minimum of a function, p. 70

Monomial
Algebraic expression formed by one number or a product of numbers and variables.
E.g. 9, x and $3xy^2$ are monomials.

Numbers

Integer
Any number belonging to the set $\mathbb{Z} = \{..., -2, -1, 0, 1, 2, 3, ...\}$.

Irrational number
A number which cannot be expressed as a ratio of two integers, and whose decimal representation is non-periodic and non-terminating.

Natural number
Any number belonging to the set $\mathbb{N} = \{0, 1, 2, 3, ...\}$.

Rational number
A number which can be written in the form a/b where a and b are integers, and b is not equal to 0. Its decimal representation can be terminating (finite) or non-terminating (infinite) and periodic.

Real number
A number belonging to the union of the set of rational numbers and the set of irrational numbers.

Numerical coefficient of a term
Numerical value multiplied by the variable or variables of a term.
E.g. In the algebraic expression $x + 6xy - 4.7y$, the numerical coefficients of the first, second and third terms are 1, 6 and -4.7 respectively.

Operation on algebraic expressions, p. 133, 153, 154

Origin of a Cartesian plane
The intersection point of the two axes in a Cartesian plane. The coordinates of the origin are (0, 0).

Parabola, p. 91, 240

Parallelogram
A quadrilateral with two pairs of opposite sides parallel.
E.g. $\overline{AB} \parallel \overline{CD}$ and $\overline{AD} \parallel \overline{BC}$

Parameter
In an algebraic expression, a letter other than the variable whose numerical value can be fixed.

Polygon
A closed plane figure with three or more sides.

Regular polygon
A polygon whose sides are congruent and whose angles are congruent.

Polygons

Number of Sides	Name of Polygon
3	Triangle
4	Quadrilateral
5	Pentagon
6	Hexagon
7	Heptagon
8	Octagon
9	Nonagon
10	Decagon
11	Undecagon
12	Dodecagon

Polyhedron
A solid determined by plane polygonal faces.
E.g.

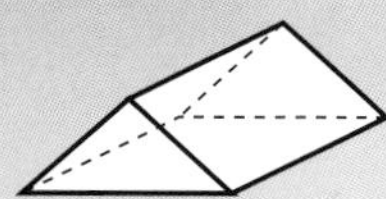
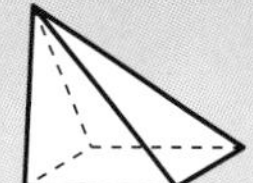
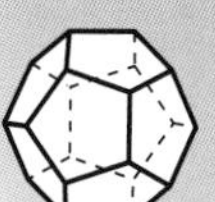

Polynomial
An expression formed by the sum of monomials.

Polynomial function - see Function.

Population
A set of living beings, objects or facts which are the object of a statistical survey.

Prism
A polyhedron with two congruent parallel faces called "bases." The parallelograms determined by the corresponding sides of these bases are called the "lateral faces."

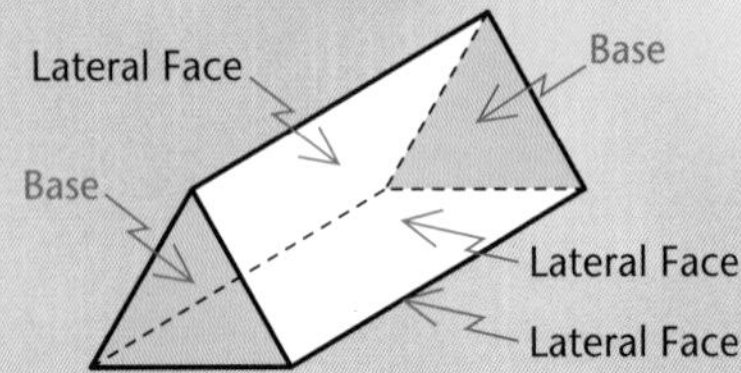

Right prism
A prism whose lateral faces are rectangles.
E.g. A right trapezoidal prism

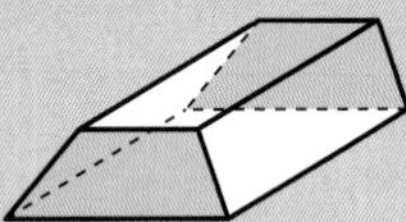

Regular prism
A prism whose bases are regular polygons.
E.g. A regular heptagonal prism

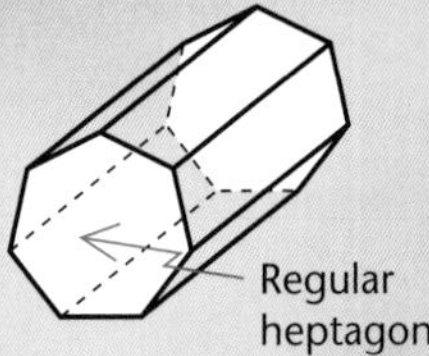

Proportion
A statement of equality between two ratios or two rates.
E.g. If the ratio of a to b, for $b \neq 0$, is equal to the ratio of c to d, for $d \neq 0$, then $a : b = c : d$ or $a/b = c/d$ is a proportion.

Properties of a function, p. 70, 79

Properties of a step function, p. 106

Properties of a quadratic function, p. 92, 197, 206

Pyramid
A polyhedron with one polygonal base, whose lateral faces are triangles with a common vertex called the apex.
E.g. Octagonal pyramid

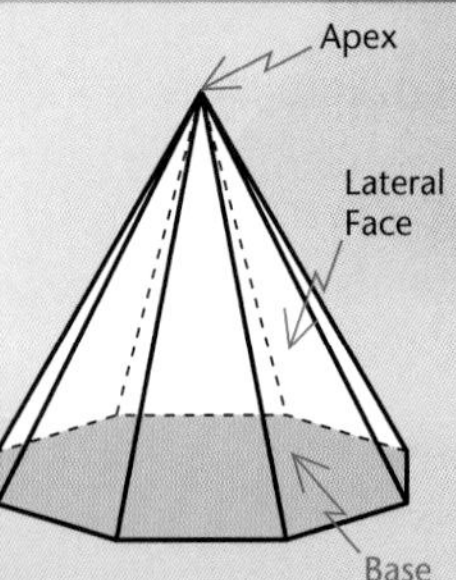

Regular pyramid
A pyramid whose base is a regular polygon.
E.g. A regular hexagonal pyramid

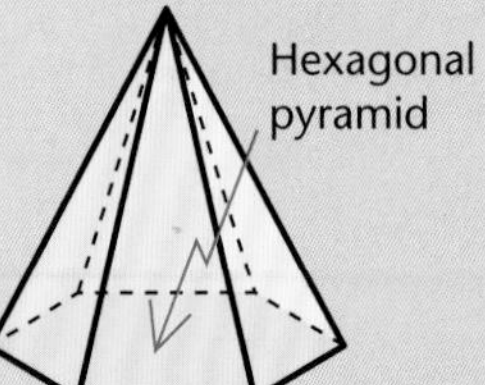

Right pyramid
A pyramid such that the segment from the apex, perpendicular to the base, intersects it at the centre of the polygonal base.
E.g. A right rectangular pyramid

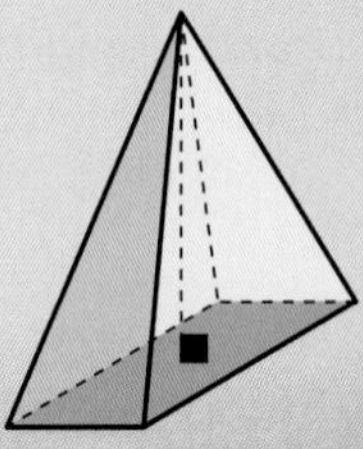

Pythagorean theorem, p. 132

Q

Quadratic formula, p. 206

R

Radius
A radius is a segment (or length of a segment) which is determined by the centre of a circle and any point on the circle.

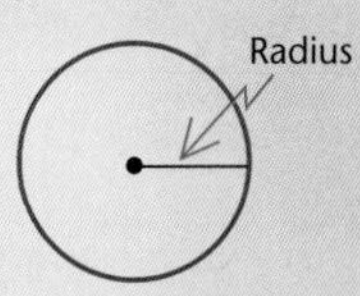

Range, p. 6

Rate of change, p. 7

Ratio
A way of comparing two quantities or two sizes of the same kind expressed in the same units and which involves division.

Rational number - see Numbers

Rational expression, p. 154

Real number - see Numbers.

Rectangle
A quadrilateral which has four right angles.

Reflection
A geometric transformation which maps an initial point to an image point such that a given line (called the reflection line) is the perpendicular bisector of the segment determined by the point and its image. The reflection of a figure is the reflection of all of its points.

Regression line, p. 41, 42

Regular polygon - see Polygon.

Regular prism - see Prism.

Regular pyramid - see Pyramid.

Rhombus
A quadrilateral with 4 congruent sides.

Right circular cone
Solid made of two faces, a circle and a sector. The circle is the base and the sector forms the lateral face.

Right circular cylinder
Solid made of three faces, two congruent circles and a rectangle. The circles form the bases and the rectangle forms the lateral face.

Right prism - see Prism.

Right pyramid - see Pyramid.

Root - see Square root of a positive number, Cube root.

Rotation, p. 196
A geometric transformation which maps an initial figure to an image using a centre, an angle and a direction of rotation.

Rules
An equation which translates a relationship between variables.

Rules for transforming inequalities, p.196

S

Sample
Subset of a population.

Sample survey
A search for information on a representative subset of a population in order to make conclusions about the entire population.

Scale
The ratio of the dimensions of a reproduction to the dimensions of a real object.
The scale can be expressed in different ways:
E.g. 1 cm = 100 km indicates that 1 cm on the reproduction corresponds to 100 km in the real object.

Scatter plot, p. 14

Sign of a function, p. 79

Slant height of a regular pyramid
Segment from the apex perpendicular to any side of the polygon forming the base of the pyramid. It corresponds to the altitude of a triangle which forms a lateral face.

Slant height of a right circular cone
Segment (or length of segment) defined by the apex and any point on the edge of the base.

Sphere
The set of all points in space at a given distance (radius) from a given point (centre).

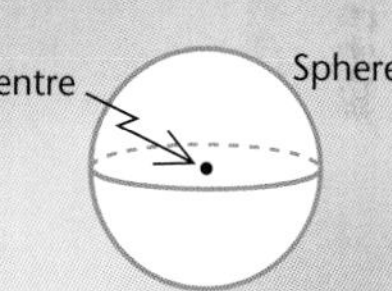

Square
A quadrilateral whose sides and angles are congruent.

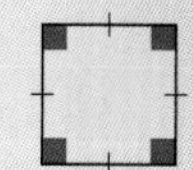

Square root of a positive number
The number a is a square root of a positive number b, if $a^2 = b$. All numbers b larger than 0 have two square roots, one positive written $\sqrt{b}$, and the other negative, written $-\sqrt{b}$.
E.g. The square roots of 25 are 5 and –5.

Solutions of second-degree equations in one variable, p. 169, 206

Surface area (or total area) of a solid, p. 132

T

Terms

Like terms
Constants or terms composed of the same variables raised to the same exponents.
E.g. 1) $8ax^2$ and ax^2 are like terms
2) 8 and 17 are like terms

Trajectory
A curve describing the movement of a point or the centre of gravity of an object in space.

Translation
A geometric transformation which maps an initial figure to an image given a specified direction and length.

Trapezoid
A quadrilateral having at least one pair of parallel sides.
E.g. $\overline{AB}$ // $\overline{CD}$

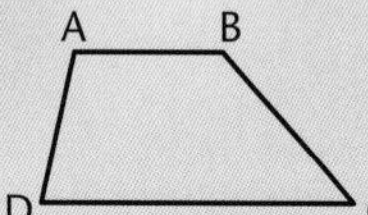

Isosceles trapezoid
A trapezoid whose legs are congruent.

Right trapezoid
A trapezoid with two right angles.

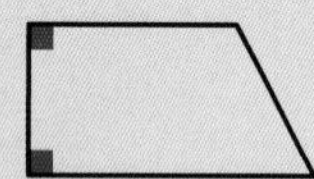

Triangle
A polygon with three sides.

Classification of Triangles

Properties	Name	Samples
No congruent sides	Scalene	
Two congruent sides	Isosceles	
All sides are congruent	Equilateral	
Three acute angles	Acute triangle	
One obtuse angle	Obtuse triangle	
One right angle	Right triangle	
All angles congruent	Equiangular	

Trinomial
A polynomial with three terms.

U

Units of capacity
The litre is the basic unit of capacity in the metric system (SI). This measurement corresponds to the capacity of a container with a volume of 1 dm^3. The multiples and fractions of a litre are described with the usual prefixes (milli-, centi-, deci-, deca-, hecto-, kilo-).
E.g. 1 dL corresponds to $\frac{1}{10}$ L.

Units of length, of area and of volume
The metre, the square metre and the cubic metre are the basic units of length, area and volume respectively in the metric system (SI). The multiples and fractions of these units are described with the usual prefixes whose significance depends on the unit being considered.

E.g. 1 dm corresponds to $\frac{1}{10}$ m.

1 dm^2 corresponds to $\frac{1}{100}$ m^2.

1 dm^3 corresponds to $\frac{1}{1000}$ m^3.

V

Variables

Variables that are directly proportional, p.71

Variable directly proportional to the square of another variable, p. 92

Variables that are inversely proportional, p.71

Statistical or quantitative variables
A variable to which you can associate a number.

Vertex of a solid
In geometry, a point common to at least two edges of a solid.

Vertex of a parabola
The point where a parabola intersects its axis of symmetry.

Volume of a solid, p. 132

X

***x*-axis (horizontal)**
A scaled line which allows you to determine the *x*-value (abscissa) of any point in the Cartesian plane.

***x*-intercept**
In a Cartesian plane, an *x*-intercept is the *x*-value (abscissa) of a intersection point of a curve with the *x*-axis.

***x*-value (abscissa)**
The first coordinate of a point in the Cartesian plane.
E.g. x-value (abscissa) of the point (5,-2) is 5.

***y*-axis (vertical)**
A scaled line which allows you to determine the *y*-value (ordinate) of any point in the Cartesian plane.

***y*-intercept**, (initial value), p. 70

***y*-value (ordinate)**
The second coordinate of a point in the Cartesian plane.
E.g. The *y*-value (ordinate) of the point (5, -2) is -2.

Zero of a function (*x*-intercept), p. 70

Zero of a quadratic function, p. 197, 206

Photography Credits

T Top **B** Bottom **L** Left **R** Right **C** Centre **BG** Background

Cover

© Shutterstock

Vision 1

Introduction TL © Shutterstock **Introduction TR** © Shutterstock **Introduction CL** © Shutterstock **Introduction CR** © Shutterstock **4 BR** © David Lees/Corbis **5 TL** © Shutterstock **5 TR** © Shutterstock **5 CR** © Shutterstock **8 TR** © Shutterstock **8 M** © akg-images **8 CB** © akg-images **11 CR** © Images.com/Corbis **16 CR** © Shutterstock **17 TC** © Corbis **19 TR** © Shutterstock **20 TR** © Floresco Productions/Corbis **21 BL** 36941822© 2008 Jupiter Images and its representatives **22 TR** © Shutterstock **32 TR** 37856904© 2008 Jupiter Images and its representatives **33 BR** © Shutterstock **34 BR** © Shutterstock **36 CR** © Shutterstock **38 CL** ©Bettmann/Corbis **44 BC** © Shutterstock **45 TR** © Shutterstock **46 CR** © Layne Kennedy/Corbis **48 CL** © Shutterstock **50 TL** © akg-images **52 CR** © UCLA Departement of Epidemiology, School of Public Health **52 BL** © Nick Sinclair/SPL/Publiphoto **53 TL** © Matthias Kulka/zefa/Corbis **53 BL** © Bettmann/Corbis **54 BL** © Shutterstock **57 CR** © Shutterstock **58 TR** © Firstlight **58 BL** © Shutterstock **60 CL** © Shutterstock **60 BR** © Shutterstock **62 CL** © Shutterstock

Vision 2

Introduction TL © Shutterstock **Introduction TR** © Shutterstock **Introduction CL** © Shutterstock **Introduction CR** © Shutterstock **68 TR** © Shaun Best/Reuters/Corbis **69 TR** © PHST-Chantale Hamel **72 CR** © Steeve Lemay **73 TR** © Shutterstock **74 CL** © Visuals Unlimited/Corbis **74 CR** © Firstlight **75 FP TC** 30437794© 2008 Jupiter Images and its representatives **75 FP BL** © Shutterstock **75 FP BR** © Shutterstock **76 TR** © Shutterstock **76 BR** © Shutterstock **80 CR** © Shutterstock **81 TR** © Mauro Fermariello/SPL/Publiphoto **81 BR** 7655387© 2008 Jupiter Images and its representatives **82 CR** © Shutterstock **84 TR** 36113517© 2008 Jupiter Images and its representatives **86 CL** © Mike Powell/Getty Images **86 CR** © Olivier Maire/epa/Corbis **87 CR** © Gero Breloer/dpa/Corbis **89 TC** © Corbis **95 TL** 39202889© 2008 Jupiter Images and its representatives **96 CL** © Firstlight **96 BR** © Asif Hassan/Getty images **97 TR** 24230596© 2008 Jupiter Images and its representatives **98 BL** © Lucy Nicholson/Reuters/Corbis **99 TR** 22758579© 2008 Jupiter Images and its representatives **100 FP G** © Shutterstock **101 TL** © Firstlight **107 BR** 26256365© 2008 Jupiter Images and its representatives **108 TL** 30898139© 2008 Jupiter Images and its representatives **110 TC** © Shutterstock **111 BR** © Shutterstock **114 TL** © Bettmann/Corbis **114 CR** © Shutterstock **115 TL** © Clipart **115 CR** Achille Cazin, *Les Forces physiques* © Librairie Hachette, 1871 **116 TL** © Royal Astronomical Society/SPL/Publiphoto **116 CR** © STScI/NASA/Corbis **117 TL** © Bettmann/Corbis **118 TR** © Shutterstock **119 FP B** © Shutterstock **120 TR** © Shutterstock **122 BR** © Rudy Sulgan/Corbis **124 TC** © Shutterstock **126 M** © Marc Muench/Corbis **127 TR** © Public domain **127 M** © Steeve Lemay

Vision 3

Introduction TL © Shutterstock **Introduction TR** © Shutterstock **Introduction CL** © Shutterstock **Introduction CR** © Shutterstock **131 CR** © Shutterstock **135 TC** © Steeve Lemay **136 TR** © Shutterstock **136 BL** © National Gallery Collection, avec l'aimable autorisation de la National Gallery, Londres/Corbis **139 BC** © Adrienne Hart-Davis/SPL/Publiphoto **144 CR** © Steeve Lemay **145 TL** © Shutterstock **145 TC** Thierry Baudry © Galerie « Beaux-objets.com » **145 TR** © Shutterstock **146 TR** © Shutterstock **147 BC** © Shutterstock **148 TR** © Snark/Publiphoto **159 CR** Public domain **161 TL** © Bettmann/Corbis **161 TR** ©

SPL/Publiphoto **164 TL** © Shutterstock **164 TC** © Shutterstock **164 TR** © Shutterstock **166 M** © Fridmar Damm/zefa/Corbis **167 TL** Public domain **171 B FP** © Shutterstock **172 BC** © Shutterstock **175 TR** © DEA Picture Library/Getty Images **175 BR** © Photo Stationnement Place Alexis Nihon **176 BL** © Shutterstock **177 TR** © Collection Roger Viollet/Topfoto/Ponopresse **177 CL** © James L. Amos/Corbis **178 CL** © Shutterstock **180 TL** © Musée J.-A. Bombardier **180 CR** © Shutterstock **181 TL** © George Hall/Corbis **181 TR** © Celaya/Cervera/Gomez **181 BR** © Firstlight **182 TR** © Perrine Poiron «Reproduction autorisée par Les Publications du Québec» **183 CR** © Shutterstock **184 TR** © Shutterstock **187 M** © Gilbert S. Grant/PhotoResearchers/Publiphoto **187 BR** © Bettmann/Corbis **188 CR** © Shutterstock

Vision 4

Introduction TL © Richard Cummins/Corbis **Introduction TR** © Atlantis Phototravel/Corbis **Introduction CL** © Shutterstock **Introduction CR** © Shutterstock **194 TL** © Shutterstock **194 TR** © Richard T. Nowitz/Corbis **194 CL** © Shutterstock **194 CR** © Shutterstock **195 CR** © Mark Karass/Corbis **198 TR** © C.Cuthbert/SPL/Publiphoto **200 BL** © 7673243 © 2008 Jupiter Images and its representatives **203 TR** © Joe McDonald/Corbis **208 CR** © Shutterstock **209 B** © William Manning/Corbis **210 TR** © Shutterstock **212 CR** © Nasa **213 MH** © Shutterstock **217 BR** © Shutterstock **218 TR** © Shutterstock **218 BR** © Shutterstock **219 TR** © Shutterstock **219 CR** © Shutterstock **220 TR** © Shutterstock **220 CR** © Shutterstock **221 TL** © Bettmann/Corbis **222 M** © Shutterstock **224 CL** © Firstlight **224 CR** © Shutterstock **230 TR** © Shutterstock **231 BR** 34782262 © 2008 Jupiter Images and its representatives **232 TR** © Chris Hellier/Corbis **233 CL** © Duomo/Corbis **235 CR** 60489243 © 2008 Jupiter Images and its representatives **236 TR** Steeve Lemay **237 TR** © Shutterstock **242 TC** © Moodboard/Corbis **243 TR** © Shutterstock **244 BR** © Shutterstock **245 TR** © M. Bond/SPL/Publiphoto **246 TL** © SPL/Publiphoto **246 CR** 37067746 © 2008 Jupiter Images and its representatives **247 CR** © Public domain **248 TL** © Frank Robichon/epa/Corbis **248 CR** © Panneton-Valcourt **249 CR** © Sophie Bassouls/Sygma/Corbis **250 BR** © John C. Fernandez **251 CR** © Shutterstock **252 TL** © Firstlight **252 CR** © Ciniglio Lorenzo/Sygma/Corbis **253 BL** © Dante Fenolio/PhotoResearchers/ Publiphoto **254 TR** © Joao Relvas/epa/Corbis **255 CL** © Shutterstock **257 TL** © Shutterstock **258 TC** © Shutterstock

Learning and evaluation situations

262 B © Superstock **263 TR** © Tom Grill/Corbis **263 BL** © Keren Su/Corbis **264 TR** © Shutterstock **264 BL** © Shutterstock **265 TR** 32352413 © 2008 Jupiter Images and its representatives **266 TR** © Kai Pfaffenbach/Reuters/Corbis **266 CL** © Shutterstock **266 BC** © Duomo/Corbis **267 TR** ©Matthew Impey/Colorsport/Corbis **267 CL** © Dimitri Iundt/TempSport/Corbis **267 CR** © G. Rancinan/Corbis Sygma **268 TR** © Gérard Julien/Getty Images **269 TR** © P. Psaila/SPL/Publiphoto **269 CL** © Luc Léger **270 B** © Nasa/SPL/Publiphoto **271 TR** © Shutterstock **271 CL** © Shutterstock **271 M** © Kenneth M. Highfill/PhotoResearchers/Publiphoto **271 CR** © Shutterstock **272 CR** © Shutterstock **273 TR** © Peikko® **274 B** © Peter Bassett/SPL/Publiphoto **275 TR** © Sam Ogden/SPL/Publiphoto **275 BR** © Shutterstock **276 TL** © David Smith, The human Cannonball in performance at the Canadian National Exhibition in Toronto, Canada **276 TR** © David Smith, The human Cannonball in performance at the Canadian National Exhibition in Toronto, Canada **277 TR** © M.-J. Roy – Centre des sciences de Montréal